GSNI — Geological Survey of Northern Ireland

The Geology of Northern Ireland
Our Natural Foundation

Second Edition
Edited by W. I. Mitchell

Geological Survey of Northern Ireland

Belfast 2004

First published 1972
ISBN 0-85272-454-3

The grid, where it is used on the figures,
is the Irish Grid taken from Ordnance Survey of
Northern Ireland mapping.

Design by;
Kunnert & Tierney, Belfast.
Printed by;
W. & G. Baird Ltd., Greystone Press, Antrim.

Bibliographical reference

The Geology of Northern Ireland-Our Natural Foundation. 2004.
Mitchell, W. I. (ed.). (Second Edition)
Geological Survey of Northern Ireland, Belfast.

Contents

Acknowledgements

The following geologists provided excellent advice and encouragement whilst reviewing chapters of the new book:

Dr. Bernard Anderson (formerly Queen's University Belfast (QUB), Chapters 1, 3, 8, 17),
Mr. John Mendum (British Geological Survey (BGS), Chapter 2), Dr. Jim Floyd (BGS, Chapter 4),
Dr. Ian Meighan (QUB, Chapters 5, 15), Dr. Mike Stephenson (BGS, Chapter 6),
Dr. Ian Somerville (University College Dublin, Chapter 7),
Dr. Geoff Warrington (formerly BGS, Chapters 9, 10, 11), Dr. Jim Riding (BGS, Chapters 12, 13, 16),
Dr. Paul Lyle (University of Ulster (UU), Chapter 14),
Prof. Marshall McCabe (UU, Chapter 18),
Mr. Sam Holloway (BGS, Chapter 19), Mr. Nick Robins (BGS, Chapter 20) and
Dr. Alastair Ruffell (QUB, Chapter 22).
Dr. Ian Meighan kindly provided information on geoarchaeology for Chapter 18 (Quaternary).
The final review of all the chapters by Prof. Tony Bazley has greatly improved the book.

In addition the GSNI has received assistance and advice from staff in the BGS and from associates in museums, universities and institutes throughout Ireland and Britain.
I hope that the following list is exhaustive.

Mr. Tim Cullen (BGS, Photography),
Mr. Brian Routledge (Ulster Museum, Belfast (UM), Photography),
Mr. Hugh Crilly (GSNI, Cartography), Mr. Andy Hulbert (BGS, Cartography),
Ms. Janis Smyth (formerly GSNI, Cartography), Dr. Alan Brandon (formerly BGS, Chapter 7),
Mr. Alex Donald (GSNI, IT support), Ms. Dee Flight (BGS, Chapter 21),
Dr. Jasper Knight (Edge Hill College, Chapter 18),
Dr. Steve McCarron (Trinity College Dublin, Chapter 18),
Dr. Patrick McKeever (GSNI, Photographs), Dr. John Morris (Geological Survey of Ireland-GSI),
Mr. Derek Reay (GSNI), Dr. Ian Somerville (Photographs), Mr. Geoff Warke (GSNI, Photographs),
Mr. Mark Williams (BGS, Chapter 3), Dr. Neil Clark (Hunterian Museum, Glasgow),
Dr. Mike Howe (BGS), Mr. Ken James (UM), Dr. Matthew Parkes (GSI), Dr. Mike Simms (UM),
Mrs. Pauline Taylor (BGS), Dr. Mark Woods (BGS).

Permission to use company data in (Figure 16.2, Boreholes 2 and 3) was received from Ballymoney Power.

Front cover   Landsat TM5 image and Chapter 15, Photograph 1 © Natural Environment Research Council;
Back cover   Photographs of Dunluce Castle and Strangford Lough, Chapter 12, Photograph 1 © Environment and Heritage Service, Department of the Environment for Northern Ireland; Chapter 23, Photograph 6 © Esler Crawford and Rivers Agency, Department of Agriculture for Northern Ireland.
Chapter 18, Photograph 1 © Environment and Heritage Service, Department of the Environment for Northern Ireland

Foreword

The Geology of Northern Ireland
Our Natural Foundation

In the years since the first edition of *The Geology of Northern Ireland* was published in 1972 many new theories have become generally accepted in geology, and perhaps the most significant of these is the understanding of plate tectonics. This, in conjunction with an increasing knowledge of other geological processes, has required a re-examination of the geological history of Northern Ireland.

The first edition was the earliest publication to describe the detailed geology and landscape of Northern Ireland for both geologists and non-geologists. That it is only now necessary to update it is a tribute to the author, the then Director of the Geological Survey of Northern Ireland, Harry Wilson.

The Geology of Northern Ireland - Our Natural Foundation gives a comprehensive account of the rocks and deposits shown on the 1997 edition of the 1:250,000 scale geological map of Northern Ireland and is written primarily for geologists and geoscientists. However, it is also intended to be of value to planners, civil engineers and environmental scientists who require an overview of the geology of Northern Ireland. In addition, we hope that it will attract the interest of walkers, naturalists, cavers, climbers and other outdoor-based pursuits that spend time on the bedrock and superficial deposits that are our natural foundation.

In addition to providing a comprehensive account of the geology of the region, *The Geology of Northern Ireland* complements other GSNI publications, including 'A Story through Time' and the 'Explore' and 'Walk' guides from the Landscapes from Stone project. The publication also includes new and unpublished information contained in the archive of the GSNI.

Northern Ireland represents a small area of the Earth's surface but yet contains a wide array of rock types, of many different geological ages, which are reflected in the variety of landscapes present. These extend from the high moorland of the Antrim Plateau with the magnificent Glens of Antrim along the north and eastern coastal fringes, to the rolling fields of Counties Down and Armagh, which are pierced by the Mountains of Mourne and Slieve Gullion in the south and east. In the northwest, the rounded and glaciated peaks of the Sperrin Mountains give way to the maze of waterways of the Fermanagh Lakeland in the southwest. All of these landscapes reflect the interaction between the underlying rocks and geological processes that give rise to the multitude of environmental niches that support our widely varied natural flora and fauna.

The Geology of Northern Ireland endeavors to present detailed geological information in a systematic and user-friendly way. Each chapter, commencing with the oldest rocks and progressing through time to the final glacial episode, allows the reader to understand the setting of each geological period on national, regional, local and individual locality scale. It is hoped that the provision of general information, supported by detailed maps, will facilitate visits to areas too long regarded as being 'off-the-beaten-track' and will act as a guide to localities of outstanding geological significance. Therefore, in almost every chapter, sites of national or international significance are described and augmented by photographs, large-scale maps and grid references. The book also provides an up-to-date account of the results of mineral and hydrocarbon exploration and reflects on the prospects of new discoveries being made in Northern Ireland.

In compiling *The Geology of Northern Ireland*, the GSNI have drawn heavily on the expertise and experience of staff of the British Geological Survey and of academic staff at universities in Ireland and Britain. Their efforts are gratefully acknowledged.

Detailed knowledge of the geology of an area can help reduce risk in all scales of development. The GSNI hope that *The Geology of Northern Ireland - Our Natural Foundation* will highlight the value of geological information. A geologist is never more than a phone call away!

David Falvey, PhD
Executive Director
British Geological Survey
Keyworth
Nottingham NG12 5GG

Eur Geol Garth Earls
Director
Geological Survey of Northern Ireland
Colby House, Stranmillis Court,
Belfast BT9 8BJ

Introduction

Northern Ireland, despite being a mere 0.00001% of the land area of planet Earth, presents an opportunity to study an almost unparalleled variety of geology in such a small area (Figure 1). The diverse ages of the rocks present in Northern Ireland is illustrated in this book by the contents menu. Their stratigraphical record commences in the Mesoproterozoic and includes representatives in all of the systems up to and including the Palaeogene (Table 1). If the Cambrian age attributed to upper parts of the Dalradian Supergroup in Scotland is substantiated then it is likely that their correlatives in Northern Ireland will fall within that system.

Geology does not stop at political boundaries and the 1:250,000 geological map demonstrates the continuity of major geological structures and lineaments that dominate the geology of Northern Ireland into the Republic of Ireland. The distribution of the

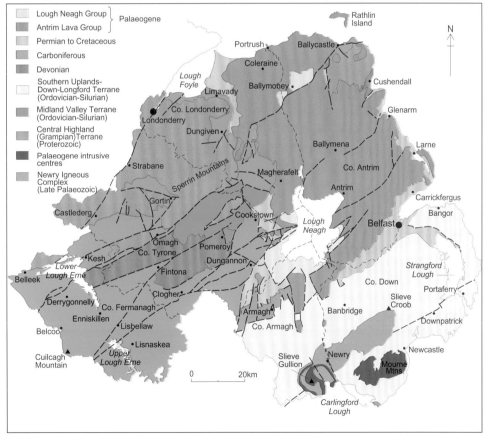

Figure 1
Simplified geological map of Northern Ireland.

geological units described in the book is depicted on the revised edition of the 1:250,000 scale geological map of the northern part of Ireland, which was published in 1997. The book largely describes the geology of Northern Ireland constituting the six counties of the ancient province of Ulster and including Antrim, Armagh, Down, Fermanagh, Londonderry and Tyrone. However, it also includes a description of the Palaeogene Carlingford Complex which, although occurring entirely in Co. Louth in the Republic of Ireland, is one of three, closely spaced, intrusive complexes that together form the cross-border topographical and cultural heritage region of Mourne, Gullion and Cooley.

If one envisages Northern Ireland without the cover of late Palaeozoic and younger rocks then the basement is partitioned into areas that represent remnants of three major terranes (Chapter 1). Commencing some 600 million years ago (Ma) the continents, of which the rocks forming these terranes are representative, were distributed around the ancient Iapetus Ocean. The effects of plate movements through time carried the continents across the Earth's surface, gradually closing the Iapetus Ocean. Thus, some 400Ma, those terranes came together during the Caledonian Orogeny as one continental mass, which included Ireland and Britain. The oldest rocks in Northern Ireland, the Meso- to Neoproterozoic Moine and Dalradian supergroups, which constitute the northern terrane, form the Sperrin Mountains and extend westwards into Co. Donegal (Chapter 2). They are also exposed in an inlier in northeast Co. Antrim and from there extend northeastwards across the North Channel and form the Highlands of Scotland. The central terrane is an extension southwest into Ireland of the Midland Valley Terrane in Scotland. Basement rocks of this terrane are superbly exposed in the Tyrone Igneous Complex (Chapter 3), unlike in Scotland where they are everywhere concealed by Devonian and Carboniferous rocks. Isolated inliers of highly fossiliferous Ordovician and Silurian sedimentary rocks occur at Pomeroy and Lisbellaw and correlate with contemporaneous rocks in eastern North America and the west coast of Scotland. The history of the formation of the southern terrane is one of the most controversial issues to influence the geological history of Ireland and Britain. The Ordovician and Silurian rocks are disposed in an accretionary prism and are a southwesterly continuation of the Southern Uplands of Scotland into Counties Down and Armagh in Northern Ireland (Chapter 4).

When the younger Phanerozoic cover rocks are superimposed on the basement complex it is evident that Northern Ireland can be divided into four areas with quite distinctive geological characteristics, and ages of rocks that are not usually found in any of the other quadrants (Figure 2).

1) The **northwest quadrant** is composed of Dalradian rocks, the early Ordovician Tyrone Igneous Complex and late Ordovician-early Silurian Pomeroy Inlier.
2) The **southeast quadrant** is composed of Ordovician and Silurian rocks of the Southern Uplands-Down-Longford Terrane with younger intrusive complexes.
3) The **southwest quadrant** is composed largely of Carboniferous rocks and a Devonian component.
4) The **northeast quadrant** has Palaeogene basalt lava and lacustrine sedimentary rocks of the Antrim Plateau at surface and is underlain by rocks of Permian to Cretaceous age.

About 400Ma, after the closure of the Iapetus Ocean, the Newry Igneous Complex was intruded into the Southern Uplands-Down-Longford Terrane in south Counties Armagh and Down (Chapter 5). Later Palaeozoic deposition occurred in two episodes. Firstly, during the Devonian, red-bed sediments were deposited in a continental desert environment (Chapter 6). Uplift and extensive erosion preceded the early part of the Carboniferous

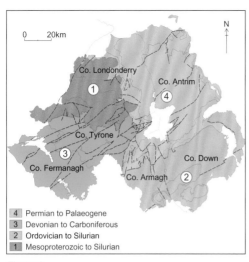

Figure 2
Geological divisions of Northern Ireland.

0   20km

N

Co. Londonderry

Co. Antrim

① ④

Co. Tyrone

③ Co. Down

Co. Fermanagh

Co. Armagh ②

4 Permian to Palaeogene
3 Devonian to Carboniferous
2 Ordovician to Silurian
1 Mesoproterozoic to Silurian

period when predominantly marine sedimentary rocks were deposited in response to episodes of marine transgression (Chapter 7). The first tangible evidence of tectonic activity related to the Variscan Orogenic Cycle can be identified in the Lower Carboniferous succession but maximum uplift and deformation only reached a climax in the end-Carboniferous-Early Permian period (Chapters 7 and 8).

The present distribution of virtually all post-Carboniferous rocks in Northern Ireland is restricted to the northeast quadrant. While the surface rocks of the Antrim Plateau are composed of Palaeogene basalt lava, the underlying Permian, Triassic, Jurassic and Cretaceous rocks form a narrow outcrop at the margins of the plateau (Chapters 9-12). For the first time in the structural history of Ireland, sedimentary basins, and in particular those of Permian and Mesozoic age, owed their formation and orientation not to the reactivation of underlying Caledonoid basement structures but to the opening of the North Atlantic Ocean (Chapter 17). While structural preservation of these rocks is partly responsible for their present distribution, their relatively soft nature compared to older rocks made them more susceptible to erosion, particularly during the Pleistocene glaciations. Although Permian and Triassic rocks are exposed on all sides of the Antrim Plateau, detailed information on their relative ages, lithostratigraphy and physical properties is only known from deep boreholes. Late Permian and Mesozoic sedimentation in Northern Ireland appears to be continuous and changes from deposition initially of red-bed sedimentary rocks with infrequent marine incursions to an open marine environment in the Early Jurassic when most of Ireland may have been submerged (Chapters 10 and 11). The Cimmerian uplift affected Northern Ireland from Jurassic into Early Cretaceous times and restricted the deposition of greensand and chalk to the Late Cretaceous (Chapter 12).

In early Palaeogene times Northern Ireland was part of the North Atlantic Igneous Province and came under the influence of the Iceland Plume. However, the earliest vestiges of magmatism are not found at the base of the lavas forming the Antrim Plateau but in the thin, reddish-coloured bed of clay that intercedes between the chalk and the lava, known as the Clay-with-Flints. Formerly believed to consist of a residue derived by weathering of the chalk and to represent a fossil soil or palaeosol horizon, analyses have revealed a volcanic origin for much of the clay component (Chapter 13). The overlying basalt lava forms the Antrim Plateau and is responsible for protecting the underlying softer rocks from erosion. The lava flows were produced by volcanic activity related to the Iceland Plume and in addition to being formerly more extensive were probably considerably thicker than their present 800m (Chapter 14). Early Palaeogene intrusive igneous complexes are restricted to the Carlingford, Slieve Gullion and Mourne Mountains centres (Chapter 15). They individually form separate areas of mountainous terrain and, though related in time, each has a different petrogenetic history. Minor intrusions, particularly basic dykes, intrude all older rocks in Northern Ireland and are related to the extrusion of the basalt lavas. At the end of the period of basaltic volcanism, mid- to late Palaeogene uplift and faulting segmented the lava pile. The final events in the tectonic history of Northern Ireland are related to the formation of Oligocene sedimentary basins that formed on the basalt lava plateau in response to episodes of dextral strike-slip faulting. The remnants of these basins may be of huge economic significance for Northern Ireland in that they contain significant reserves of lignite (Chapter 16).

In the late Pleistocene in Northern Ireland, the final 100,000 years of our history, the impact of global climatic cooling resulted in the advance of continental glaciers across northern Europe and Ireland and Britain. At least 80% of bedrock is covered by deposits left by the ice sheets and their meltwater, and by younger Holocene deposits such as alluvium and peat (Chapter 18). It is at this stage in the history of Northern Ireland that Man arrived and his impact on the environment, and in particular on the natural vegetation, is recorded in those Holocene deposits.

The final five chapters in the book commence with an outline of the deep structure of Northern Ireland (Chapter 19) and link this with a history of hydrocarbon exploration and the prospects of finding accumulations of oil and gas (Chapter 22). The history of mineral exploration in Northern Ireland concentrates on the search for gold deposits but also provides an introduction to the availability and types of bulk minerals (Chapter 21). For a long time it was believed that Northern Ireland lacked significant reserves of fuel minerals. The discovery of almost 1 billion tonnes of lignite in three separate Oligocene basins has highlighted the importance of this indigenous fuel for the future. Although it is often said that it never seems to stop raining in Northern Ireland the importance of groundwater to the economy and the quality of life cannot be overestimated (Chapter 20). The final chapter in the book describes a range of geological hazards that occur in Northern Ireland and offers a note of caution that future development should be cognisant of risk associated with geology.

Chapter 1

Basement Structure and the Terrane Model

T. B. ANDERSON, T. P. JOHNSTON and W. I. MITCHELL

"The Precambrian and Lower Palaeozoic foundations of the British Isles may be viewed as a series of suspect terranes whose exposed boundaries are prominent fault systems of various kinds, each with an unproven amount of displacement." (1).

Introduction

The geological foundations of Ireland and Britain, known as the Caledonides, were assembled in the Caledonian Orogeny. Like most orogenic belts, the Caledonides consist of a collage of suspect terranes, each with a distinctive stratigraphy and structural, metamorphic and igneous history (1, 2, 3, 4). A suspect terrane may be defined as an area characterised by an internal continuity of geology (including petrology, metallogeny, geophysical properties and palaeomagnetic record) that is bounded either by faults, or mélange representing a trench complex, or cryptic suture zones. Terranes now juxtaposed across such boundaries commonly display geological structures and histories so strikingly different it implies that they were once very widely separated. Although movements on the bounding faults and suture zones are commonly estimated in hundreds of kilometres they can rarely be determined with precision. Many of the suspect terranes are best envisaged as buoyant fragments of crust which were accreted to the adjacent continents when the surrounding oceanic crust was returned to the mantle by oceanic closure and subduction.

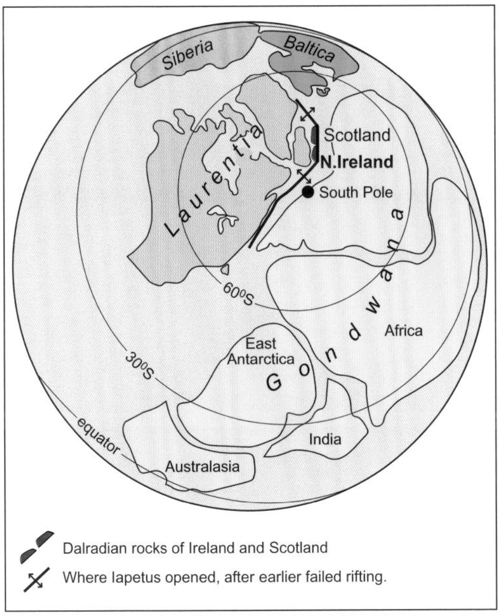

Dalradian rocks of Ireland and Scotland

Where Iapetus opened, after earlier failed rifting.

Figure 1.1
Distribution of the continents in Neoproterozoic times. (*c.* 600Ma).

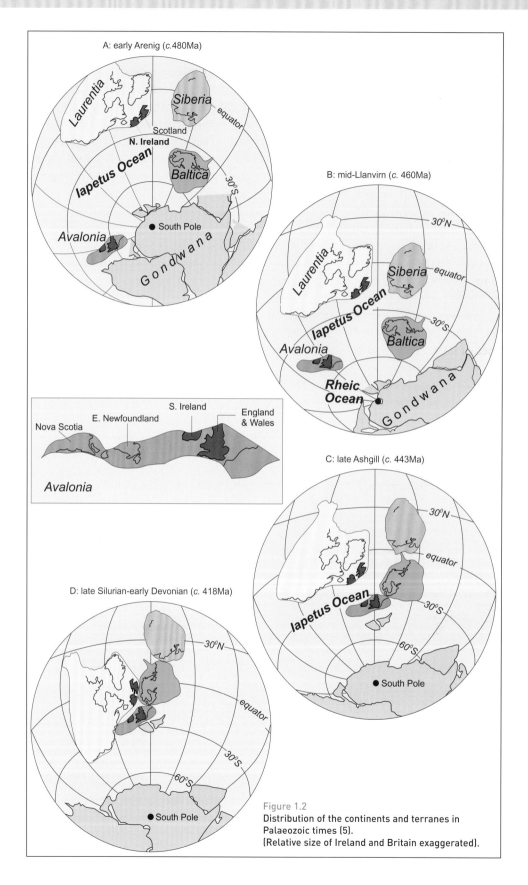

A: early Arenig (c.480Ma)

Laurentia

Siberia
equator

Scotland
N. Ireland

Iapetus Ocean

Baltica

30°S

● South Pole

Avalonia

Gondwana

B: mid-Llanvirn (c. 460Ma)

30°N

Laurentia

Siberia
equator

Iapetus Ocean

30°S

Avalonia

Baltica

Rheic Ocean

Gondwana

Nova Scotia

E. Newfoundland

S. Ireland

England & Wales

Avalonia

C: late Ashgill (c. 443Ma)

30°N

equator

30°S

Iapetus Ocean

60°S

● South Pole

D: late Silurian-early Devonian (c. 418Ma)

30°N

equator

30°S

60°S

● South Pole

Figure 1.2
Distribution of the continents and terranes in Palaeozoic times (5).
(Relative size of Ireland and Britain exaggerated).

Rise and fall of the Iapetus Ocean

The Iapetus Ocean (Figure 1.1) probably first opened in late Neoproterozoic (Vendian) time as a consequence of rifting caused by the separation of Baltica (North European Plate) and Siberia from Laurentia (North American Plate) (5). Evidence for the existence of the Iapetus Ocean and for the continental plate closures come from studies of faunal provincialism and palaeomagnetism. The reconstruction of events starts in early Arenig time (Figure 1.2A) with Avalonia in its original position as a marginal sliver of the continent of Gondwana and the Iapetus Ocean attaining its maximum width of about 5000km. However, this changed through mid-Ordovician time as Avalonia drifted northwards (Figure 1.2B) and palaeomagnetic data locate the southern margin of Laurentia, including the northern part of Ireland and Scotland at latitude 15-20°S, with eastern Avalonia including southern Ireland, England and Wales, in latitudes of 60°S (6). By late Ordovician-early Silurian time (Figure 1.2C) the Iapetus Ocean had narrowed significantly resulting in a breakdown of faunal provinces with the spread of a cosmopolitan benthic community to the shores of all the major continents (7).

However, it was not until latest Silurian time that the Iapetus Ocean finally closed. Thus, by the Early Devonian, the Caledonian suspect terranes that had been brought together from opposite sides of that ocean by strike-slip shuffling had come together and the geological framework of Ireland and Britain was completed (Figure 1.2D). Much of the early Caledonian deformation recorded in the rocks of Ireland and northern Britain is attributed to across-strike compression, probably induced by the collision and accretion of offshore terranes or arcs with the Laurentian margin (3). In contrast, deformation of the

Figures 1.3 A-D
Palaeozoic palaeogeographical reconstruction of northern Ireland and Britain (15).

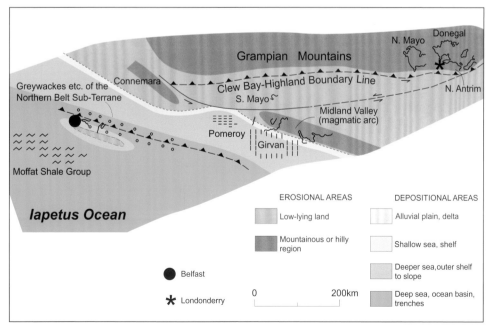

Figure 1.3A
Llanvirn (Llandeilian: c.460Ma)

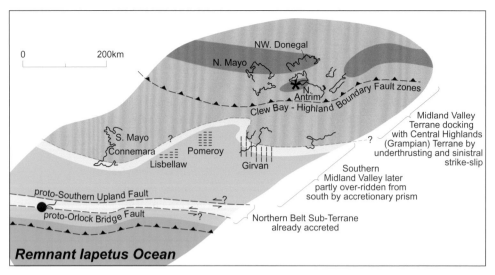

Figure 1.3B
Late Ashgill - early Llandovery (c. 440Ma)

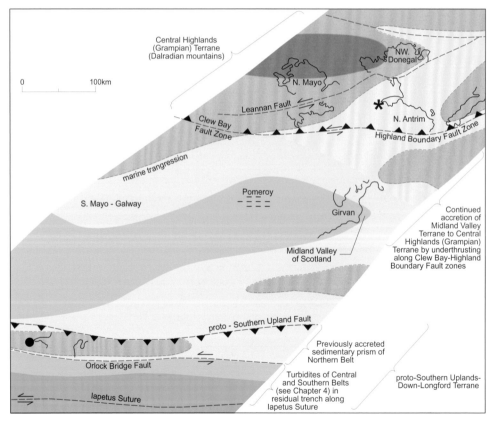

Figure 1.3C
Late Llandovery (c. 427Ma)

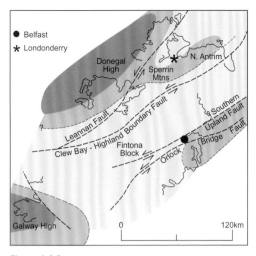

Figure 1.3 D
Early Devonian (*c.* 400Ma)

marine sediments composing the Southern Uplands-Down-Longford Terrane appears to be related almost entirely to their diachronous incorporation into an accretionary prism on that same continental margin, but with little if any evidence of collision tectonics (8).

Terrane assembly in Ireland
Assembly and docking of the terranes that form the basement in Northern Ireland commenced in mid-Ordovician time and continued for 80Ma through the Silurian and finished in the Early Devonian, about 380Ma ago (Figure 1.3A-D). Closure of the Iapetus Ocean was effected, at least in part, by large sinistral strike-slip movement (3) on the terrane-bounding faults and along internal faults (9, 10). The composite continental crust that resulted from those movements formed a basement for subsequent erosion and deposition during the remainder of Ireland's geological history.

Northern Ireland straddles three of the seven suspect terranes (11) that together constitute the Caledonian Orogen in Ireland (Figure 1.4). From north to south these are referred to as the Central Highlands (Grampian) Terrane, Midland Valley Terrane and the Southern Uplands-Down-Longford Terrane (Figure 1.5).

Central Highlands (Grampian) Terrane
The Central Highlands or Grampian Terrane consists of Moinian (Mesoproterozoic) and Dalradian (Neoproterozoic-Cambrian) rocks (Chapter 2) and Caledonian igneous intrusions. The southern margin of the terrane is marked by the concealed Fair Head-Clew Bay Line which is interpreted as the southwesterly extension (3), or major splay (10), of the Highland Boundary Fault in Scotland (Figure 1.4). This regional magnetic lineament, which extends southwestwards to Clew Bay in Co. Galway, is located 10km north of the Variscan Omagh Thrust Fault, but is concealed beneath Dalradian rocks that were thrust southwards over the Midland Valley Terrane (Chapter 8).

Midland Valley Terrane
The Midland Valley Terrane in Scotland lies between the Highland Boundary Fault and the Southern Upland Fault (Figure 1.4). In Northern Ireland, as in Scotland, Upper Palaeozoic, Mesozoic and Palaeogene rocks cover much of the terrane. However, in Co. Tyrone a late Ordovician to early Silurian succession is exposed at Pomeroy (Chapter 3) with part of an early Ordovician ophiolite and island arc volcanic complex (Tyrone Igneous Complex) at its base (12). At the core of the Tyrone Igneous Complex is the fault-bounded Central Inlier. This consists of schist and gneiss of Moinian affinity (Chapter 2) and originally formed part of the Central Highlands (Grampian) Terrane.

5

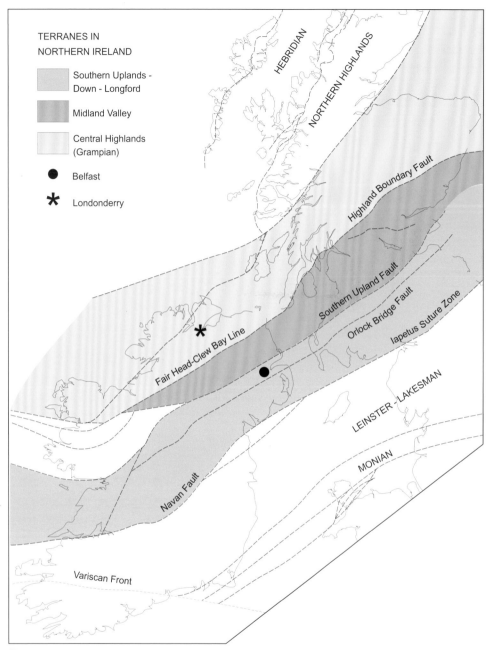

Figure 1.4
Configuration of terranes in the northern parts of Ireland and Britain (15).

Southern Uplands-Down-Longford Terrane

The Southern Uplands-Down-Longford Terrane (Figure 1.4, Chapter 4) lies between the Southern Upland Fault and the Navan Fault (Iapetus Suture Zone) and in Ireland is also referred to as the Central Terrane (11). It is interpreted as a fore-arc accretionary prism of Ordovician and Silurian marine sediment. As the ocean closed by northwards subduction of oceanic crust, clastic sediment scraped in slices from the ocean floor was diachronously accreted to the over-

6

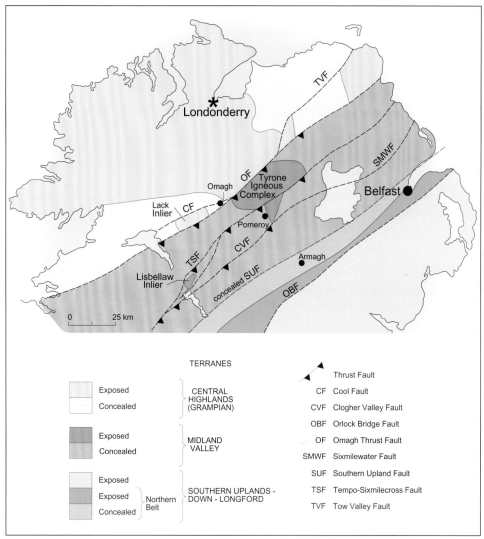

Figure 1.5
Configuration of basement terranes in northern Ireland.

riding Laurentian continent. The terrane is segmented into northeast-southwest orientated tracts separated by major strike-parallel faults. Within each tract the rock successions generally young to the north and successive tracts become incrementally younger towards the south by one or two graptolite zones each time. These apparently contradictory observations are the essential Southern Uplands paradox, ultimately resolved by the introduction of the accretionary prism model (13, 14). The widespread folding and faulting of rocks in the accretionary prism is almost entirely related to the process of subduction and accretion.

Closure of the Iapetus Ocean ceased following the oblique collision of the Laurentian and Avalonian foreland margins in late Silurian time. In response to the collision a continuous mountain range, the Caledonides, developed from the Appalachians through New England, Nova Scotia, Newfoundland, Greenland, Ireland, Scotland (Caledonia), to Scandinavia and Spitzbergen. Dismembered and eroded remnants of those mountains are found today in all of these areas.

7

References

1) Coney, P. J., Jones, D. L. and Monger, J. W. H. 1980. Cordilleran suspect terranes. *Nature*, **288**, 329-33.

2) Williams, D. M. 1984. The stratigraphy and sedimentology of the Ordovician Partry Group, southeastern Murrisk, Ireland. *Geological Journal*, **19**, 173-86.

3) Hutton, D. W. H. 1987. Strike-slip terranes and a model for the evolution of the British and Irish Caledonides. *Geological Magazine*, **124**, 405-25.

4) Murphy, F. C., Anderson, T. B., Daly, J. S., Gallagher, V., Graham, J. R., Harper, D. A. T., Johnston, J. D., Kennan, P. S., Kennedy, M. J., Long, C. B., Morris, J. H., O'Keefe, W. G., Parkes, M. A., Ryan, P. D., Sloan, R. J., Stillman, C. J., Tietzch-Tyler, D., Todd, S. P. and Wrafter, J. P. 1991. Appraisal of Caledonian suspect terranes in Ireland. *Irish Journal of Earth Sciences*, **11**, 11-41.

5) Cocks, L. R. M. 2000. The Early Palaeozoic geography of Europe. *Journal of the Geological Society, London*, **157**, 1-10.

6) Woodcock, N. H. 2000. Terranes in the British and Irish Ordovician. *In*: Fortey, R. A., Harper, D. A. T., Ingham, J. K., Owen, A. W., Parkes, M. A., Rushton, A. W. A. and Woodcock, N. H. *A Revised Correlation of Ordovician Rocks in the British Isles*, The Geological Society Special Report No. 24.

7) Cocks, L. R. M., McKerrow, W. S. and van Staal, C. R. 1997. The margins of Avalonia. *Geological Magazine*, **134**, 627-36.

8) Anderson, T. B. 2001. Structural interpretations of the Southern Uplands Terrane. *Transactions of the Royal Society of Edinburgh: Earth Sciences*, **91**, 363-73

9) Anderson, T. B. 1987. The onset and timing of Caledonian sinistral shear in County Down. *Journal of the Geological Society, London*, **144**, 817-25.

10) Ryan, P. D., Soper, N. J., Snyder, D. B., England, R. W. and Hutton, D. H. W. 1995. The Antrim-Galway Line: a resolution of the Highland Border Fault enigma of the Caledonides of Britain and Ireland. *Geological Magazine*, **132**, 171-84.

11) Harper, D. A. T. and Parkes, M. A. 2000. Ireland. *In*: Fortey, R. A., Harper, D. A. T., Ingham, J. K., Owen, A. W., Parkes, M. A., Rushton, A. W. A. and Woodcock, N. H. *A Revised Correlation of Ordovician Rocks in the British Isles*, The Geological Society Special Report No. 24.

12) Hutton, D. H. W., Aftalion, M. and Halliday, A. N. 1985. An Ordovician ophiolite in County Tyrone, Ireland. *Nature*, **315**, 210-12.

13) Mitchell, A. H. and McKerrow, W. S. 1975. Analogous evolution of the Burma Orogen and the Scottish Caledonides. *Geological Society of America Bulletin*, **86**, 302-15.

14) McKerrow, W. S., Leggett, J. K. and Eales, M. H. 1977. Imbricate thrust model of the Southern Uplands of Scotland. *Nature*, **136**, 755-70.

15) Bluck, B. J., Gibbons, W. and Ingham, J. K. 1992. Terranes. *In*: Cope, J. C., Ingham, J. K. and Rawson, P. F. (eds.). *Atlas of Palaeogeography and Lithofacies, Geological Society of London*, Memoirs, **13**, 1-4.

Chapter 2

Central Highlands (Grampian) Terrane - Metamorphic Basement

M. R. COOPER and T. P. JOHNSTON

Introduction

The Mesoproterozoic and Neoproterozoic metamorphic basement in Northern Ireland consists of deformed and metamorphosed sedimentary and volcanic rocks. Their distribution here is viewed as a continuation of similar lithologies and stratigraphical sequences in Scotland and northwest Ireland (1). In Scotland the southern boundary of this terrane is the Highland Boundary Fault. In Northern Ireland geophysical evidence indicates that the Fair Head-Clew Bay Line (Chapters 1 and 19) is the southwesterly continuation of that fault although basement rocks do occur south of that line in the Central Inlier of Co. Tyrone (2). The rocks are divided into a **Pre-Dalradian Basement** and the **Dalradian Supergroup**.

Pre-Dalradian Basement

The oldest rocks in Northern Ireland occur in two fault-bounded inliers in Counties Fermanagh and Tyrone and are tentatively assigned to the Moine Supergroup. In Co. Fermanagh the **Lough Derg Group** is part of the stratigraphical sequence in the **Lough Derg Inlier** while in Co. Tyrone the outcrop of the **Corvanaghan Formation** is restricted to the **Central Inlier** (Figure 2.1). Their precise age is not known but because the rocks have experienced higher grade metamorphism than the Dalradian rocks in Northern Ireland they are presumed to be significantly older. The evidence for a high pressure-high temperature (granulite facies) metamorphic event coupled with a radiometric date of 895±60Ma (Rb-Sr whole-rock isochron) points to a Grenvillian age for the rocks (3). In both inliers there is evidence of polyphase deformation and a high-grade regional metamorphic event overprinted by a later (Caledonian) retrogressive event.

Lough Derg Inlier (Lough Derg Group: Slishwood Division)

The Lough Derg Inlier straddles the Fermanagh-Donegal border between Lough Derg and Lower Lough Erne (Figure 2.2). Carboniferous rocks lie unconformably on the Lough Derg Group along its western and southern margins. On its southeast side the Pettigoe Fault juxtaposes the inlier with Carboniferous rocks in the Kesh-Omagh area while the Lough Derg Slide has transported inverted Dalradian Southern Highland Group rocks southwestwards across the north of the inlier in south Co. Donegal.

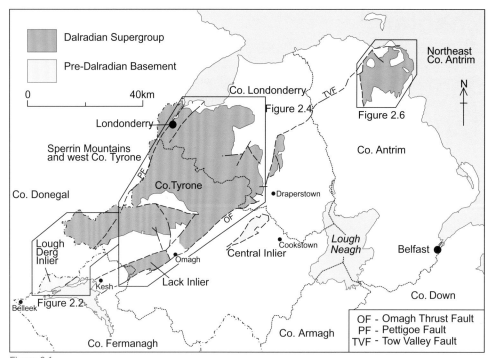

Figure 2.1
Distribution of Pre-Dalradian Basement and Dalradian rocks in Northern Ireland.

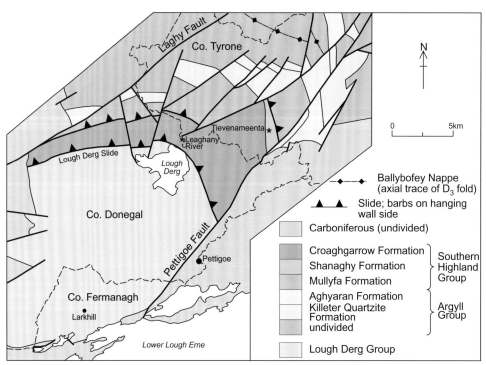

Figure 2.2
Geological map of the Pre-Dalradian Basement and Dalradian rocks in Co. Fermanagh and south Co. Donegal (16).

Photograph 1
Banded gneissose psammite of the Lough Derg Group.
Croagh mountain [G985 630], 6km northeast of
Belleek, Co. Fermanagh.
(Pen 15cm long).

The Lough Derg Group consists of medium- to coarse-grained, grey, buff and pink siliceous, feldspathic and micaceous psammites with mica schist bands (Photograph 1). Although locally gneissose and with dominantly granoblastic textures, indicative of considerable deformation and recrystallization, the psammites still retain evidence of original sedimentary structures including cross laminations and slump features. In many exposures, micaceous laminae often impart a flaggy character to the psammites and probably lie parallel to bedding.

The psammites in the Lough Derg Inlier are cut by metabasite dykes up to several metres wide and contain discrete metre-wide pods or trains of boudins parallel to the regional bedding/schistosity (Photograph 2). Mineralogically, the metabasite bodies are amphibolites with at least 75% hornblende and represent basic magma that was intruded into the sediments prior to the main deformation (4).

Photograph 2
Metabasite pod in gneissose psammite of the Lough Derg Group.
Croagh mountain [G985 630], 6km northeast of Belleek, Co. Fermanagh. (Hammer 36cm long).

Irregular and normally lenticular quartz-feldspar pegmatite veins are late-stage features that transect most other major structures and lithologies in the Lough Derg Inlier. They are composed of quartz, alkali-feldspar (microcline), biotite and muscovite and are up to 3m wide such as at Larkhill [H013 633] (Figure 2.2). Locally, the veins contain up to 65% modal potash feldspar, which in the 19th Century provided raw material for the manufacture of porcelain in the Belleek Pottery (5).

The rocks of the Lough Derg Group contain evidence of a complex deformational and thermal history during which an early formed gneissose banding was subjected to polyphase folding and deformation. During the Caledonian Orogeny the rocks were subsequently folded into a regional antiform plunging northeastwards (4). There is also evidence of at least two major metamorphic events. An early, possibly Grenvillian, event is represented by granulite facies mineral assemblages but is overprinted by younger retrogressive amphibolite facies mineral assemblages of probable Caledonian age (6). Current stratigraphical correlation, supported by radiometric dates, indicate that the Lough Derg Group is part of the Slishwood Division that includes some of the rocks of the Ox Mountains Inlier, located to the southwest (3).

Central Inlier (Corvanaghan Formation)

The Central Inlier in Co. Tyrone (Figure 2.1) is a fault-bounded fragment of pre-Caledonian Proterozoic continental crust that is surrounded by Ordovician rocks of the Tyrone Igneous Complex (Chapter 3). While the bounding faults appear to have mainly transverse movements the northeast margin of the inlier is delineated by a low-angle fault which thrusts rocks of the Corvanaghan Formation northeastwards onto the Tyrone Plutonic Group.

The Central Inlier consists of gritty, medium- to coarse-grained, grey and pinkish grey psammite with minor schistose and pelitic rocks of the **Corvanaghan Formation**. They are exposed in Corvanaghan quarry [H718 812] 10km WNW of Cookstown. Coarse lithologies commonly display a gneissose texture with pink (K-feldspar) and grey (quartz) banding and segregation. The rocks have undergone at least three separate fold phases with the major regional structure comprising an eastward-plunging, open antiform (7). Mineral assemblages indicate peak metamorphism at sillimanite grade.

The age and stratigraphical position of the Corvanaghan Formation are uncertain and on early geological maps the rocks of the Central Inlier were not distinguished from the Dalradian rocks of the Sperrin Mountains (7, 8). However, based on the evidence of high metamorphic grade and an unpublished Rb-Sr date of 640Ma (D. H. W. Hutton pers. com.) for muscovite and feldspar in late-stage, cross-cutting pegmatite veins, an early Neoproterozoic or older age is now believed to be more likely.

Dalradian Supergroup

Most of the Central Highlands (Grampian) Terrane in Northern Ireland consists of mid- to late Neoproterozoic rocks of the Dalradian Supergroup which extend from the east coast of Scotland to the Atlantic coast of Co. Donegal. In Northern Ireland the rocks crop out in the Sperrin Mountains, Lack Inlier and northeast Co. Antrim (Figure 2.1). The regional fold structures that affect the Dalradian rocks here and in Scotland seem to be of similar structural age and disposition (Figure 2.3).

Stratigraphy

The thick succession of predominantly clastic marine sediments that now forms the rocks of the **Dalradian Supergroup** was deposited in a rift basin. They are divided into the Argyll

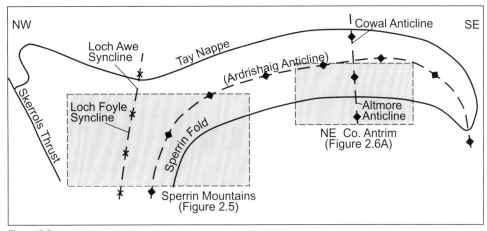

Figure 2.3
Diagrammatic cross-section to illustrate the structure of the Dalradian rocks in the southwest Highlands of Scotland and the location of equivalent structures in Northern Ireland.

Group and the Southern Highland Group (Table 2.1). In addition to the correlation with successions in Scotland wider correlations have also been made between the Dalradian Supergroup and the Fleur de Lys Supergroup in Newfoundland (9).

The rocks in the **Argyll Group** provide evidence of changing tectonic and depositional conditions at the Laurentian margin. The initial relatively stable shelf environment, which prevailed here during deposition of the Crinan Subgroup (Table 2.1), gave way to more unstable conditions. Between 700-600Ma, prior to the opening of the Iapetus Ocean, regional instability resulted from the separation of Laurentia from Baltica. Evidence of crustal stretching and thinning is found in major facies changes in the Tayvallich Subgroup (Table 2.1) in particular the appearance of metabasite (dolerite) intrusions and submarine pillow lavas that reflect upsurges of basaltic magmatism. This magmatism, and the erosion of basic igneous rocks along the continental margin, was closely associated with the formation of contemporaneous volcaniclastic sediments (green beds) that are confined to a narrow stratigraphical interval in the upper part of the Argyll Group and lower part of the Southern Highland Group.

Scotland		West Co. Tyrone/ South Co. Londonderry	Sperrin Mountains		Northeast Co. Antrim
			North	South	
Group	Subgroup	Formations			
Southern Highland			Londonderry	Mullaghcarn	Glendun
		Croaghgarrow	Ballykelly	Glengawna	Runabay
				Glenelly	
		Shanaghy			
		Mullyfa	Claudy	Dart	Altmore
Argyll	Tayvallich	Aghyaran	Dungiven Limestone		Torr Head Limestone
	Crinan	Killeter Quartzite	Newtownstewart		Owencam
					Murlough Bay
	Easdale				

Table 2.1
Correlation of Dalradian rocks in Northern Ireland (17).

The **Southern Highland Group** consists mainly of turbidites that were deposited in a tectonically unstable off-shelf environment. The basal part consists mainly of coarse-grained proximal arenites, with green beds, which pass upward into a very thick succession of finer grained lithologies of the outer fan depositional environment.

Argyll Group

Sperrin Mountains

The oldest Dalradian rocks in the Sperrin Mountains belong to the **Newtownstewart Formation** and are exposed in the core of the recumbent Sperrin Fold (Figures 2.3 and 2.4). They consist of pale grey, thickly bedded, quartzose psammite with thin pelite interbeds which outcrop between Ballynamallaght and Newtownstewart, with some of the best exposures in quarries at Letterbrat [H471 923], 2km northwest of Plumbridge, and Cashty Wood [H371 814] in the Baronscourt Estate.

The **Dungiven Limestone Formation** (Table 2.1), the highest formation in the Argyll Group, is a regionally important marker which correlates with limestone formations in northeast Co. Antrim, Co. Donegal and Scotland. The formation is lithologically diverse and although limestone is a major constituent it is associated with pelite, semi-pelite, psammite, quartzite, basaltic pillow lavas and volcaniclastic sediments. All of these lithologies are exposed on the east flank of Butterlope Glen [H493 947], 5km north of Plumbridge (Photograph 3). A lithologically distinctive limestone composed of black calcite crystals, up to 1cm in diameter, within clear calcite vein-breccia matrix occurs in a disused quarry in Banagher Glen [C669 048] 6km SSW of Dungiven (Photograph 4), and in the banks of the River Roe [C693 082] upstream of Dungiven Priory. Primary bedding in the limestone is defined by lines of graphite particles that were slightly disrupted by early diagenetic and near surface crystal growth and by variations in the amount of clastic sediment present.

Photograph 3
View looking north into Butterlope Glen [H493 947], 3.5km NNE of Plumbridge, Co. Tyrone.

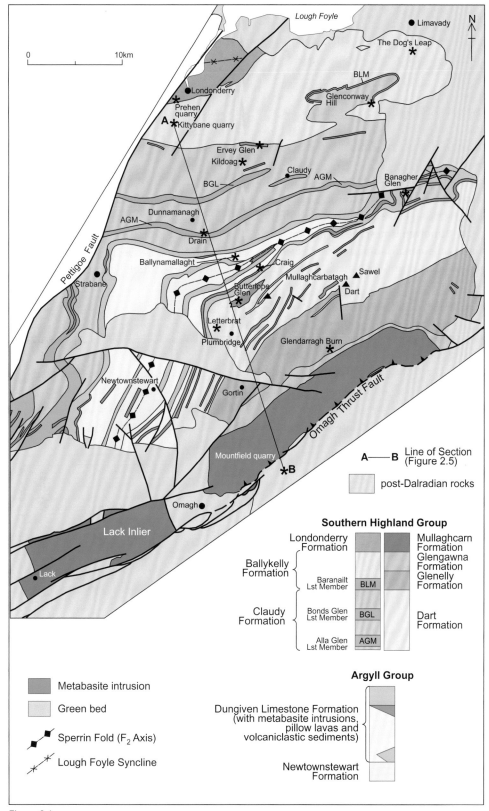

Figure 2.4
Geological map of the Dalradian rocks of the Sperrin Mountains (17).

15

Basaltic pillow lavas occur at several localities. The best example is at Craig [H523 981], about 8km northeast of Plumbridge, where the pillows, individually up to 1m in diameter and consisting of fine-grained, equigranular, metabasalt, retain the characteristic triple junction, chilled margins, gas vesicles and radial fracture pattern. They probably equate with lavas in the Dungiven and Banagher Glen areas of the Sperrin Mountains and are correlated with lavas at Artigarvan and Strabane (10).

Photograph 4
Black calcite in recrystallised limestone of the Dungiven Limestone Formation. Disused quarry on west bank of Owenrigh River [C669 048], Banagher Glen, 5km SSW of Dungiven, Co. Londonderry. (Pen 15cm long).

Southern Highland Group
The Southern Highland Group is the youngest stratigraphical division of the Dalradian in Ireland and Scotland. The stratigraphy of the Southern Highland Group is less clearly defined than the Argyll Group and consists of a thick succession of turbiditic arenites and pelitic metasediments with rare volcaniclastic (green bed) and calcareous schist units. In the Sperrin Mountains the stratigraphy of the Southern Highland Group differs markedly across the axial trace of the recumbent **Sperrin Fold** (Figures 2.4 and 2.5). An absence of distinctive marker horizons allied to lateral facies changes makes correlation difficult between formations and results in the different nomenclature north and south of the fold axis (Figure 2.4 and Table 2.1).

South Sperrin Mountains
South of the axial trace of the Sperrin Fold the Southern Highland Group comprises four formations (Table 2.2). The rocks lie on the inverted southern limb of the major regional Sperrin Fold (Figure 2.5). The transition from the underlying Dungiven Limestone Formation (Argyll Group) into the lowest levels of the **Dart Formation** can be traced from Butterlope Glen to the summit of Mullaghcarbatagh [H518 949]. At the base of the Dart Formation (11) is the **Glenga Amphibolite Member** (Table 2.2), which is interpreted as a locally resedimented volcaniclastic siltstone and sandstone (Photograph 5). The remainder of the formation consists of granule to pebble size conglomerate (Photograph 6), psammite with graded bedding, schistose semipelite and the volcaniclastic **Henry's Bridge Member**.

The **Glenelly Formation** comprises silvery to greenish grey schistose pelite and semipelite with minor psammite and limestone. Plagioclase porphyroblasts (albite-oligoclase) are ubiquitous in the rocks of this formation with more localised occurrences of small euhedral garnet and randomly distributed needles of tourmaline. There are four lithologically distinctive members which reflect variations in the depositional environment (Table 2.2). The **Oughtboy Burn Member** is a volcaniclastic unit (green bed) which indicates a change in the sediment source, possibly to a basic igneous hinterland. The **Clogherny**, **Golan Bridge** and **Garvagh Bridge members** all contain beds of limestone and schistose calcareous semipelite indicating episodes of basin shallowing in the midst of essentially deeper water sedimentation.

16

Photograph 5
Amphibolitic green beds (Glenga Amphibolite Member) of the Dart Formation. Mullaghcarbatagh mountain [H518 949], 5km northeast of Plumbridge, Co. Tyrone. (Hammer head 17cm long).

Photograph 6
Quartz pebble microconglomerate of the Dart Formation. West and south-facing slopes of Oughtnager [H505 946], 4km northeast of Plumbridge, Co. Tyrone. (Lens cap 5cm wide).

The **Glengawna Formation** (Table 2.1) is about 400m thick and is well exposed in Glendarragh Burn [H591 892] in Glenlark, 5.5km ENE of Gortin (11). The base of the formation is marked by the contrast between silvery grey lithologies of the Glenelly Formation and the black graphitic schistose pelites of the Glengawna Formation. At higher levels in the formation, pale grey quartzose psammite, semipelite and grey graphitic schistose pelite grade up into the Mullaghcarn Formation.

The **Mullaghcarn Formation**, the highest formation in this section in the south Sperrin Mountains (Figure 2.4) also forms the Lack Inlier, west of Omagh (11, 12) and consists of schistose semipelite, psammite and pelite. Bedding is not easily recognisable and the rocks show evidence of increasing strain close to the Omagh Thrust Fault. Garnet porphyroblasts from the D1 deformation are common in the Lack Inlier and are rotated passively by an S2 cleavage with a later overprint by biotite. Hornblende-bearing green beds occur close to the top of the formation at Largy [H282 661].

17

Member (thickness in type area)		Stratotype	Lithology
Southern Highland Group / Glenelly	Garvagh Bridge (c. 18m)	Garvagh Burn [H620 937] and disused quarry [H621 936]	Schistose, pale grey, calcareous and semipelite; beds and lenses of impure metalimestone
	Golan Bridge (c. 10m)	Golan Burn upstream from bridge [H526 271] and at waterfall [H523 872] 300m from bridge	Schistose semipelite, silvery grey; feldspathic psammite, fine-grained, locally calcareous and thin beds of impure metalimestone
	Clogherny (c. 40m)	Barnes Burn downstream from the bridge at [H563 904]	Schistose semipelite, calcareous, pale green to white and medium- to very coarse-grained psammite, minor chlorite and tourmaline
	Oughtboy Burn (c. 70m)	Oughtboy Burn [H592 952]	Volcaniclastic semipelite (green bed), dark green to buff, chloritic, feldspar porphyroblasts, biotite and chlorite
Dart	Henry's Bridge (c. 50m)	Glensass Burn for 250m upstream from Henry's Bridge [H515 917]	Volcaniclastic semipelite (green bed), dark greenish brown, chloritic
	Glenga Amphibolite (c. 100m)	Mullaghcarbatagh (517m) summit [H518 947] and col to east	Schistose amphibolite, dark green, fine-grained, beds of pale brown schistose, feldspathic and calcareous semipelite

Table 2.2
Lithostratigraphy of members within the Dart and Glenelly formations in the south Sperrin Mountains (11).

North Sperrin Mountains and North Co. Londonderry

North of the axial trace of the Sperrin Fold the Southern Highland Group is divided into three formations (Figure 2.4 and Table 2.3). Bedding dips are towards the north and the rocks young northwards in a normal stratigraphical succession (Figure 2.4). The basal **Claudy Formation** is exposed in Kildoag quarry [C497 084], 4.5km WNW of Claudy and consists of psammite units up to 1m thick alternating with laminae of silvery grey phyllitic semipelite and rare layers of greyish black phyllitic pelite up to 1m thick. The presence of chlorite, white mica and biotite porphyroblasts indicates metamorphism under upper greenschist facies

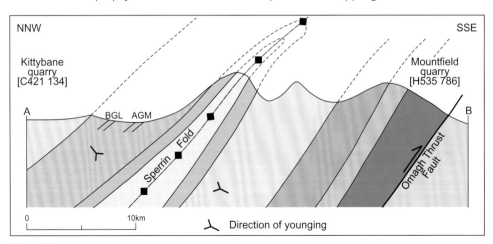

Figure 2.5
Simplified cross-section of the Dalradian rocks in the Sperrin Mountains.
(see line of section A-B on Figure 2.4)

18

conditions. Two limestone units form markers in the Claudy Formation. The **Alla Glen Limestone Member** is exposed in the partially flooded quarry at Drain [C458 019], 2km southeast of Dunnamanagh and the **Bonds Glen Limestone Member** in quarries in Bond's Glen [C491 067], 5km west of Claudy. Bedding surfaces are conspicuous in the limestone and phyllitic semipelite layers preserve a coplanar slaty cleavage (S1). Both surfaces are crenulated by a northwards-dipping S2 cleavage that is axial planar to minor F2 folds plunging towards the ENE. The top of the Claudy Formation is exposed in the Crunkin Burn at Ervey [C522 121] and is marked by a thin epidote-rich volcaniclastic semipelite (green bed) (13).

The base of the succeeding **Ballykelly Formation** is marked by the **Baranailt Limestone Member** which is exposed in a stream [C635 148] on the northeast flank of Glenconway Hill (14). Structurally the **Ballykelly Formation** is situated on the southeast limb of the Lough Foyle Syncline (Figure 2.3). The formation is exposed in Kittybane quarry [C421 134] 1km northeast of New Buildings. At The Dog's Leap, on the River Roe [C674 204] south of Limavady, mixed psammite and pelite show the regionally penetrative S2 cleavage strongly crenulating and transposing an earlier composite bedding/S1 (pressure solution) fabric.

The outcrop of the succeeding **Londonderry Formation** lies at the core of the Lough Foyle Syncline (Figure 2.4) with typical lithologies (Table 2.3) exposed in Prehen quarry [C423 147] southwest of Londonderry. These rocks have experienced relatively low levels of metamorphism and the dominant fabric is a penetrative S2 cleavage that is sub-parallel to a composite bedding/S1 fabric but dips more steeply to the northwest. The S2 cleavage is axial planar to southeasterly verging minor folds and its intersection lineation with the earlier fabric plunges at up to 15° to the northeast. Sedimentary structures such as grading are common and these, combined with bedform geometry, indicate that the strata are the right-way-up and young to the northwest.

	Formation	Lithology	Member	Lithology
Southern Highland Group	Londonderry	Meta-arenite, greenish grey, coarse to granule grade, thin schistose and phyllitic semipelite and pelite		
	Ballykelly	Meta-arenite, coarse-grained at base becoming fine- to medium-grained at top	Baranailt Limestone	4-10m of meta-limestone and meta-dolostone, pale grey, crystalline; thin schistose semipelite
	Claudy	Psammite, quartz and feldspar rich, coarse detrital grains of blue and grey quartz and pink and white feldspar;minor semipelite,limestone and green beds	Bonds Glen Limestone	Up to 100m of meta-limestone, pale to dark bluish grey, medium- to coarse-grained, in beds up to 0.75m thick separated by thin dark grey to black pelite, pyritous
			Alla Glen Limestone	Banded meta-limestone, pale grey to greyish blue, coarsely crystalline, units up to 1m thick, separated by laminae of grey to black graphitic phyllitic semipelite and pelite

Table 2.3
Lithostratigraphy of the Southern Highland Group in the north Sperrin Mountains and north Co. Londonderry (14).

West Co. Tyrone

The Dalradian succession of central and south Donegal (15) extends south and eastwards into west Co. Tyrone and south Co. Londonderry (16). In west Co. Tyrone the Dalradian rocks lie on the inverted southern limb of the Ballybofey Nappe (Figure 2.2). The youngest strata (Table 2.4) are thrust southeastwards over the Moinian rocks of the Lough Derg Inlier along the Lough Derg Slide (15).

The lowest stratigraphical unit in west Co. Tyrone, the **Killeter Quartzite Formation** (Argyll Group), is correlated with the Newtownstewart Formation in the Sperrin Mountains (17).

The most distinctive lithostratigraphical unit in west Co. Tyrone, the **Aghyaran Formation** (Table 2.4), is equivalent to the Dungiven Limestone Formation in the Sperrin Mountains and the Torr Head Limestone Formation in northeast Co. Antrim.

The Southern Highland Group in west Co. Tyrone is divided into three formations (Table 2.4). Extensive exposures of all three formations occur in the vicinity of Tievenameenta [H164 758] ENE of Lough Derg (Figure 2.2). The distinctive mixed lithologies of the **Shanaghy Formation**, and its contacts with adjacent formations, can be traced north for 2km from the sub-Carboniferous unconformity [H166 753], onto the east flank of the hill at Tievenameenta. Lying east of the outcrop of the Shanaghy Formation are scattered exposures of the Mullyfa Formation while the Croaghgarrow Formation is exposed on the hill at Tievenameenta. The widespread occurrence of garnet and biotite in west Co. Tyrone indicates that metamorphic grade is in the upper greenschist to lower amphibolite facies. Kyanite also occurs in the **Croaghgarrow Formation** as bladed crystals up to 2cm long in schist and as felted masses in tourmaline-rich pegmatites, on the east bank of the Leaghany River [H096 755], suggesting that locally the metamorphic grade may have reached the lower or middle amphibolite facies.

Northeast Co. Antrim

The Dalradian inlier in northeast Co. Antrim (18) is unconformably overlain by Carboniferous, Cretaceous and Palaeogene strata at its margins (Figure 2.6). The succession, which is divided into six formations (Table 2.5), lies on the lower, inverted limb of the Altmore Anticline (Figures 2.3 and 2.6) which is regarded as the southwesterly continuation of the Cowal Anticline from southwest Scotland (7, 19).

Group	Sub-Group	Formation (thickness)	Lithology
Southern Highland		Croaghgarrow (1100-3500m)	Schistose psammite and semipelite, pale greenish grey, graded pebbly psammite; numerous quartz segregations
		Shanaghy (40-200m)	Schistose amphibolite, medium grey-green, siliceous, volcaniclastic; dark green-black amphibole-rich metabasite intrusions; numerous quartz segregations and quartz-feldspar pegmatites
		Mullyfa (750-2500m)	Psammite, bedded (up to 75cm) and graded, blue quartz pebbles up to 2cm across in layers; thin pink and pale grey quartzite, schistose pelite, rare meta-limestone
Argyll	Tayvallich	Aghyaran (400-1000m)	Interbedded meta-limestone (up to 25cm) and meta-dolomite. Quartzite and associated psammite locally pebbly and graphitic near base
	Crinan	Killeter Quartzite (0-1100m)	Feldspathic quartzite in beds up to 50cm thick, rare graded pebbly beds

Table 2.4
Lithostratigraphy of the Dalradian rocks in west Co. Tyrone (16, 17).

The lowest two formations of the **Argyll Group**, the **Murlough Bay** and **Owencam formations**, consist mainly of coarse-grained schistose psammite and semipelite. The most distinctive and youngest unit in the Argyll Group is the **Torr Head Limestone Formation** (Photographs 7 and 7A), which correlates with the Dungiven Limestone Formation in the Sperrin Mountains, the Culdaff Limestone in Co. Donegal and Loch Tay Limestone in Scotland (20). Clastic sediments in the limestone and at the base of the overlying Altmore Formation indicate deposition on a shallow marine, storm-influenced shelf.

The **Southern Highland Group** in the inlier is represented by the **Altmore, Runabay** and **Glendun formations** which consist mainly of pebbly and coarse-grained psammite. Although the sediment at the base of the Altmore Formation was deposited in shallow water the remainder of the Southern Highland Group succession was deposited as turbidite

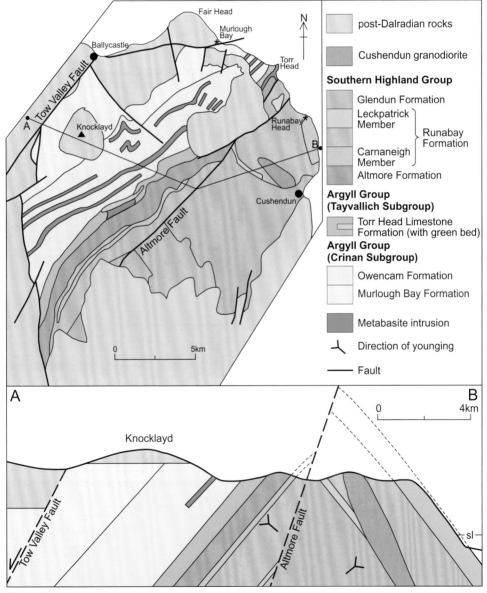

Figure 2.6
Geological map and diagrammatic cross-section of the Dalradian rocks in northeast Co. Antrim (18).

21

Group	Sub-Group	Formation (thickness)	Lithology
Southern Highland		Glendun (1100-3500m)	Psammite, graded and pebbly schist and pelite, pale greenish grey; numerous quartz segregations
		Runabay (40-200m)	Schistose psammite and feldspathic grit; two green bed members; numerous quartz segregations and feldspar pegmatites
		Altmore (750-2500m)	Feldspathic gritty psammite, coarse-grained, bedded (up to 75cm) and graded, thin layers of blue quartz pebbles up to 2cm. Thin pink and pale grey quartzite, schistose pelite, rare meta-limestone
Argyll	Tayvallich	Torr Head Limestone	Meta-limestone, dark blue-grey to black, coarsely crystalline, graphitic, with laminae of clastic quartz grains and pods and lenses of chert
	Crinan	Owencam	Schistose coarse-grained psammite with pebbly and granule grade layers, grading and channelling common; rare semipelite; top 2m represented by meta-limestone, calcareous schistose semipelite and pelite
		Murlough Bay	Feldspathic grit, coarse-grained, very thick beds, psammite and semipelite

Table 2.5
Lithostratigraphy of the Dalradian rocks in northeast Co. Antrim (18).

fans in a rapidly subsiding basin. The **Runabay Formation** contains two distinctive volcaniclastic (green bed) members. At the base of the formation the **Carnaneigh Green Bed Member** consists of pale grey and green bedded schistose chlorite-epidote rich semipelite. The **Leckpatrick Green Bed Member** occurs at the top of the formation and comprises mid- to dark green, schistose, chlorite-hornblende rich semipelite with albite and biotite porphyroblasts (21). Both green bed members are composed of volcaniclastic material derived by erosion of coeval extrusive and intrusive mafic rocks or from contemporaneous basic volcanicity.

Deformation of the Dalradian

The Dalradian rocks in Northern Ireland were intensely deformed and metamorphosed during the Grampian Orogeny (Figure 3.3). At least four separate phases of deformation and associated structures are recognised in the Dalradian rocks in Northern Ireland. Folds and cleavages resulting from the earliest deformation (D1) are, at best, barely discernible and are generally obscured in a composite fabric defined by bedding surfaces (Ss) and the sub-parallel first schistosity (S1). D2 was the dominant deformation of the Grampian Orogeny in Northern Ireland and was associated with the formation of major regional southeast-facing recumbent anticlines, the Sperrin Fold in the Sperrin Mountains and the Altmore Anticline in northeast Co. Antrim. These structures are analogous to the Tay Nappe in Scotland, which formed as a result of D2 flattening, tightening and extension of an earlier D1 anticline (22). A penetrative schistosity, which developed throughout the southern part of the Sperrin Mountains and in northeast Co. Antrim, strongly crenulates the earlier formed composite Ss/S1 surfaces.

In the south Sperrin Mountains, the D3 deformation resulted in southeasterly-verging minor folds and a number of low-angle, northwards inclined thrust surfaces such as the Omagh Thrust Fault, which transported Dalradian rocks to the SSE over the early Ordovician Tyrone Igneous Complex (23). In west Co. Tyrone and central and south Co. Donegal the Ballybofey Nappe is the dominant D3 structure controlling the disposition of Dalradian strata (Figure 2.2). This sub-recumbent structure closes and faces towards the southeast and is disrupted by several northeast-trending late Caledonian faults (24). The lowest structural levels of the Dalradian succession in west Co. Tyrone are in tectonic contact with the Lough Derg Group along the Lough Derg Slide (15, 16).

Photograph 7
Torr Head [D234 406] in northeast Co. Antrim with the North Channel and the Mull of Kintyre (Scotland) in the background. 11km east of Ballycastle, Co. Antrim.

Post- D3 structures in Northern Ireland mainly take the form of localised sets of kink bands and late stage brittle fractures.

Regional Metamorphism

The pattern of regional metamorphism in the Dalradian Supergroup in Northern Ireland reflects a thermal and pressure gradient increasing from lower greenschist facies in the north to lower amphibolite facies in the south, close to the Omagh Thrust Fault (10). Metamorphic minerals including albite, muscovite, biotite, epidote, chlorite and actinolite occur throughout a large part of the Sperrin Mountains and are indicative of greenschist facies metamorphism. However, in the southern part of the Sperrin Mountains and in the Lack Inlier, garnet (almandine) porphyroblasts are indicative of slightly higher grade metamorphism in the upper greenschist to lower amphibolite facies. The garnets commonly have chloritic alteration rims indicating a later retrogressive phase possibly linked to late Caledonian movements on the Omagh Thrust Fault.

Photograph 7A
Thin bedded limestone at the top of the inverted Torr Head Limestone Formation with psammite and gritty psammite of the Altmore Formation below. Torr Head [D234 406], 11km east of Ballycastle, Co. Antrim. (Hammer head 17cm long).

References

1) Hutton, D. H. W. 1987. Strike-slip terranes and a model for the evolution of the British and Irish Caledonides. *Geological Magazine.* **125**, 405-25.

2) Bluck, B. J., Gibbons, W. and Ingham, J. K. 1992. Terranes. In: Cope, J. C. W., Ingham, J. K. and Rawson, P. F. (eds.). *Atlas of Palaeogeography and Lithofacies. Geological Society of London, Memoirs,* **13**, 1-4.

3) Max, M. D. and Long, C. B. 1985. Pre-Caledonian basement in Ireland and its cover relationships. *Geological Journal.* **20**, 341-66.

4) Anderson, J. G. C. 1948. The occurrence of Moinian rocks in Ireland. *Quarterly Journal of the Geological Society of London.* **103**, (for 1947), 171-88.

5) Boswell, P. G. H. 1918. British resources of sands and rocks used in glass-making. 2nd edition. London.

6) Sanders, I. S., Daly, J. S. and Davies, G. R. 1987. Late Proterozoic high pressure granulite facies metamorphism in the north-east Ox Inlier, north-west Ireland. *Journal of Metamorphic Petrology,* **5**, 69-85.

7) Wilson, H. E. 1972. *The Regional Geology of Northern Ireland.* HMSO, Belfast.

8) Cobbing, E. J. C. 1964. The Highland Boundary Fault in east Tyrone. *Geological Magazine,* **101**, 496-501.

9) Kennedy, M. J. 1975. The Fleur de Lys Supergroup: stratigraphic comparisons of Moine and Dalradian equivalents in Newfoundland and the British Caledonides. *Journal of the Geological Society, London,* **131**, 305-10.

10) Hartley, J. J. 1938. The Dalradian rocks of the Sperrin Mountains and adjacent areas in Northern Ireland. *Proceedings of the Royal Irish Academy.* **44B**, 141-71.

11) Geological Survey of Northern Ireland, 1995. Draperstown, Northern Ireland Sheet 26. Solid Geology. 1:50,000. (Keyworth, Nottingham: British Geological Survey).

12) Geological Survey of Northern Ireland, 1995. Omagh, Northern Ireland Sheet 33. Solid Geology. 1:50,000. (Keyworth, Nottingham: British Geological Survey).

13) Arthurs, J.W. 1976. The geology and metalliferous mineral potential of the Sperrin Mountains area. *Geological Survey of Northern Ireland, Special Report*

14) Geological Survey of Northern Ireland, 1981. Limavady, Northern Ireland Sheet 12 and part of Sheet 6. Solid. 1:50,000. (Southampton: Ordnance Survey for the Geological Survey of Northern Ireland).

15) Alsop, G. I. and Hutton, D. H. W. 1990. A review and revision of Dalradian stratigraphy in central and southern Donegal, Ireland. *Irish Journal of Earth Sciences.* **10**, 181-98.

16) Geological Survey of Northern Ireland, 1994. Kesh, Northern Ireland Sheet 32. Solid Geology. 1:50,000. (Keyworth, Nottingham: British Geological Survey).

17) Geological Survey of Northern Ireland, 1997. Northern Ireland. Solid Geology (second edition). 1:250,000. (Keyworth, Nottingham: British Geological Survey).

18) Geological Survey of Northern Ireland, 2002. Ballycastle, Northern Ireland Sheet 8. Solid Geology (second edition). 1:50,000. (Keyworth, Nottingham: British Geological Survey).

19) Arthurs, J.W. 1976. The geology and metalliferous mineral potential of north-east Antrim. *Geological Survey of Northern Ireland, Special Report*

20) McCallien, W. J. 1931. A contribution to the correlation of the Dalradian rocks of Scotland. *Geological Magazine.* **68**, 153-75.

21) Wilson, H. E. and Robbie, J. A. 1966. *Geology of the Country around Ballycastle.* Memoir of the Geological Survey of Northern Ireland. HMSO, Belfast.

22) Stephenson, D. and Gould, D. 1995. *British regional geology: the Grampian Highlands (4th edition).* (London: HMSO for the British Geological Survey).

23) Alsop, G. I. and Hutton, D. H. W. 1993. Major southeast-directed Caledonian thrusting and folding in the Dalradian rocks of mid-Ulster: Implications for Caledonian tectonics and mid-crustal shear zones. *Geological Magazine.* **130**, 233-44.

24) Alsop, G. I. 1991. Gravitational collapse and extension along a mid-crustal detachment: the Lough Derg Slide, north-west Ireland. *Geological Magazine.* **128**, 345-54.

Chapter 3

Midland Valley Terrane

M. R. COOPER and W. I. MITCHELL

Introduction

Basement rocks of the Midland Valley Terrane in Northern Ireland comprise the Proterozoic **Central Inlier** and early Palaeozoic **Tyrone Igneous Complex** (1, 2, 3). Both geological units are bounded by faults (Figure 3.1) and have very different geological origins. At its southern margin, the Tyrone Igneous Complex is overlain unconformably by late Ordovician and early Silurian sediments of the **Pomeroy Inlier** (1). Further west, the fault-bounded **Lisbellaw Inlier** consists of early Silurian sedimentary rocks (4).

The Corvanaghan Formation of the Central Inlier (5) is lithologically, structurally and metamorphically distinct from the Tyrone Igneous Complex. It is tentatively assigned to the Moine Supergroup and is possibly an exhumed slice of the Central Highlands (Grampian) Terrane (Chapter 2).

The Tyrone Igneous Complex is broadly divided into two parts. The basal **Tyrone Plutonic Group** comprises basic igneous rocks including **gabbro, dolerite** and **basalt**. Their field relationships reflect a complex thermal and tectonic history and they are believed to

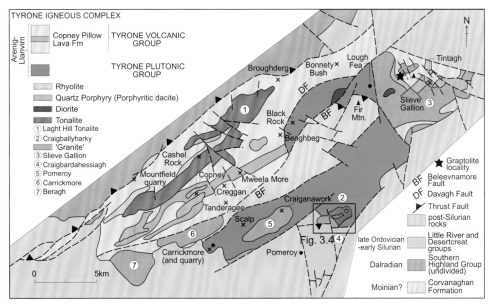

Figure 3.1
Geological map of the Central Inlier (Corvanaghan Formation), Tyrone Igneous Complex and Pomeroy Inlier.

25

represent a portion of an early Ordovician **ophiolite** (oceanic crust) (6). The **Tyrone Volcanic Group** forms the upper part of the Tyrone Igneous Complex and consists of basic to intermediate pillow lavas and volcaniclastic tuffs, rhyolites, banded chert, jasper and argillaceous sediment. The sequence is interpreted as being deposited in a **volcanic arc** setting. Graptolites from the Tyrone Volcanic Group give an Arenig-Llanvirn age (7). The Tyrone Igneous Complex and Central Inlier are intruded by volcanic arc-related plutonic and higher level granitoid intrusions. Zircon dating (U/Pb) indicates that their intrusion occurred at 470-465Ma (mid-Arenig to early Llanvirn), soon after the formation of the ophiolite and volcanic arc sequence and provides a minimum age for the Tyrone Plutonic Group.

The Tyrone Igneous Complex is one of an association of complexes in Great Britain and Ireland that have oceanic affinities. They all contain sections of ophiolite, as well as examples of volcanic arc, accretionary prism and fore-arc basin deposits. However, the Tyrone Igneous Complex is one of the largest and most varied in that it includes part of an ophiolite, a volcanic arc sequence, arc-related granitoids and a portion of continental crust. The Tyrone Igneous Complex is thus closely related to the Highland Border Complex and the Ballantrae Igneous Complex of Scotland and to the Clew Bay Complex of western Ireland, in that they all fall along or are located to the southeast of the Highland Boundary Fault-Fair Head-Clew Bay Line (8).

Tyrone Igneous Complex
Tyrone Plutonic Group

The **Tyrone Plutonic Group** forms the southern half of the Tyrone Igneous Complex (Figure 3.1). In the northeast part of its outcrop the rocks consist mainly of variably tectonised and

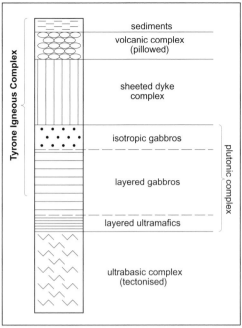

Figure 3.2
Idealised section of an ophiolite showing the extent of the Tyrone Igneous Complex.

Photograph 1
Intensely folded hornblende schist (Tyrone Plutonic Group) grades into 'normal', coarse-grained hornblende gabbro. Scalp hill [H635 745], 3km northeast of Carrickmore, Co. Tyrone. Hammer length 33cm.

Photograph 2
Black Rock from the Beaghbeg Road [H685 837], 13km NNE of Carrickmore, Co. Tyrone.

Photograph 3
Tyrone Plutonic Group showing sharp contact between early dolerite and a later intrusive very coarse-grained, hornblende gabbro. Black Rock [H685 837], 13km NNE of Carrickmore, Co. Tyrone. Hammer shaft width 3cm.

metamorphosed gabbro and hornblende gabbro (3) with both layered and isotropic varieties present. Dolerite, in the form of a sheeted dyke complex, appears confined to the southwest around Carrickmore (1). This association of rock types and their field relationships strongly supports the idea that they represent the upper layers of an ophiolite (Figure 3.2).

Gabbros, with **cumulate layering** (9) reflecting textural and compositional variations, form ice-scoured knolls at Scalp [H635 745] northeast of Carrickmore (Figure 3.1). Metre-scale and centimetre-scale layering is composed of alternating dark mafic and pale felsic bands. While there appears to be no regular relationship between the bands, sections of metre-scale layering are always separated by a thin zone of monomineralic bands. At Scalp, there is every gradation from normal layered gabbro to intensely deformed gabbro resembling hornblende schist (Photograph 1). Epidote-amphibolite

27

metamorphic assemblages are developed without any accompanying deformation and may be the result of metasomatic alteration by circulating hot brines.

At Black Rock [H685 837], coarse-grained hornblende gabbro is in contact with, and contains xenoliths of, an early-formed suite of dolerite and is intruded by younger, 1-2m wide, basalt and dolerite dykes (Photographs 2 and 3). Also of note here, is the irregular form of intrusions and veins of pegmatitic gabbro. This assemblage of cross-cutting rock types may have formed in a transitional zone between a plutonic magma chamber and the sheeted dyke complex during the formation of the ophiolite. Intrusions of **porphyritic granitoid** and fine-grained **dacite** also invade the gabbro and dolerite (Photograph 4). The **sheeted dyke complex**, which is best exposed in Carrickmore quarry [H609 721], consists of parallel, northeast-southwest trending dolerite dykes that are either vertical or dip steeply southwards (6). The dykes average 1m in thickness and intrude one another forming two-sided chilled margins, and more commonly, one-sided chilled margins that are characteristic of sheeted dyke complexes.

Tyrone Volcanic Group

The **Tyrone Volcanic Group** consists of volcanic, volcaniclastic and thin, occasionally fossiliferous, argillaceous sedimentary rocks (Figure 3.1). Its outcrop is bounded in the north by the Omagh Thrust Fault and by the Beleevnamore and Davagh faults in the south.

Within the Tyrone Volcanic Group there is evidence of at least three volcanic cycles. The base of each cycle is defined by a basic volcanic component, composed largely of pillowed basaltic lavas, while at the top are laminated chert, jasper and black mudstone. The background lithology consists of pale-greenish grey, schistose, chlorite-epidote-sericite **tuff** which range

Photograph 4
Dolerite and gabbro (Tyrone Plutonic Group) intruded by fine-grained, porphyritic granitoid. Black Rock [H685 837], 13km NNE of Carrickmore, Co. Tyrone. Hammer head length 18cm.

Photograph 5
Augened 'acid' clast in coarse-grained volcanic breccia/lapilli tuff of the Tyrone Volcanic Group. Beaghbeg [H674 828], south side of hill top, 10.5km NNW of Pomeroy, Co. Tyrone. (Pen 15cm long).

28

Photograph 6
The locality at Creggan from the Creggan Road [H623 782], 6km north of Carrickmore, Co. Tyrone.

Photograph 7
One of several exposures of volcanic breccia of the Tyrone Volcanic Group. Angular clasts consist mainly of felsitic lithology with rare basalt and jasper in a coarse-grained chloritic matrix. Creggan [H623 782], 6km north of Carrickmore, Co. Tyrone.
(Pen 15cm long).

from fine-grained ash to coarse-grained lapilli tuff. The Group also contains clast- and matrix-supported **volcanic breccias** composed of angular and rounded fragments of rhyolite and dacite in a tuffaceous, or more rarely, ignimbritic matrix. The deposits are laterally impersistent and most likely formed close to explosive vents. Rock crags southeast of Beaghbeg [H674 828] are formed of coarse-grained lapilli tuff with isolated clasts up to 5cm in diameter of angular, pale pink to grey felsite (Photograph 5), and rare examples of banded cream coloured chert and jasper. At Creggan [H623 782], crudely bedded, clast- and matrix-supported breccias contain numerous clasts of buff-weathering felsitic and rare fragments of basalt and jasper (Photographs 6 and 7).

The base of the lowest volcanic cycle is represented by the **Copney Pillow Lava Formation** (Figure 3.1) which forms the prominent knolls between Copney Hill [H600 777] and Creggan [H623 782]. At Mweela More [H641 792], north of the Cookstown Road (Photograph 8), there are spectacular examples of undeformed pillow lavas consisting of fine- to medium-

Photograph 8
Mweela More [H641 792] from the A505, Cookstown Road 7.3km NNE of Carrickmore, Co. Tyrone.

grained, locally porphyritic basalt (Photograph 9). The triple junctions between some of the pillows contain pale pink to red chert or fine-grained hyaloclastite breccia. Thin layers of grey and green, banded chert occur with pillow lavas at the base of the southernmost crag at Mweela More (Photograph 10).

The top of the lowest cycle is represented by the **Tanderagee Siliceous Ironstone Formation** (1) which is exposed at Tanderagee [H624 763] (Figure 3.1) and consists of thin beds of jasper and banded chert. The top of the second cycle is represented southwest of Bonnety Bush [H726 888] by a bed of jasper at least 1m thick, with millimetre-scale banding, interbedded with pale green and grey tuffs and laminae of black mudstone. The occurrence of beds of black chert and graphitic pelite at Broughderg [H671 878] may represent the top of the third cycle (Figure 3.1).

A small exposure of dark grey to black, **graphitic mudstone** in Sruhanleanantawey Burn [H791 878] on Slieve Gallion contains fragments of the graptolites *Tetragraptus serra and Sigmagraptus* s.l. (7). They indicate a Lower Ordovician (Arenig to Llanvirn) age for the mudstone and, by implication, for the surrounding volcanic rocks of the Tyrone Volcanic Group.

Photograph 9
Pillow lavas of the Tyrone Volcanic Group composed of fine- to medium-grained basalt showing well preserved triple junction. Mweela More [H641 792], 7.3km NNE of Carrickmore, Co. Tyrone.

Photograph 10
Finely laminated chert of the Tyrone Volcanic Group exposed at base of southernmost crag. Mweela More [H641 792], 7.3km NNE of Carrickmore, Co. Tyrone.

30

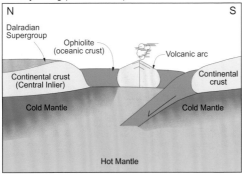

A: Early Arenig (c. 475-470Ma)

N   S

Dalradian
Supergroup
          Ophiolite
          (oceanic crust)   Volcanic arc

Continental crust   Continental
(Central Inlier)   crust

Cold Mantle   Cold Mantle

Hot Mantle

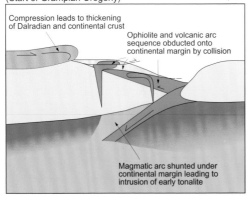

B: Middle to late Arenig (c. 470-465Ma)
(Start of Grampian Orogeny)

Compression leads to thickening
of Dalradian and continental crust

          Ophiolite and volcanic arc
          sequence obducted onto
          continental margin by collision

          Magmatic arc shunted under
          continental margin leading to
          intrusion of early tonalite

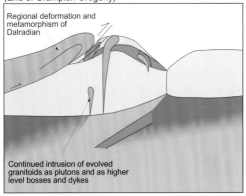

C: Late Arenig to early Llanvirn (c. 465Ma)
(End of Grampian Orogeny)

Regional deformation and
metamorphism of
Dalradian

Continued intrusion of evolved
granitoids as plutons and as higher
level bosses and dykes

Figure 3.3
Plate tectonic amalgamation of the Tyrone Igneous
Complex on the Laurentian continental margin during
the Grampian Orogeny.

Each cycle thus commences with submarine lavas. The succeeding volcaniclastic rocks are largely of submarine origin but may include a minor subaerial component. The laminated chert and jasper probably accumulated in a volcanic environment as colloidal gel deposited within the surrounding tuffs. At a later stage, as water levels deepened within the basin, black mudstone was deposited in quiet euxinic conditions during periods of reduced volcanic activity. As a single succession of volcanic and sedimentary rocks, the Tyrone Volcanic Group becomes progressively more acidic from base to top while within each cycle there is a trend from basic to acidic between the base and top. These cycles are believed to have been active in an island arc or back-arc setting on the northern margin of the Iapetus Ocean (Figure 3.3A).

Early Palaeozoic arc-related intrusives

The Tyrone Plutonic and Tyrone Volcanic groups are intruded by a small number of arc-related, early Caledonian intrusions (10). While these plutonic intrusions of tonalite, granodiorite and granite mostly cut the Central Inlier and ophiolite, related higher level bosses, sills and dykes of porphyritic dacite and rhyolite are restricted to the volcanic arc sequence. These field relationships suggest that the ophiolite and volcanic arc sequence were already obducted over the Central Inlier prior to the intrusion of these intrusives (Figures 3.3B and 3.3C).

The **Laght Hill Tonalite** (Figure 3.1) is a high-level intrusion consisting of three interconnected sill-like bodies. At Cashel Rock [H600 808], the greenish grey, coarse-grained tonalite is composed of white quartz, pale grey plagioclase (altered to white mica) and green hornblende. The rock contains a penetrative fabric. Tonalite at Cashel Rock is intruded by weakly flow-banded rhyolites that are identical to silicic clasts found in the volcanic breccias of the

31

Tyrone Volcanic Group. The rhyolite also contains partially assimilated xenoliths of tonalite.

At Craigballyharky and Craigbardahessiagh (Figure 3.4), the relationship between the later intrusions of tonalite, granodiorite and gabbro and the older basaltic pillow lavas of the Tyrone Plutonic Group (Figure 3.4) is evident. West of the summit of Craigballyharkey [H734 756], coarse-grained pinkish white tonalite is composed of altered feldspar (60%), quartz (30%) and hornblende (7%). Between the gabbro and tonalite, quartz-diorite is present and consists of reduced sodic plagioclase feldspar (25%), hornblende (25%) and increased quartz (45%). However, the suggested magma mingling relationship at Craigballyharky, between tonalite and gabbro (11, 6) is not convincing. Diffuse boundaries between the tonalite and host gabbro appear to be the result of erosion of a sheeted rock association (Photograph 11). At the diffuse contact, ocelli comprising quartz megacrysts appear to have moved from the quartz-diorite into the gabbro (11). In addition, hornblende coronas developed on the megacrysts are more likely to be the result of post-crystallization metasomatic growth. Although sharp contacts are commonly observed between the tonalite and gabbro, the absence of a chilled margin to the younger tonalite intrusion suggests that at the time of its intrusion the ophiolite was hot but not molten.

The slightly younger, very coarse-grained Craigbardahessiagh granodiorite [H722 743] is composed of equal proportions of brown turbid feldspar and quartz with minor biotite and hornblende (10%).

The four granite plutons at Beragh, Carrickmore, Pomeroy and Slieve Gallion are petrographically similar (Figure 3.1). The pinkish grey Pomeroy granite exposed

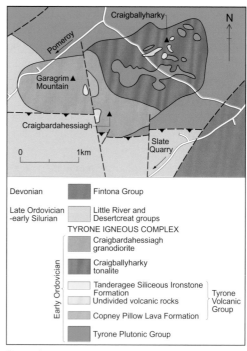

Figure 3.4
Geological map of the intrusive complex of the Tyrone Igneous Complex at Craigbardahessiagh and Craigballyharky (1).

Photograph 11
The apparently diffuse boundary between ocelli-bearing quartz-diorite (left of picture), one of a suite of arc-related intrusives, and gabbro of the Tyrone Plutonic Group probably formed as a result of recent erosion of the sheeted rock association. Summit of Craigballyharkey [H733 757], 5km northeast of Pomeroy, Co. Tyrone. (Compass 18cm long).

at Craiganawork [H677 759] is typical of the group and is composed of large crystals of alkali (35%) and plagioclase feldspar (25%), biotite (5%) and quartz. A coarse northeast-southwest trending fabric dips steeply to the northern boundary of the pluton and is defined by ribbons of large quartz grains. On Slieve Gallion, the undeformed pinkish red, biotite granite exposed at Tintagh [H810 872] is in contact with pink, porphyritic rhyolite.

The **Cushendun Granodiorite** is located 2km northwest of Cushendun in Co. Antrim (Figure 2.6). It is exposed on Cushleake Mountain [D233 434] where petrographically the rock is a porphyritic dacite (fine-grained granodiorite) composed of euhedral phenocrysts of zoned plagioclase feldspar (40%), quartz (4%) and biotite (<1%) in a fine-grained groundmass of anhedral quartz and alkali feldspar (40%). Hornblende commonly occurs as clusters of small prisms which may be xenoliths. A K/Ar biotite age of 462±6Ma (12) suggests that emplacement was contemporaneous with the arc-related magmatism of the Tyrone Igneous Complex.

The Grampian Orogeny

The presence of Arenig-Llanvirn graptolites in the Tyrone Volcanic Group (7) and the age range of the granitoid suite indicate that the volcanic arc sequence formed in the early Arenig, and was possibly contemporaneous with the ophiolite. These facts, when allied to the field relationships of the three components of the Tyrone Igneous Complex, are convincing evidence for Grampian orogenic collision in mid- to late Arenig times. The ensuing amalgamation of the Tyrone Igneous Complex and Central Inlier on the Laurentian continental margin as shown in Figure 3.3 was relatively rapid. The subsequent subduction of the still active volcanic arc beneath the Laurentian continental margin is thought to have driven the intrusion of the arc-related granitoid intrusives (Figure 3.3B).

The late Ordovician-early Silurian sedimentary cover sequence

The Ordovician and Silurian rocks of the Pomeroy Inlier (Figures 3.1 and 3.5; Table 3.1) rest unconformably on the Tyrone Plutonic Group and on the granitoid intrusive complex at Craigbardahessiagh. Uplift and unroofing of the Central Inlier and Tyrone Igneous Complex had occurred by mid-Caradoc times, in the 5-15 million years after obduction and magmatism. Some 50km to the southwest, is the fault-bounded inlier of Silurian rocks at Lisbellaw (Table 3.1). Although composed of sedimentary rocks resembling those in the Southern Uplands-Down-Longford Terrane, the Lisbellaw rocks underwent a radically different tectono-thermal history being relatively uncleaved and with much lower organic carbon maturation levels.

		Pomeroy	Lisbellaw
Silurian	Llandovery	Little River Group	Lisbellaw Formation
Ordovician	Ashgill	Desertcreat Group	
	Caradoc		

Table 3.1
Stratigraphy of the Lower Palaeozoic rocks at Pomeroy and Lisbellaw.

Pomeroy Inlier

The Pomeroy succession (Table 3.1) consists of over 400m of late Ordovician rocks of the **Desertcreat Group** conformably overlain by about 600m of Silurian rocks of the **Little River Group** (13).

Desertcreat Group

The **Bardahessiagh Formation** (Figure 3.5), including the **'Junction Beds'** (Table 3.2), comprises a conglomerate at the base of the succession, overlain mostly by coarse-grained sandstone that passes up into fine-grained sandstone and grey mudstone that constitute the Junction Beds. Fossils consist mainly of large, thick-shelled brachiopods (13) such as *Bilobia, Bimuria, Campylorthis, Isophragma, Rostricellula* and *Sowerbyites* (Fossils 1-6) and rare trilobites.

The mid-Caradoc (Burrellian Stage) brachiopod and trilobite fauna in the Bardahessiagh Formation is of Laurentian aspect and has much in common with faunas found in rocks of similar age at Girvan in Scotland (14) and in North America.

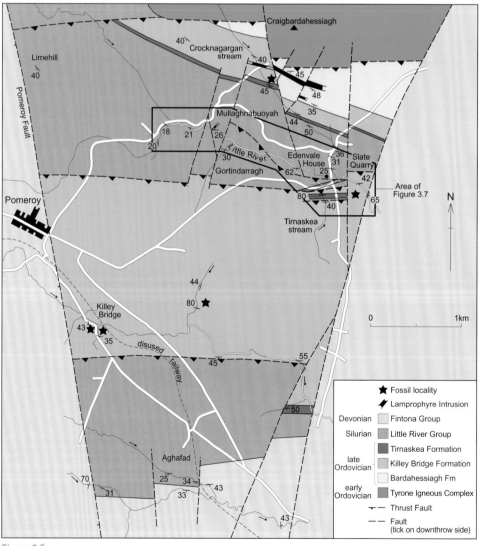

Figure 3.5
Geological map of the Ordovician and Silurian rocks of the Pomeroy Inlier.

34

	Stage	Substage	Formation	Lithology
Ashgill	Hirnantian		Tirnaskea (33m)	Siltstone, grey, calcareous, blocky, sparsely fossiliferous; 3m of pale green mudstone at the top
Ashgill	Rawtheyan		Killey Bridge (up to 250m)	Siltstone and mudstone, grey, calcareous, micaceous flags, very fossiliferous; sandstone, coarse-grained, brown, 3m thick, fossiliferous
Ashgill	Cautleyan			
Ashgill	Pusgillian			
Caradoc	Streffordian	Onnian		
Caradoc	Streffordian	Actonian		
Caradoc	Cheneyan	Marshbrookian		
Caradoc	Cheneyan	Woolstonian		
Caradoc	Burrellian	Longvillian	'Junction Beds'	Sandstone and siltstone, grey, calcareous, reddish brown staining, thin to flaggy bedding, parallel laminations, very fossiliferous
Caradoc	Burrellian	Soudleyan	'Junction Beds'	Mudstone, grey, micaceous, fossiliferous
Caradoc	Burrellian	Soudleyan	'Junction Beds'	Sandstone, grey, to reddish brown stained, fine-grained, silty, fossiliferous
Caradoc	Burrellian	Soudleyan	Bardahessiagh (c. 160m)	Sandstone, very coarse-grained, grey, micaceous, bioturbated, very sparsely fossiliferous; conglomerate, clast supported, abundant vein quartz clasts
Caradoc	Burrellian	Harnagian		
Caradoc	Aurelucian	Costonian		
Caradoc	Aurelucian	Velfreyan		

Table 3.2
Litho- and chronostratigraphy of the Ordovician Desertcreat Group in the Pomeroy Inlier.

The **Killey Bridge Formation** (Figure 3.5, Table 3.2) comprises grey siltstone and mudstone. Subordinate sandstone in the Killey Bridge stream [H702 710] contains brachiopods including the typical Ashgill form *Schizophorella* (Fossil 7). Exposed in the Little River, about 210m east of the Slate Quarry Bridge, silty mudstones contain abundant, well preserved fossils including numerous small brachiopods (Fossils 8-15), trilobites (Fossil 16), bivalves, gastropods, orthocone nautiloids, corals, bryozoa and the Ashgill zonal graptolite *Dicellograptus anceps*. Faunas in the formation are Ashgill (Table 3.2). Compared to faunas in the Bardahessiagh Formation the Ashgill assemblage was more cosmopolitan and included many genera of brachiopods and trilobites that, in the Caradoc, were restricted to the margins of either Baltica or Avalonia and to separate Baltic or Anglo-Welsh faunules respectively.

The **Tirnaskea Formation** (Table 3.2) is a relatively hard pyritous grey siltstone (Figure 3.5, Table 3.2) with rare fossils including trilobites, ostracods and bryozoa (13). The top of the formation and contact with the succeeding Little River Group represents the conformable Ordovician-Silurian systemic boundary and is exposed in the Crocknagargan stream section [H724 734]. This section also exposes the middle and upper levels of the formation (15). A fauna of small brachiopods of Rawtheyan age in the middle part of the formation includes *Dedzetina*, *Sericoidea*, *Proboscisambon* and *Protozyga*. The upper part contains *Eostropheodonta* and *Dysprosorthis* along with the trilobite *Mucronaspis* indicating a Hirnantian age. The faunas lived in deep, cold water in a dark, poorly oxygenated and nutrient-starved environment.

Little River Group

The Silurian **Little River Group** (16) consists of dark grey graptolitic mudstones with rare thin sandstones (Table 3.3). Although the graptolite faunas have been studied in detail

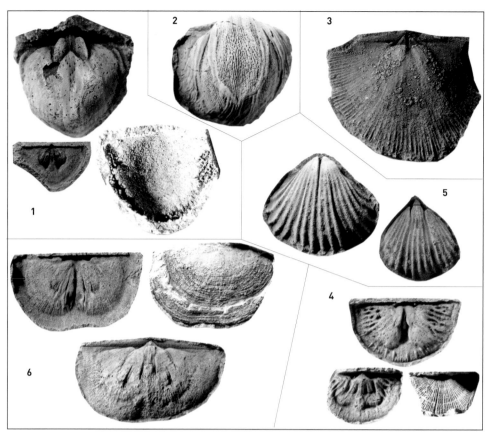

Fossils 1-6
Late Ordovician (mid-Caradoc) brachiopods from the Bardahessiagh Formation:
1 *Bilobia etheridgei* (x3) **2** *Bimuria youngiana recta* (x1.5) **3** *Campylorthis discreta* (x1.75)
4 *Isophragma pseudoretroflexum* (x1.5) **5** *Rostricellula ambigua* (x1.5)
6 *Sowerbyites hibernicus* (x1.5).

(Figure 3.6) only an informal lithostratigraphy is available (16). Lithological divisions are characterised in four main parts of the outcrop. The exposure of the **Crocknagargan 'beds'**, representing the base of the Little River Group, in the Crocknagargan stream (op. cit.) comprises poorly graptolitic mudstone. In the Slate Quarry river [H727 729], higher strata in this unit contain a more diverse graptolite fauna (Table 3.3) and are succeeded by at least 100m of the **Slate Quarry 'beds'** with 2m of the **Edenvale 'beds'** at the south end of the exposure. The base of the Edenvale 'beds' is represented by the *Dimorphograptus* band (16), comprising 1m of calcareous mudstone with thin, bands of pale yellow bentonite. The most continuous exposure of this Group is in the Little River (Figure 3.5) where long sections in the **Edenvale** and **Mullaghnabuoyah 'beds'** contain diverse graptolite faunas (Figure 3.7, Table 3.3). The **Lime Hill 'beds'** are exposed only in a stream section [H694 739] at Lime Hill (Figure 3.5) which is the type locality for the graptolite species *Stimulograptus (Graptolithus) sedgwickii* and *Lagarograptus (Graptolithus) tenuis* (16). Unusually for the Little River Group, these graptolitic mudstones also contain a sparse shelly fauna including bivalves and inarticulate and rhynchonnelid brachiopods. **Unnamed 'beds'** (Table 3.3) at the top of the Little River Group are confined (Figure 3.5) to the stream at Aghafad [H709 696]. Historically, because of their composition they were often included in the early Devonian Fintona Group but the presence of late Llandovery graptolites proves their early Silurian age.

36

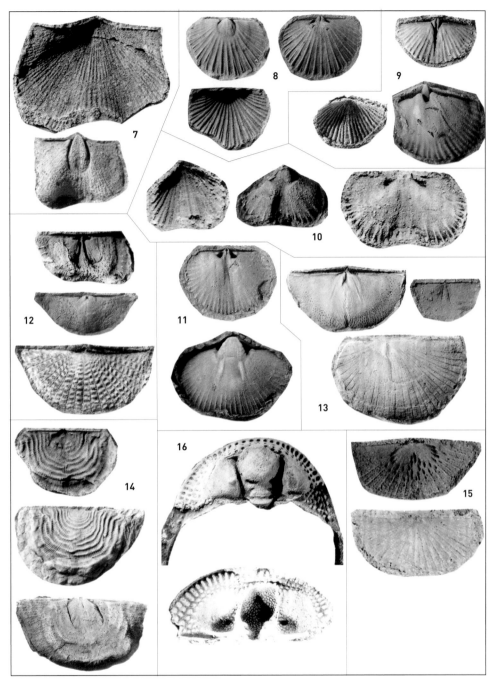

Fossils 7-16
Late Ordovician (early Ashgill) fossils from the Killey Bridge Formation:
<u>Brachiopods</u>: **7** *Schizophorella fallax fallax* (x1.5) **8** *Plaesiomys porcata lata* (x2)
9 *Skenidioides* cf. *greenhoughi* (x4) **10** *Dicoelosia simulata* (x6) **11** *Dalmanella testudinaria ripae* (x3)
12 *Rugosowerbyella ambigua* (x3), **13** *Sowerbyella thraivensis* (x3), **14** *Leptaena rugosa*,
15 *Chonetoidea radiatula* (x6).
<u>Trilobite</u>: **16** *Tretaspis seticornis* (x3 and x5.)

Lisbellaw Inlier

The **Lisbellaw Formation** consists of 300m of grey and greenish grey fossiliferous mudstone and silty mudstone with some greywacke beds usually less than 5cm thick (Figure 3.8). Near the middle of the succession, the 40m thick **Leambreslen Conglomerate Member** (18) comprises conglomerate beds ranging from 10cm to over 6m thick. The conglomerate is exposed in the centre of Lisbellaw and in the Council quarry [H295 411] west of the village, where 25m of conglomerate is overlain by 25cm of greywacke sandstone. Each bed has a sharp base with flute and groove marks and commonly grades up into coarse greywacke sandstone proving the succession is not inverted. The conglomerates are clast-supported with a medium- to coarse-grained matrix and only rarely show imbrication of pebbles. More than 90% of the well-rounded clasts consist of purplish and greenish grey quartzite up to 57cm in diameter, with minor vein quartz, jasper and granite. Palaeocurrent data suggest that the sediments were derived from the north and northeast (19).

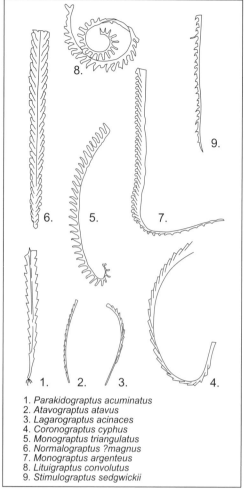

1. *Parakidograptus acuminatus*
2. *Atavograptus atavus*
3. *Lagarograptus acinaces*
4. *Coronograptus cyphus*
5. *Monograptus triangulatus*
6. *Normalograptus ?magnus*
7. *Monograptus argenteus*
8. *Lituigraptus convolutus*
9. *Stimulograptus sedgwickii*

Figure 3.6
Early Silurian (Llandovery) graptolite zonal index species from Pomeroy (all x2) (after 17).

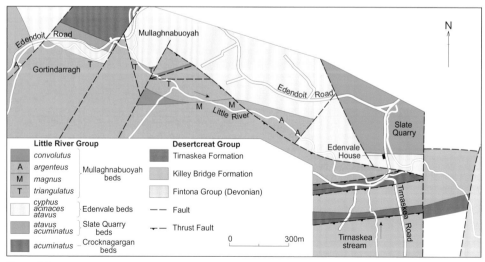

Figure 3.7
Detailed geological map of the Ordovician and Silurian rocks in the Little River section at Pomeroy.

38

Graptolite Biozone				Lithological Unit	Lithology	Graptolite First Occurences
Early Silurian	Llandovery	Telychian	crenulata s.l.			
			griestoniensis			
			crispus			
			turriculatus s.l.	Unnamed beds	Conglomerate, small to medium pebbles of white vein quartz in coarse granule matrix; sandstone, greenish grey, coarse-grained, silty, lithic intraclasts, ripples; mudstone, thin, sparse graptolite fauna	*Monograptus* cf. *parapriodon*, cf. *Petalolithus intermedius*, *?Pseudoglyptograptus* sp.
		Aeronian	sedgwickii s.l.	Lime Hill beds	Mudstone, medium grey to blue-black, micaceous, pyritous; mud-pellet conglomerate; bentonite, thin pale yellow; bivalves, orthocone nautiloids, ?brachiopods; rich graptolite fauna	*Campograptus* cf. *lobiferus*, *Lagarograptus tenuis*, *Stimulograptus distans*, *?S. halli*, *S. sedgwickii*
			convolutus	Mullaghnabuoyah beds	Mudstone, medium grey, massive, poorly graptolitic; siltstone, medium grey, hard; sandstone, quartz-rich, calcareous	*Glyptograptus tamariscus incertus*, *Lituigraptus convolutus*, *Monoclimacis crenularis*, *Monograptus limatulus*, *Petalolithus folium*, *P. palmeus*, *Torquigraptus denticulatus*
			argenteus (aka. leptotheca)			*Campograptus* cf. *clingani*, *C. communis*, *'Climacograptus' scalaris*, *Lituigraptus* cf. *convolutus*, *Pseudorthograptus insectiformis*
			magnus		Mudstone, dark grey, low amplitude ripples, arthropod tracks, bivalves, rich graptolite fauna with rhabdosomes orientated $15°$- $195°$, pyritous	*Monograptus triangulatus fimbriatus*, *Normalograptus? magnus*, *Petalolithus palmeus latus*, *P. ovatoelongatus*, *Pristiograptus jaculum*, *Rastrites longispinus*
			triangulatus		Siltstone, greenish to olive grey, flaggy, pyritous; mudstone, grey	*'Monograptus attenuatus'*, *Monograptus triangulatus*, *Monograptus revolutus*, *Pribylograptus* cf. *leptotheca*, *Pristiograptus concinnus*, *P. regularis*, *Rastrites* cf. *approximatus*
		Rhuddanian	cyphus	Edenvale beds	Mudstone, blue-black to grey, banded in places; rich graptolite fauna	*Coronograptus gregarius* s.l., *Dimorphograptus confertus swanstoni*, *Lagarograptus* cf. *acinaces*, *Metaclimacograptus hughesi*, *Rivagraptus cyperoides*, *Pseudorthograptus mutabilis*
					Mudstone, bluish black to dark grey, calcareous, massive, thin K-bentonites; referred to the *Dimorphograptus* band(18)	*Coronograptus cyphus*, *Dimorphograptus erectus*, *Raphidograptus toernquisti*
			acinaces		Mudstone, alternating dark (pyritous) and light (silty) laminae, poor graptolite fauna; siltstone, pale grey laminae	*'Climacograptus' medius*, *Cystograptus vesiculosus penna*, *Pribylograptus incommodus*, *Paraclimacograptus innotatus*
			atavus	Slate Quarry beds	Mudstone, bluish black to dark grey, rich graptolite fauna	*'Climacograptus' rectangularis*, *Atavograptus atavus*, *Huttagraptus strachani*, *'Coronograptus' praematurus*, *Raphidograptus extenuatus*
					Mudstone, thinly banded dark, medium and pale grey, sandstone laminae, (<5mm) pale grey,fine-grained; rich graptolite fauna; two sandstone beds, greenish brown and grey, pyritous, up to 15cm thick	*Diplograptus modestus diminutus*
			acuminatus		Mudstone, dark bluish grey, purple tinged	Climacograptids and diplograptids
				Crockna-gargan beds	Mudstone, dark and light grey laminae, interbedded with siltstone, greenish grey; sparse graptolite fauna	*Akidograptus ascensus*, *'Climacograptus' miserabilis*, *'C.' tuberculatus*, *Cystograptus vesiculosus*, *Diplograptus modestus*, *Glyptograptus tamariscus* -'like'
						Parakidograptus acuminatus, *'Climacograptus' normalis*

Table 3.3
Litho-, chrono-, and biostratigraphy of the Silurian Little River Group in the Pomeroy Inlier.

The oldest graptolite faunas occur (4) in mudstones in the stream east of Homeville [H303 420] and belong to either the *atavus* Biozone or to the *cyphus* Biozone and include *Normalograptus* sp., *Paraclimacograptus innotatus* and *Pribylograptus?* sp. Thin mudstone beds in the conglomerate in the council quarry (Figure 3.8) contain a graptolite fauna of *Monograptus triangulatus* and *Pseudorthograptus mutabilis* of the early Aeronian *triangulatus* Biozone. Mudstones interbedded with greywacke in the by-pass quarry [H301 412] (Figure 3.8) also contain a graptolite fauna of the *triangulatus* Biozone including *M. triangulatus*, *Atavograptus* cf. *atavus*, *Coronograptus gregarius*, *Glyptograptus sinuatus*,

Metaclimacograptus cf. *hughesi*, *Pribylograptus* sp. and *Raphidograptus toernquisti* (4). The youngest graptolite fauna occurs in mudstone in the slate quarry [H297 417] and apart from trilobite remains contains *Petalolithus folium* and *Pribylograptus leptotheca* of the *argenteus / leptotheca* Biozone. The graptolite faunas range from the mid- to late Rhuddanian (*atavus or cyphus* biozones) to the mid-Aeronian *leptotheca* Biozone (20).

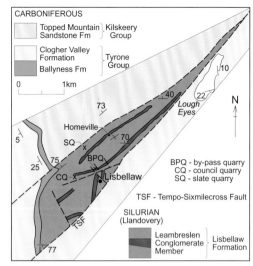

Figure 3.8
Geological map of the Silurian rocks in the Lisbellaw Inlier (18).

References

1) Geological Survey of Northern Ireland 1979. Pomeroy, Northern Ireland Sheet 34. Solid Geology. 1:50,000. (Southampton: Ordnance Survey for the Geological Survey of Northern Ireland).

2) Geological Survey of Northern Ireland 1983. Cookstown, Northern Ireland Sheet 27. Solid Geology. 1:50,000. (Southampton: Ordnance Survey for the Geological Survey of Northern Ireland).

3) Geological Survey of Northern Ireland, 1995. Draperstown, Northern Ireland Sheet 26. Solid Geology. 1:50,000. (Keyworth, Nottingham: British Geological Survey).

4) Harper, J. C. and Hartley, J. J. 1938. The Silurian Inlier of Lisbellaw, County Fermanagh, with a note on the age of the Fintona beds. *Proceedings of the Royal Irish Academy*, **45B**, 73-87.

5) Hartley, J. J. 1933. The geology of North-Eastern Tyrone and adjacent portions of Co. Londonderry. *Proceedings of the Royal Irish Academy*, **B41**, 218-85.

6) Hutton, D. H. W., Aftalion, M. and Halliday, A. N. 1985. An Ordovician ophiolite in County Tyrone, Ireland. *Nature*, **315**, 210-12.

7) Hutton, D. H. W. and Holland, C. H. 1992. An Arenig-Llanvirn age for the black shales of Slieve Gallion, County Tyrone. *Irish Journal of Earth Sciences*, **11**, 187-89.

8) Geological History of Britain and Ireland. Woodcock, N. H. and Strachan, R. (eds.). 2000. Blackwell Science Ltd.

9) Cobbing, E. J. 1969. Schistosity and folding in a banded gabbro from Tyrone. *Bulletin of the Geological Survey of Great Britain*, **30**, 89-97.

10) Geological Survey of Northern Ireland. 1997. Geological Map of Northern Ireland. Solid Geology. (second edition). 1:250,000. (Keyworth, Nottingham: British Geological Survey).

11) Angus, N. S. 1962. Ocellar Hybrids from the Tyrone Igneous Series, Ireland. *Geological Magazine*, **99**, 9-26.

12) Harrison, R. K. and Wilson, H. E. 1978. *The granodiorite intrusion of Cushleake Mountain, County Antrim, Northern Ireland*. Institute of Geological Sciences Report No. 78/7.

13) Mitchell, W. I. 1977. *The Ordovician Brachiopoda from Pomeroy, Co. Tyrone*. Monograph of the Palaeontographical Society.

14) Ingham, J. K. 2000. Scotland: the Midland Valley Terrane-Girvan. In: Fortey, R. A., Harper, D. A. T., Ingham, J. K., Owen, A. W., Parkes, M. A., Rushton, A. W. A. and Woodcock, N. H. (eds.). *A Revised Correlation of Ordovician Rocks in the British Isles*, The Geological Society Special Report No. 24.

15) Harper, D. A. T., Mitchell, W. I. and Rong, Jia-Yu. 1994. New faunal data from the highest Ordovician rocks at Pomeroy, County Tyrone, Northern Ireland. *Scottish Journal of Geology*, **30**, 187-90.

16) Fearnsides, W. G., Elles, G. L. and Smith, B. 1907. The Lower Palaeozoic rocks of Pomeroy. *Proceedings of the Royal Irish Academy*, **26** (B), 97-128.

17) Loydell, D. K. 1998. Early Silurian sea-level changes. *Geological Magazine*, **135**, 447-71.

18) Geological Survey of Northern Ireland 1982. Enniskillen, Northern Ireland Sheet 45. Solid Geology. 1:50,000. (Southampton: Ordnance Survey for the Geological Survey of Northern Ireland).

19) Simon, J. B. 1986. Provenance and setting of some Ordovician and Silurian conglomerates in Northern Ireland. *Scottish Journal of Geology*, **22**, 63-76.

20) Williams, M. and Taylor, P. 2002. Graptolites from the Lisbellaw Inlier, Co. Fermanagh. *British Geological Survey Internal Report*, IR/02/089.

Chapter 4

Southern Uplands-Down-Longford Terrane

T. B. ANDERSON

Introduction

Beneath the drumlin cover, much of the bedrock of Counties Down and Armagh consists of Lower Palaeozoic marine sedimentary rocks. These are part of the Southern Uplands-Down-Longford Terrane (Figure 4.1), which is one of the most distinctive terranes in the collage assembled by orogeny in the Ordovician, Silurian and Devonian periods to form the Irish and British Caledonides.

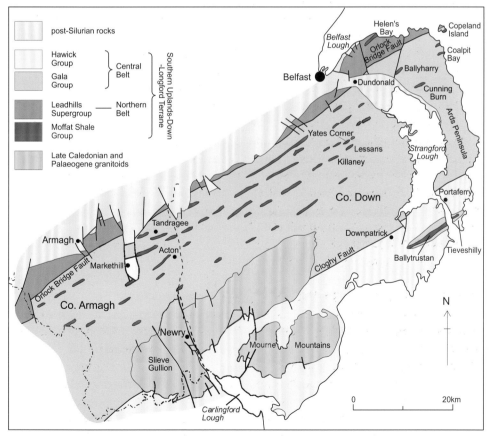

Figure 4.1
The Southern Uplands-Down-Longford Terrane in Northern Ireland.

The terrane is an allochthonous prism composed almost entirely of thick, well-bedded Ordovician and Silurian turbidite sequences comprising greywacke sandstone, siltstone and mudstone. In addition there are several thin formations consisting of chert and spilitic lavas, and black and grey mudstone with bentonites (ash falls from a volcanic arc). Throughout most of the terrane the beds strike ENE-WSW with almost uniformly steep dip which combines with the apparently monotonous nature of the thick turbidite successions to pose difficult stratigraphical and structural problems.

Although the dominant turbidite successions are largely unfossiliferous, a few graptolites occur in the interlayered mudstone and rare shelly fossils have been found as clasts in coarse sandstone beds. Chert and lavas of the **Crawford Group**, cropping out in the northwestern part of the terrane, are the oldest rocks in a stratigraphic succession whose base is not exposed. These remnants of oceanic crust are succeeded by the **Moffat Shale Group**, a stratigraphically condensed succession of grey and black mudstone less than 150m thick, which is overlain conformably by turbidites. Rich graptolite faunas in the Moffat Shale Group provided the basis for Lapworth's classic studies of graptolite palaeontology and Ordovician stratigraphy in the latter half of the 19th Century (1). The high biostratigraphical resolution provided by the graptolite faunas remains key to the understanding of the lithostratigraphy and structure of the terrane.

Understanding the sequence of graptolite zones subsequently facilitated Peach and Horne's division of the Southern Uplands of Scotland into Northern, Central and Southern Belts (2). The Northern Belt consists entirely of Ordovician strata, the Central Belt is early Silurian (Llandovery) with numerous, small, Ordovician mudstone inliers, and the Southern Belt is of mid- and late Silurian (Wenlock and Ludlow) age. Although all three belts can be traced into and across the northern part of Ireland, only the Northern and Central Belts crop out in Counties Down and Armagh. Across both belts the high-resolution graptolite palaeontology unequivocally demonstrates that, despite successions which dominantly young northwards, progressively younger sediments crop out towards the south.

The late 19th Century geologists attempted to explain the relative ages and distribution of the graptolite faunas in the Southern Uplands of Scotland by arranging the strata around numerous upright tight or even isoclinal folds (2). Thus on contemporary Geological Survey maps of the Southern Uplands, and of Counties Down and Armagh, the many outcrops of the Moffat Shale Group were interpreted as forming the cores of tight periclinal anticlines and so appear in plan view as boat-shaped inliers within the younger turbidites. Subsequent recognition of a variety of way-up sedimentary indicators in the turbidite successions of southwest Scotland and of Co. Down challenged this interpretation and demonstrated that the strata face or young predominantly to the northwest (3). Folds certainly occur but their northwest-facing limbs tend to be much the thicker.

Tectonostratigraphic models: the 'Southern Uplands Controversy'

The apparent contradiction between palaeontological and sedimentological evidence is the fundamental Southern Uplands paradox. It can be solved only by the insertion of numerous major faults parallel to the strike (3, 4). The strata indeed young predominantly to the north but the strike-parallel faults repeatedly throw down younger beds on their southern side (Figure 4.2). These major **strike-parallel faults**, typically spaced at between 1 and 5km, segment the terrane into a number of **blocks** or **tracts** of similar width (5). Detailed mapping has confirmed the presence of such faults and has highlighted subtle differences in stratigraphy and lithology between the adjacent fault-bounded tracts. The tracts in the Northern Belt and at least in the northern parts of the Central Belt expose successions of

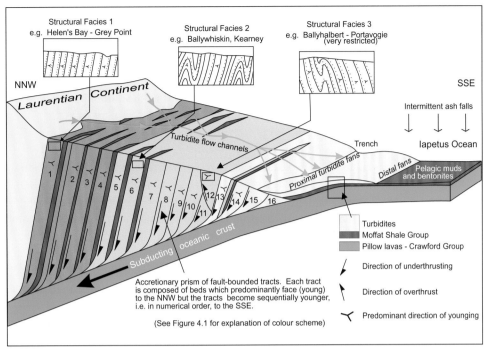

Figure 4.2
The accretionary prism model for the formation of the Southern Uplands-Down-Longford Terrane.

thick turbidites resting, typically with sharp, commonly tectonised, but essentially conformable boundaries, on fossiliferous black and grey mudstones of the Moffat Shale Group. In very rare cases the mudstones rest directly on spilitic pillow lava of the Crawford Group (6). The precise age of the contact between the Moffat Shale Group and the base of the succeeding turbidite sequence differs from tract to tract, decreasing incrementally southward by the equivalent of one or two graptolite zones per tract (Figure 4.3). The turbidite successions which rest on the Moffat Shale Group also differ across the tract boundaries, subtly or profoundly, in both thickness and lithology. However, within each individual tract the lithostratigraphy is relatively constant and may be correlated for many tens of kilometres ENE-WSW along strike. Each tract thus demonstrates its own unique version of the overall stratigraphic theme, with the Moffat Shale Group as the only truly common stratigraphic element.

A further very important feature of the tectonostratigraphic pattern is that *all* successions are terminated stratigraphically downward and upward by faults. The oldest basement rocks in the Southern Uplands-Down-Longford Terrane are the outcrops of pillow lavas of possible Arenig age, which are seafloor 'basement' and represent the surface onto which the marine successions were deposited and from which they were subsequently stripped (7).

These observations and relationships were initially addressed in the Southern Uplands accretionary prism model (8) and later refined in the light of the then newly emerging theory of plate tectonics (9). According to the model, black hemipelagic mudstone deposited on the floor of the Iapetus Ocean was carried toward the fore-arc trench as the oceanic plate was subducted northwestward beneath Laurentia. As each segment of the oceanic plate approached the trench it came within reach of turbidity currents bringing detritus from the continental margin located to the north and northeast. Thick turbidite fans, advancing

43

diachronously southward, were thus deposited directly and rapidly on the black mudstones. As the oceanic plate continued to be subducted, packets of these sediments were detached from the descending slab from time to time and accreted to the Laurentian continental margin as a growing stack of underthrust slices. The northwestern Ordovician tracts accreted first, while sedimentation continued to the southeast. Sedimentary evolution and subsequent deformation both migrated diachronously northwest to southeast across Iapetus for some 40Ma until that ocean finally closed. The model explained the major features of the terrane and its unusual tectonostratigraphic pattern.

However, the model, at least in the simple form outlined above, does not explain the occurrence, in southwest Scotland, of volcanic arc detritus in some late Ordovician turbidites whose sole-markings consistently indicate a southeasterly provenance. This and other observations prompted the development of an alternative interpretation of the Southern Uplands-Down-Longford Terrane as a back-arc basin thrust stack (10). This model contends that the Southern Uplands turbidites and mudstones accumulated in a back-arc situation between the Laurentian continent and an outboard volcanic arc, deriving clastic detritus from both. Convergence and ultimate collision between arc and continent during the Silurian Period generated a rising stack of thrust sheets progressively overthrusting one another to the southeast until the basin was consumed and inverted.

The ensuing debate between proponents of the two models has become known as the 'Southern Uplands Controversy'. It is important to recognise that, whichever is preferred, both models require the pattern of sedimentation, subsequent accretionary deformation and associated thrusting to migrate northwest to southeast as the Iapetus Ocean, or back-arc basin, closed.

Stratigraphy
Modelling the stratigraphy and structure of the Southern Uplands-Down-Longford Terrane in a plate tectonic context imparted new impetus to mapping and research in the latter half of the 20th Century and this in turn produced a plethora of lithostratigraphical formation and member names. In Scotland these formations and members have now been systematically organised into a few groups and supergroups (11, 12). The following account of the Lower Palaeozoic stratigraphy attempts to extend that rationalism into Counties Down and Armagh.

In Northern Ireland the oldest rocks exposed in the **Northern Belt** and the northern parts of the **Central Belt** belong to the **Crawford Group** and the **Moffat Shale Group**. The Crawford Group is confined to outcrops in the Acton Inlier of Co. Armagh and at Cultra in Co. Down. The **Moffat Shale Group** is much more widespread, cropping out at more than 30 localities (Figure 4.1), typically broken and imbricated by faulting and invariably surrounded by younger turbidites. The Moffat Shale Group is divided into four formations (11), Glenkiln Shale, Lower Hartfell Shale, Upper Hartfell Shale and Birkhill Shale. In the Northern Belt tracts, the Group is stratigraphically succeeded by several different turbidite formations, collectively assigned to the **Leadhills Supergroup**. The Northern Belt is separated from the Central Belt in both Scotland and Ireland by the **Orlock Bridge Fault**, the extent and the fabric of the fault rocks indicative of a large, sinistral strike-slip displacement (13). South of the fault there is a sequence of tracts in which turbidite formations of the **Gala Group**, of a siliceous or quartz-rich petrography, rest on progressively younger units of the Moffat Shale Group (5). South of the **Cloghy Fault** (the equivalent of the Laurieston Fault in Scotland), turbidites of the **Hawick Group** are generally fine-grained, rich in carbonate and, except for the Portaferry Tract, are not seen to rest on the Moffat Shale Group.

44

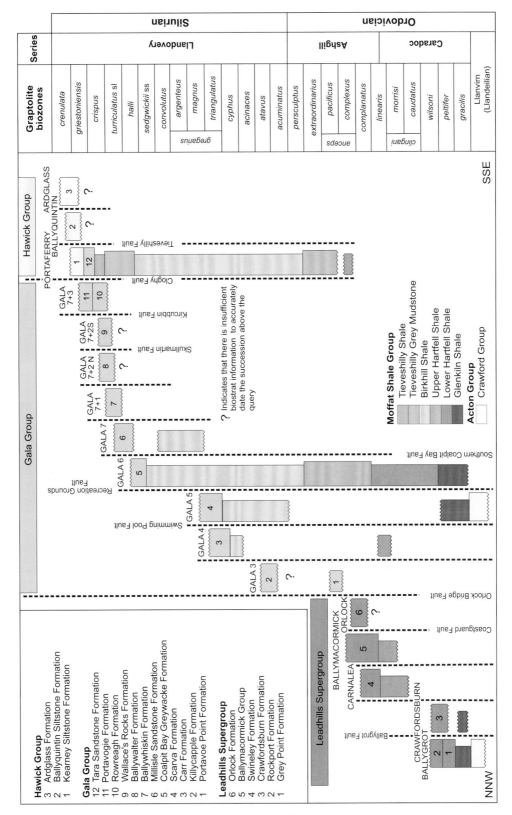

Figure 4.3
Correlation chart of the Ordovician and Silurian rocks in the Southern Uplands-Down-Longford Terrane.

This classification is somewhat unconventional in that the Moffat Shale Group is the temporal equivalent of large parts of both the Leadhills Supergroup and Gala Group in the same area. In addition the Leadhills Supergroup, Gala and Hawick Groups are composed of numerous formations which do not form part of a single continuous succession but rather occur in separate fault-defined tracts. It is nevertheless, a successful pragmatic approach to the unusual nature of the prism stratigraphy.

Crawford Group

The oldest rocks of the Southern Uplands-Down-Longford Terrane in Northern Ireland occur in the **Acton Inlier** (14). Exposed in the bed and banks of a stream [J043 412] 1.4km west of Acton (Figure 4.1) are some 5m of purplish red and green mudstone, thin black chert and pale grey to cream weathering radiolarian chert. The purplish red mudstone contains a sparse conodont fauna that includes *Periodon aculeatus, Protopanderodus varicostatus, Pygodus anserinus* and *P. serra*, and straddles the boundary between the *Pygodus serra-P. anserinus* biozones (Bergstrom, pers. comm., 1974) and so indicates a late Llanvirn (mid-Llandeilian) age. These mudstones and cherts clearly resemble and correlate with the Kirkton Formation in the Crawford Group of southwest Scotland (11).

On the west side of Helen's Bay at Horse Rock [J459 831] about 25m of pillow lavas (6) and a thin conglomerate with spilite clasts of the Crawford Group are succeeded by *gracilis* Biozone mudstones of the Moffat Shale Group. This, the only exposure of pillow lava on the coast of Co. Down, affords excellent natural cross sections of pillow shapes, some of them clearly demonstrating that the lavas are overturned, younging down to the north.

Moffat Shale Group in Counties Down and Armagh

The best exposure, and most complete development, of the Moffat Shale Group is at **Coalpit Bay**, 1km south of Donaghadee (Figure 4.4). Swanston and Lapworth in 1876 recognised that all four formations of Lapworth's 'Moffat Series' are present with faunas typical of most, if not all, of the graptolite biozones (15).

The early Caradoc Glenkiln Shale Formation (*gracilis* and *peltifer* biozones) crops out at low water mark in the core of an east-west trending anticline in the more southerly of the two small peninsulas projecting into Coalpit Bay, some 50m ESE of the end of a disused sewage outfall. The Ordovician Moffat Shale Group succession can then be traced stratigraphically upward and southward through the Lower and Upper Hartfell Shale Formations as far as a prominent, locally multiple, dark red lamprophyre dyke. The Lower Hartfell black mudstone yields graptolite faunas of the *wilsoni* and *complanatus* biozones and includes a 0.3m thick grey limestone bed. The almost structureless, pale grey, "barren mudstones" of the Upper Hartfell include several thin sheared black mudstones of the "*anceps* Band" near the base of the formation.

The dyke is intruded along, or lies close to, the faulted boundary between the Ordovician barren mudstones to the north and the Silurian Birkhill Shale Formation to the south. At outcrop the faulted nature of the boundary is not immediately obvious but the mudstones immediately to the south of the dyke yield rich graptolite faunas of the *cyphus* Biozone, so implying the absence or excision of some five lower Birkhill graptolite biozones at the systemic boundary. Intermittent exposures of folded grey-black siltstones, mudstones, shales and a thin limestone bed of the Birkhill Formation continue to the low cliffs on the southern margin of the bay. At the base of the cliff and particularly in the small pit which gives the bay its name, they are richly fossiliferous and interlayered with many thin beds of soft bentonite (Photograph 1). The conformable contact with the overlying coarse quartz-rich

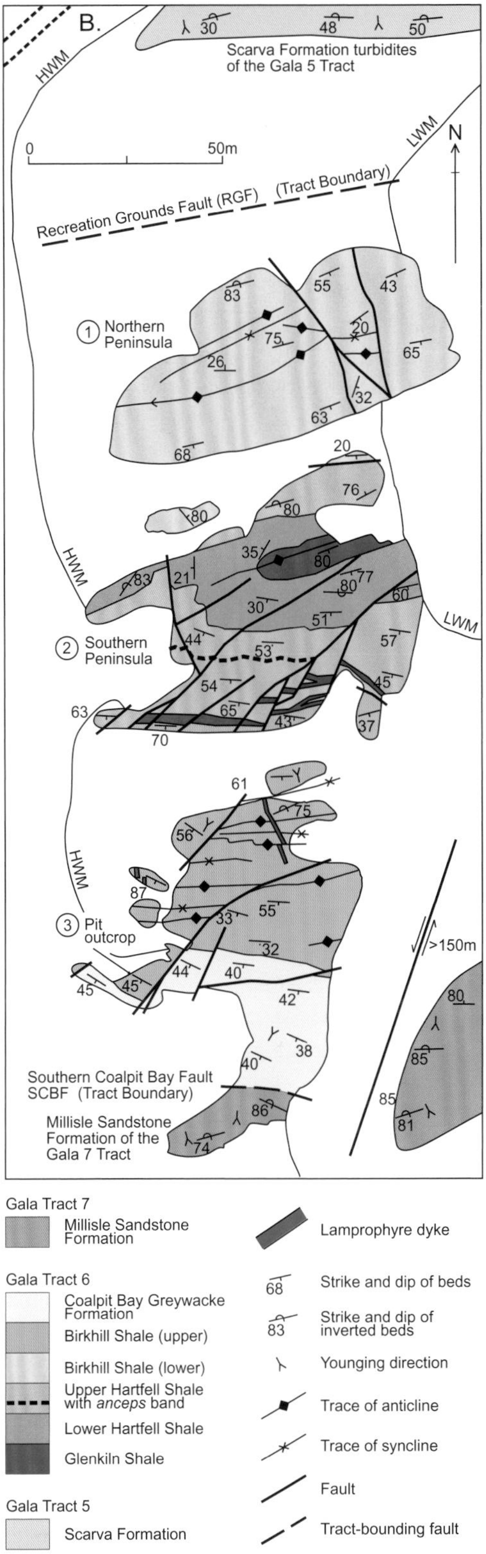
B.
Scarva Formation turbidites of the Gala 5 Tract
HWM
LWM
0
50m
N
Recreation Grounds Fault (RGF) (Tract Boundary)
1 Northern Peninsula
2 Southern Peninsula
3 Pit outcrop
>150m
Southern Coalpit Bay Fault SCBF (Tract Boundary)
Millisle Sandstone Formation of the Gala 7 Tract
Gala Tract 7
Millisle Sandstone Formation
Gala Tract 6
Coalpit Bay Greywacke Formation
Birkhill Shale (upper)
Birkhill Shale (lower)
Upper Hartfell Shale with anceps band
Lower Hartfell Shale
Glenkiln Shale
Gala Tract 5
Scarva Formation
Lamprophyre dyke
Strike and dip of beds
Strike and dip of inverted beds
Younging direction
Trace of anticline
Trace of syncline
Fault
Tract-bounding fault

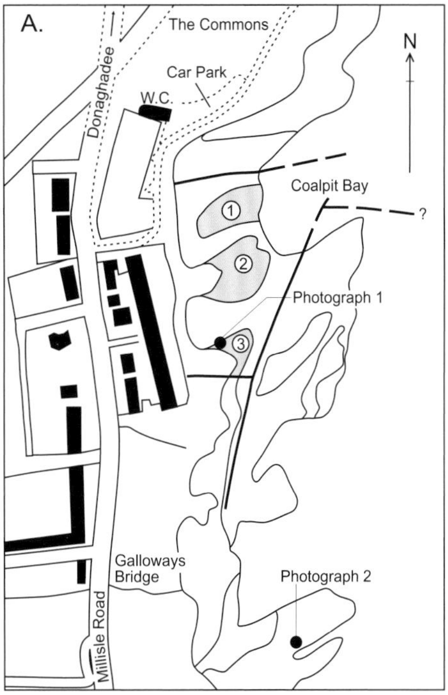
A.
The Commons
Car Park
W.C.
Donaghadee
N
Coalpit Bay
?
Photograph 1
Galloways Bridge
Millisle Road
Photograph 2

C.

	Formation	
Gala Group	**Millisle Sandstone** (1200m+) Greywacke sandstone, coarse-grained, in beds from 50cm to 1.5m thick and mudstone bands up to 50cm; superb sole markings (groove and flute casts)	Tract 7
	— SCBF —	
Gala Group	**Coalpit Bay Greywacke** (20m+) Sandstone, quartz-rich, grey, in beds up to 4m thick and grey mudstone interbeds up to 40cm; rip-up clasts and poor sole markings	Tract 6
Moffat Shale Group	**Birkhill Shale (upper)** (17m+) Siltstone, dark grey, interbedded with mudstone, greyish black; about 50 thin bentonites and one 50cm bed of grey limestone; very graptolitic towards top	Tract 6
Moffat Shale Group	**Birkhill Shale (lower)** (40m+) Mudstone, greyish black with numerous beds of soft grey bentonite up to 30cm; two beds of nodular grey, calcareous siltstone 3m and 1m thick in lower part of formation	Tract 6
Moffat Shale Group	**Upper Hartfell Shale** (30m+) Mudstone and siltstone, pale grey, weakly bedded and cleaved; rare thin bentonites; "*anceps* band" comprises three closely spaced bands of black graptolitic mudstone 4m above formation base	Tract 6
Moffat Shale Group	**Lower Hartfell Shale** (12.3m) Siltstone and mudstone, black to greyish black, interbedded with black graptolitic mudstone partings; one limestone (30cm) and one bentonite bed (15cm)	Tract 6
Moffat Shale Group	**Glenkiln Shale** (9m+) Siltstone, dark grey and cherty mudstone, grey, interbedded with graptolitic mudstone, greyish black; several beds up to 30cm of chert, pale grey, tectonically broken into angular blocks	Tract 6
	— RGF —	
Gala Group	**Scarva** (400m+) Greywacke sandstone, greyish blue, beds up to 1m thick, graded and mudstones, often silty, grey, up to 10cm	Tract 5

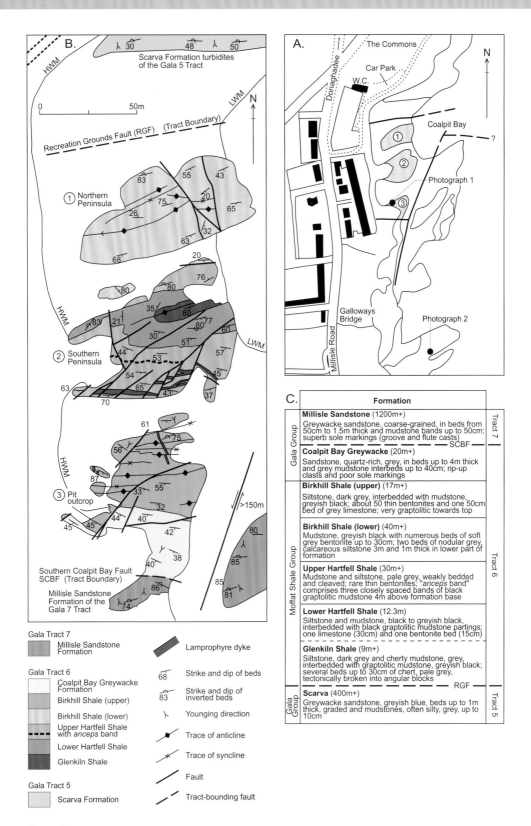

Figure 4.4

The Coalpit Bay area of Co. Down. A: Location map B: Detailed geological map C: Lithological descriptions of the main formations (in stratigraphical order).

Photograph 1
Two soft, light green bentonite beds, 5cm and 2cm thick, are displaced by small-scale, sinistral, strike-slip faults. Lying about 3m stratigraphically below overlying Gala Group turbidites, the mudstones contain numerous graptolites. Upper Birkhill Shale Formation (Moffat Shale Group) at the 'Pit' locality, Coalpit Bay [J595 788], 1km south of Donaghadee, Co. Down. (7cm scale bar).

turbidites of the Gala Group is well exposed at the pit and along strike to the east, where it is displaced by several small strike-slip faults.

Some of the lower parts of the Birkhill Shale Formation, missing in the traverse described above, are represented in the northern peninsula (Figure 4.4) which is composed of mudstone and calcareous siltstone yielding sparse faunas of the *acuminatus* and *atavus* biozones.

The Moffat Shale Group lithostratigraphy at Coalpit Bay thus compares and correlates very closely with that in the Moffat type area of Scotland.

The many other outcrops of the Moffat Shale Group in Counties Down and Armagh are useful markers of the southern edges of the fault-defined accretionary tracts. The mudstones typically occur as imbricated fault slices at the underthrust base of each tract and, except at Coalpit Bay, not as the cores of periclinal anticlines (2). At Horse Rock [J459 831], on the west side of Helen's Bay (op. cit.) black mudstone of the Moffat Shale Group, with many large olistoliths of grey sandstone are conformably succeeded by thick proximal turbidites of the Grey Point Formation (16).

Inland exposures of black mudstone in north eastern Co. Down at Lessans Cottage [J400 622], Yates Corner [J396 623] and at Ballyharry railway cutting [J501 754], contain graptolite faunas attributed to the *gracilis, peltifer, clingani* and *linearis* biozones and the mudstones thus correlate with the Glenkiln and Hartfell formations (17). In the same area, the Birkhill Shales occur in a number of inliers, notably at Yates Corner, Cunning Burn [J537 727], and Killaney [J361 588] with graptolite faunas (Figure 3.6) attributed to the *acuminatus, atavus, acinaces, cyphus, gregarius* and *convolutus* biozones (17).

48

In Co. Armagh the oldest well-preserved graptolite fauna, in the Acton Inlier, belongs to either the *gracilis* or *peltifer* biozones and occurs in sooty black mudstones that crop out in the east side of the stream valley [J045 414] 275m northeast of the conodont locality referred to above. The fauna includes *N. gracilis, Didymograptus* cf. *superstes, Hallograptus mucronatus, Orthograptus calcaratus, Dicellograptus divaricatus salopiensis, D. sextans, Climacograptus bicornis, C. antiquus lineatus* and *Pseudoclimacograptus scharenbergi*. Nowhere in the inlier is there graptolite evidence for the mid-Caradoc to early Ashgill lower part of the Hartfell Shale Formation. However, this absence is most likely due to non-exposure of the appropriate horizons as the remaining, upper, part of the Moffat Shale Group succession in the inlier consists of a thick sequence of monotonous, barren, greenish grey and grey mudstones and fine siltstones. These strata probably represent the upper part of the Hartfell Shale Formation although there is no record of black mudstones of the *anceps* Band.

An unusual and stratigraphically important outcrop of the Moffat Shale Group occurs at Tieveshilly [J612 481], near the southern tip of the Ards Peninsula (Figure 4.5). The locality is located further southeast in the terrane than any other Moffat Shale outcrop in Scotland or Ireland and has yielded copious graptolite faunas ranging in age from the *anceps* to *crispus* biozones, the latter a zone younger than currently recognised in any of the other Irish or Scottish localities (18).

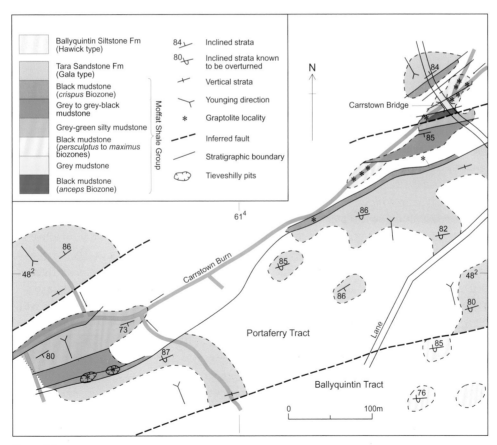

Figure 4.5
Geological map of the Carrstown Burn and Tieveshilly outcrop.

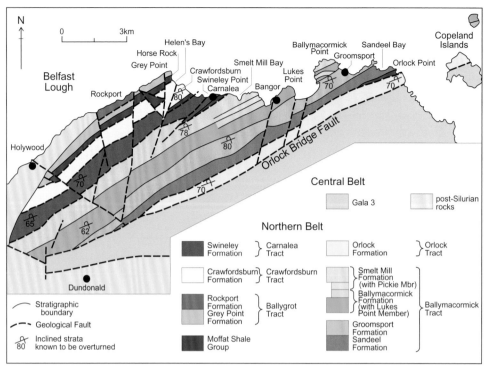

Figure 4.6
Geological map of north Co. Down (16).

Leadhills Supergroup in Counties Down and Armagh

The Leadhills Supergroup (11) is the collective name given to the several, petrographically varied, turbidite formations which rest on the Moffat Shale Group in the Northern Belt. The Southern Upland Fault, which forms the northern boundary of the Northern Belt, does not crop out in Ireland and comparison between Irish and Scottish outcrops makes it clear that the most northerly Scottish tracts also fail to crop out in Co. Down. Despite this, by using a combination of detailed petrographical analysis and the presence of the characteristic black mudstones (16), five accretionary tracts are recognised in the Northern Belt between Belfast Lough and the trace of the Orlock Bridge Fault (Figure 4.6).

The most northerly and oldest, the **Ballygrot Tract** is superbly exposed in the rocky coastal strip between the western end of Helen's Bay and Grey Point (Figure 4.1). The tract is composed of a greater range of characteristic Southern Upland lithologies than any other in Ireland, including spilitic lava, conglomerate, black mudstone, rafts (olistoliths) of sandstone embedded in black mudstone, graded, channelised pebbly and coarse-grained sandy greywacke with interbedded grey mudstone. Inland, southwestward along strike, the Northern Belt is concealed beneath Triassic rocks in the Dundonald gap. It re-emerges south of Belfast and continues WSW into Co. Armagh and Co. Monaghan as a poorly exposed, narrow strip in which tract boundaries have yet to be established. At the southwest end of the Northern Belt in Co. Cavan two distinct tracts are recognised (19).

Gala Group

Between the Orlock Bridge and Cloghy faults, in the northern part of the Central Belt (Figure 4.1), there are at least eight accretionary tracts in which the Moffat Shale Group is succeeded by thick turbidite formations of the Gala Group (Figure 4.7). These tracts are

50

Photograph 2
Southward-dipping, overturned, thick bedded greywacke sandstone with superb sole markings (large horse-shoe flutes) demonstrating current flow from lower right to top left. Shore exposures [J596 785] of the Millisle Sandstone Formation (Gala Tract 7) 400m southeast of Galloway's Bridge, Donaghadee, Co. Down. (Hammer head 17cm long).

identified as Gala 3, 4, 5, 6, 7, 7+1, 7+2 and 7+3 (5) reflecting the detailed correlation with the outcrop in the Southern Uplands of Scotland (20). Gala tracts 1 and 2 of the Scottish outcrop have not been recognised in Counties Down and Armagh and have possibly been excised by movement on the Orlock Bridge Fault. The presence of additional tracts 7+1, 7+2 and 7+3 helps to explain the fact that the outcrop of the Central Belt in Counties Down and Armagh is at least 45km across the strike and is some 15km wider than in southwest Scotland. In all these tracts the coarser sedimentary clasts that occur in the turbidites demonstrate a homogeneously quartz-rich petrography.

Four Gala tracts in Co. Down merit particular comment. The **Millisle Formation** of Gala 7 is composed of uncommonly thick bedded and coarse-grained arenites with superb sole markings (Photograph 2) and conglomerate members. The sole markings are particularly well exposed on steeply overturned, north-younging beds forming the headlands immediately south of Coalpit Bay. The same coarse arenites, readily traced for at least 60km northeastward across the North Channel and for a similar distance southwestward into Co. Armagh, are quarried for high quality skid-resistant roadstone.

The **Ballywhiskin Tract**, Gala 7+1, shows an almost perfect fining-upward sequence. Massive proximal turbidites, with individual beds up to 4m thick, strike and dip uniformly at the southern margin of the tract and young northward into progressively thinner and finer grained beds over a tract width of about 1km. The thin siltstones and mudstones in the upper part of the sequence are repeatedly folded.

Graptolites occur in dark grey mudstone interbeds in several of the Gala turbidite formations. For example, mudstone interbedded with the massive proximal turbidites of the **Ballywhiskin Formation** at Whiskin Rocks [J615 734] have yielded a *turriculatus* Biozone

51

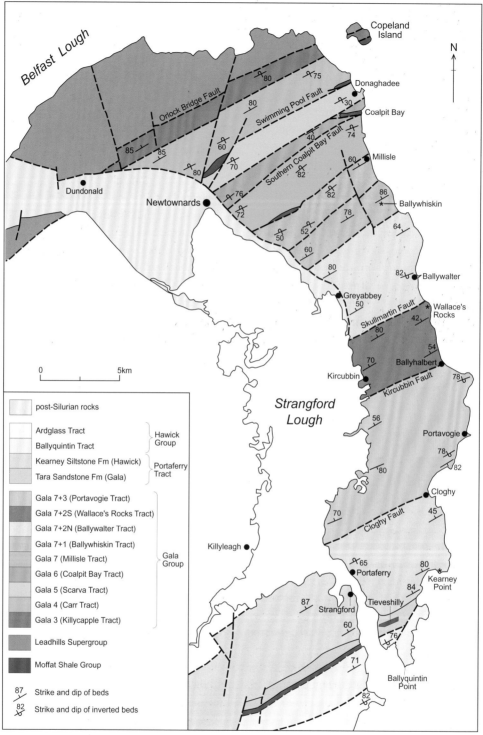

Figure 4.7
Geological map of the Ards Peninsula showing distribution of tracts in the Central Belt.

Legend:

- post-Silurian rocks
- Ardglass Tract — Hawick Group
- Ballyquintin Tract — Hawick Group
- Kearney Siltstone Fm (Hawick) — Portaferry Tract
- Tara Sandstone Fm (Gala) — Portaferry Tract
- Gala 7+3 (Portavogie Tract) — Gala Group
- Gala 7+2S (Wallace's Rocks Tract) — Gala Group
- Gala 7+2N (Ballywalter Tract) — Gala Group
- Gala 7+1 (Ballywhiskin Tract) — Gala Group
- Gala 7 (Millisle Tract) — Gala Group
- Gala 6 (Coalpit Bay Tract) — Gala Group
- Gala 5 (Scarva Tract) — Gala Group
- Gala 4 (Carr Tract) — Gala Group
- Gala 3 (Killycapple Tract) — Gala Group
- Leadhills Supergroup
- Moffat Shale Group

87 Strike and dip of beds

82 Strike and dip of inverted beds

fauna (17) and sparse *crispus* Biozone faunas have been collected at a number of localities in the **Rowreagh Formation** of the Gala 7+3 tract. The **Tara Sandstone Formation** of the **Portaferry Tract** is the most southerly formation demonstrating typical Gala Group lithological characteristics. Bands of pyritous black mudstone within the Tara Sandstone Formation at Millin Bay [J651 490] have yielded *crispus* and/or *griestoniensis* Biozone faunas (18).

Soft grey or grey-green bentonite beds occur in all the Gala Group formations in Co. Down, though they are less obvious than in the Moffat Shale outcrops (4).

Hawick Group

The distal turbidite sequences south of the Cloghy Fault demonstrate all the typical characteristics of the Hawick Group in the Southern Uplands of Scotland. The formations are largely composed of thinly bedded, fine-grained sandstone and siltstone, commonly with thick mudstone interbeds. Carbonate comprises up to 20% of the rock and is seen in thin section to have extensively replaced the original clay matrix of the greywacke. The carbonate concentrates in nodules or concretions, typically elongate and aligned parallel to bedding, which weather into rows of shallow depressions, locally merging into honeycomb patterns on joint surfaces. Thin red mudstones occur irregularly throughout the Hawick Group and rare detrital red micas can be seen on fresh surfaces of the siltstones and fine sandstones. Again, bentonite beds occur throughout the Hawick Group, being particularly common in the Ardglass Formation.

The rocks of the Hawick Group appear generally unfossiliferous, apart from a few trace fossils. South of the Cloghy Fault the Moffat Shale Group crops out only in the **Portaferry Tract** (Figure 4.7). This may be readily explained by noting that the basal thrust or *décollement* beneath the accretionary tracts in the Northern Belt and northern part of the Central Belt climbs to progressively higher stratigraphic levels in the Moffat Shale Group from northwest to southeast. Further southeast in the Central Belt the *décollement* may have cut up into the overlying turbidites, leaving the Moffat Shale Group to be completely subducted with the underlying oceanic crust. Recognition of tract boundaries in the outcrop of the Hawick Group is difficult or impossible because of the absence of Moffat Shale inliers and also because of the relatively homogeneous nature of the Hawick turbidite lithologies.

The strata exposed in the **Portaferry Tract** are arranged in a simple, straightforward and unique stratigraphic sequence (18, 20). At Tieveshilly (op. cit.) the **Moffat Shale Group** is about 80m thick. It is directly and conformably succeeded by the **Tara Sandstone Formation** (Figure 4.5), consisting of 150m of Gala-type, dark grey, quartz-rich arenites with laminae of black mudstone carrying *crispus* and *griestoniensis* Biozone graptolite faunas (18). The Tara Sandstone Formation passes up conformably into the unfossiliferous **Kearney Siltstone Formation** of Hawick Group aspect, consisting of some 600m of carbonate-rich fine sandstone, siltstone and grey mudstone with red mudstone bands near the base.

Tectonic structure

In the coastal outcrop of Co. Down the simple but important observation is that the rocks are well bedded with little evidence of changes in bed thickness and that dips are almost everywhere steep. The coherent nature of the beds may be a consequence of high pore-water pressure during and after deposition while the lack of stratal disruption and rarity of slump folding may reflect low depositional slopes (7). The generally steep dip of the beds is part of a fold style which relates to the process of accretion.

Folding

At outcrop or even at tract scale, the accretionary folding (Figure 4.2) is expressed in several distinct structural facies (21).

Facies 1: Where the turbidites are coarse-grained and thickly bedded the beds are typically uniformly steeply inclined or vertical and young consistently to the northwest. This regular pattern of strike and dip is only locally interrupted by sporadic fold pairs in which vergence is consistently to the southeast. The fold pair is composed of an anticline and a syncline with the trace of the anticline northwest of the trace of the syncline. The common 'short limb' separating the two fold traces is, with respect to the dominant northwest-younging long limbs, rotated to the southeast. Sequences of this structural facies are typified by the Ordovician Ballygrot Tract at Grey Point [J458 834] and by the Gala tracts between the Orlock Bridge Fault and Donaghadee (Figure 4.1). Although much of the Millisle Tract (Gala 7) is also essentially of this facies, the beds are commonly overturned so that they dip moderately to the south but young down to the north.

Facies 2: In this common structural facies there are many closely spaced, generally upright and upward facing, close, tight or even isoclinal folds, associated with minor faulting and shearing, particularly in the tighter fold cores and also separating adjacent folds

Photograph 3
Tight, upright F1 syncline showing differential thickening of beds into fold hinge. Kearney Siltstone Formation (Hawick Group), Kearney Point [J647 513], 5.5km east of Portaferry, Co. Down. (Hammer 33cm long).

(Photograph 3). Although the folds are generally gently plunging, the amount and direction of plunge commonly varies so that some gently plunging anticlines are locally periclinal. In Co. Down easterly plunges are dominant (20) but very steeply plunging folds, some of which are completely overturned and downward facing, characterise a 1km long coastal strip north of Ballywalter (Figure 4.1). Areas with a high density of fold hinges have been, somewhat misleadingly, described as flat belts (3), not because the dips are flat but because the fold envelope, or *faltenspiegel,* has a gentle or flat inclination. Facies 2 is best developed in the thinner bedded, fine-grained Hawick Group sandstones and siltstones, particularly in the Portaferry and Ballyquintin tracts.

Facies 3: The two preceding structural facies account for some 90% of the Lower Palaeozoic outcrop in Counties Down and Armagh. However, there are some large areas, (eg. between Ballyhalbert and Portavogie extending inland along strike to the southwest), where beds young consistently to the southeast. Even more remarkable are significant areas of Co. Armagh, for example south of Tandragee and specifically in Glasdrummond quarry [H940 388] southwest of Markethill, where the beds are horizontal or dip gently and are inverted as if on the overturned limbs of recumbent folds. The tracts of predominantly southeasterly younging strata, which also occur in Scotland, have been interpreted as packets of northwesterly overthrusted and obducted strata within the general northwesterly underthrusting and subduction of the accretionary prism (22). As yet there is insufficient evidence to justify any hypothesis attempting to explain the inverted flat-lying beds but it is relevant to note that the steeply inclined tract boundaries appear unaffected, continuing ENE-WSW across Co. Armagh. There are no obviously similar sheets of flat lying inverted strata recorded in the Scottish part of the terrane.

Cleavage

A well-developed **slaty cleavage** is present in the mudstone interbeds, locally penetrating the finer grained turbidite beds, particularly in the Hawick Group (Figure 4.8). In the Northern Belt and northern tracts of the Central Belt, the cleavage is commonly axial planar to the contemporary accretion-related folds. Where best developed (Figure 4.8), cleavage fans are alternately convergent in the fine-grained turbidites and divergent in the mudstones (Photograph 4).

In Hawick Group lithologies south of the Cloghy Fault, the cleavage commonly demonstrates a transecting relationship, in plan view striking at up to 30° clockwise of the fold axial traces (23, 24). Where the folds are strongly overturned the cleavage may cut across the northwest-younging limb so that bedding faces downward on cleavage in the north-western fold limbs and upward on the same cleavage in the southeast-younging limbs (Figure 4.8). The various hypotheses explaining the origin of the transecting geometry essentially involve horizontal sinistral shear or rotation contemporaneous with folding and accretion (23, 24, 25).

In several parts of the terrane the dominant, accretion-related folds and cleavage have been **refolded** and the later folds have associated **crenulation cleavages**. Locally it is therefore possible to establish deformation sequences in which the structures are assigned to D1, D2 or D3 deformation phases. Thus at least two crenulation cleavages are recognised deforming the original slaty cleavage in the Orlock Tract of the Northern Belt and upright, accretion-related folds in many Hawick Group exposures are refolded by both north- and south-verging fold pairs (4).

It is important to recognise that these deformation chronologies relate only to observations in a particular tract. There is ample evidence that deformation tracks

Photograph 4
Hinge area of gentle, upright F1 anticline with well developed S1 slaty cleavage refracting to form convergent fans in siltstone beds and divergent fans in the softer interlayered mudstone. Kearney Siltstone Formation (Hawick Group), Kearney Point [J644 511], 5.5km east of Portaferry, Co. Down.
(Hammer 33cm long).

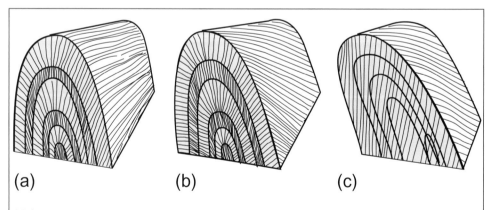

(a)   (b)   (c)

(a) Convergent and divergent fans parallel to axial surface e.g. Ballywalter, Ballyquintin

(b) Convergent and divergent fans transecting clockwise e.g. Kearney

(c) Cleavage transecting clockwise with beds facing downward on the cleavage in the northern limb
   e.g. Ardglass

Figure 4.8
Typical fold-cleavage relationships in the Southern Uplands-Down-Longford Terrane (7).

Photograph 5
Very tight, upright F1 anticline refolded by open F2 fold pair verging and gently inclined to the SSE. Kearney Siltstone Formation (Hawick Group), Whitehouse Port [J645 550], about 1km south of Cloghy, Co. Down. (Hammer 33cm long).

Photograph 6
Detail of very tight upright F1 fold hinge in Photograph 5. (Hammer length 33cm).

sedimentation diachronously from northwest to southeast across the terrane as required by both the viable terrane models (26). Thus, in the Northern Belt tracts the D1 deformation occurred before many of the Central and Southern Belt sequences had accumulated.

The later ductile deformations appear to be non-penetrative and relatively minor in scale, the fold pairs typically having short limb lengths of no more than a few metres. In the Hawick Group outcrops of southeast Co. Down, the second folds tend to be open structures, plunging gently eastward along gently inclined axial surfaces and verging southward (Photographs 5 and 6). The associated crenulation cleavage is commonly seen only at the fold hinges and in the short limbs. Third folds have a very similar style, scale, fabric and morphology except that their sense of vergence is invariably northward (4).

The well-developed slaty cleavage in many Hawick Group outcrops has acted as the mechanically essential plane of anisotropy for the genesis of an orthorhombic system of kink bands (27). The kink bands dip steeply and displace the earlier fabric both sinistrally and dextrally (Photograph 7). Profile cross sections of fine examples occur in slate on the wave-cut platform immediately west of Knockinelder Bay on the western side of Kearney Point [J644 511].

Faults

Many small faults, with variable orientation and displacement directions, occurred in association with the accretionary deformation, particularly in the hinge zones of the early folds. Groups of steeply inclined reverse faults effect imbrication of the strata on a small scale.

Photograph 7
Dextral kink band deforming a composite fabric of vertical bedding and slaty cleavage. Kearney Siltstone Formation (Hawick Group), exposed on horizontal wave-cut platform at eastern end of Knockinelder Bay [J642 514], 4.5km east of Portaferry. (Scale shows 1cm squares).

A fine example of a strike-slip duplex imbricating the Birkhill Shales occurs below and some 3m north of the low cliff on the southern edge of Coalpit Bay [J595 788].

Later brittle shear fractures include a regular and systematic set of strike-slip faults which displace fold hinges, the various elements of the ductile structural fabric and some, but not all, of the late Caledonian lamprophyre dykes. In the coastal outcrop of Co. Down, sinistral strike slip faults are twice as common as dextral and both show preferred orientations, sinistrals striking at 015° and dextrals at 125° (24). Displacements are invariably small, typically ranging up to a few hundred metres, sinistral slips tending to be larger than dextral. On occasions the strike-slip faults displace the tract boundaries such as between Gala 6 and Gala 7 so that coarse turbidites of the Millisle Formation (Gala 7) now form the low-lying intertidal outcrops eastward directly along strike from the Moffat Shale Group at Coalpit Bay (Gala 6). There is an apparent 1km sinistral displacement of tract boundaries, now concealed by Triassic rocks in the Dundonald gap and there are similar displacements of tract boundaries in Counties Armagh and Monaghan.

The fabric of the **Orlock Bridge Fault** provides further evidence of the importance of sinistral strike-slip in the later Caledonian deformation of the terrane. The fault extends for some 400km from Slieve Glah in Co. Cavan, through outcrop at Clontibret on the Co. Monaghan-Co. Armagh border, Craigantlet and Orlock and across southern Scotland to the eastern limit of the Lower Palaeozoic outcrop 11km southwest of Dunbar. The width of the zone of fault-related deformation appears to decrease eastward but it is still over 100m across at Orlock Bridge, 1km southeast of Orlock Point (Figure 4.1). In the central, most intensely deformed part of the zone, protomylonite, mylonite and ultramylonite textures are developed. The deformation overprints and deforms the local accretion-related cleavage but at Orlock Bridge it is in turn intruded by a late Caledonian lamprophyre dyke which is only marginally affected. Steeply plunging, sinistrally-verging folds indicate a large left-lateral slip (13).

Metamorphism

Throughout the Southern Uplands-Down-Longford Terrane there is ample evidence of low-grade metamorphism. Rocks now exposed at surface vary from zeolite facies to prehnite-pumpellyite facies, the latter more commonly developed in volcaniclastic greywacke and metabasic volcanic rocks such as occur in north Co. Down and in Co. Cavan (28). Illite crystallinity studies on metapelites from the turbidite sequence in southwest Scotland demonstrate regional patterns of late diagenetic to anchizonal grades that were generated by burial and underplating in an accretionary thrust stack at depths of 12km or more (29). Local shear-zone metamorphism also occurred.

Deformation and metamorphism in the Southern Uplands-Down-Longford Terrane thus appears to be largely related to diachronous, south-vergent accretion and thrusting which progressed northwest to southeast across the ocean or basin in which its sediments had been recently deposited. This deformation was increasingly modified and overprinted by sinistral strike-slip, expressed both in ductile, locally penetrative, shear fabrics and in systems of late brittle faults. There is remarkably little evidence of climactic, collisional tectonics which might have been expected to accompany the final closure of Iapetus.

References

1) Lapworth, C. 1878. The Moffat Series. *Quarterly Journal of the Geological Society of London*, **34**, 240-346.

2) Peach, B. N. and Horne, J. 1899. *The Silurian Rocks of Britain, Vol. 1. Scotland.* Memoirs of the Geological Survey of the United Kingdom, HMSO.

3) Craig, G. Y. and Walton, E. K. 1959. Sequence and structure in the Silurian Rocks of Kirkcudbrightshire. *Geological Magazine*, **96**, 209-20.

4) Anderson, T. B. and Cameron, T. D. J. 1979. A structural profile of Caledonian deformation in Down. *In*: Harris, A. L., Holland, C. H. and Leake, B. E. (eds.). *The Caledonides of the British Isles, reviewed.* Special Publication of the Geological Society of London, No. **8**, 263-7.

5) Geological Survey of Northern Ireland. 1997. Geological Map of Northern Ireland. Solid Geology (second edition). 1:250,000. (Keyworth, Nottingham: British Geological Survey).

6) Sharpe, E. N. 1970. An occurrence of pillow lavas in the Ordovician of County Down. *Irish Naturalist's Journal*, **16**, 299-301.

7) Anderson, T. B. 2001 (for 2000). Structural interpretations of the Southern Uplands Terrane. *Transactions of the Royal Society of Edinburgh: Earth Sciences*, **91**, 363-73.

8) Mitchell, A. H. G. and McKerrow, W. S. 1975. Analogous evolution of the Burma orogen and the Scottish Caledonides. *Bulletin of the Geological Society of America*, **86**, 305-15.

9) McKerrow, W. S., Leggett, J. K. and Eales, M. H. 1977. Imbricate thrust model of the Southern Uplands of Scotland. *Nature*, **136**, 755-70.

10) Stone, P., Floyd, J. D., Barnes, R. P. and Lintern, B. C. 1987. A sequential back-arc and foreland basin thrust duplex model for the Southern Uplands of Scotland. *Journal of the Geological Society of London*, **144**, 753-64.

11) Floyd, J. D. 1996. Lithostratigraphy of the Ordovician rocks in the Southern Uplands: Crawford Group, Moffat Shale Group, Leadhills Supergroup. *Transactions of the Royal Society of Edinburgh: Earth Sciences*, **86**, 153-65.

12) Floyd, J. D. 2001 (for 2000). The Southern Uplands terrane: a stratigraphical review. *Transactions of the Royal Society of Edinburgh: Earth Sciences*, **91**, 349-62.

13) Anderson, T. B. and Oliver, G. J. H. 1986. The Orlock Bridge Fault: a major late Caledonian sinistral fault in the Southern Uplands terrane, British Isles. *Transactions of the Royal Society of Edinburgh: Earth Sciences*, **77**, 203-22.

14) Geological Survey of Northern Ireland 1985. Armagh, Northern Ireland Sheet 47. Solid Geology. 1:50,000. (Southampton: Ordnance Survey for the Geological Survey of Northern Ireland).

15) Swanston, W. and Lapworth, C. 1877. On the Silurian rocks of the County Down. *Proceedings of the Belfast Naturalists Field Club*, **Appendix 1876-77**, 107-48.

16) Craig, L. E. 1984. Stratigraphy in an accretionary prism: the Ordovician rocks in North Down, Ireland. *Transactions of the Royal Society of Edinburgh: Earth Sciences*, **74**, 183-91.

17) Smith, R. A., Johnston, T. P. and Legg, I. C. 1991. Geology of the country around Newtownards. *Memoir of the Geological Survey of Northern Ireland*, Sheet 37 and part of sheet 38 (Northern Ireland).

18) Anderson, T. B. and Rickards, R. B. 2000. The stratigraphy and graptolite faunas of the Moffat Shales at Tieveshilly, Co. Down, Northern Ireland, and their implications for the modelling of the Southern Uplands-Down-Longford Terrane. *Irish Journal of Earth Sciences*, **18**, 69-88.

19) Geraghty, M. 1997. *A geological description of Monaghan - Carlingford to accompany the Bedrock Geology 1:100,000 Scale Map Series, sheet 8 and 9, Monaghan and Carlingford, with contributions by J. Farrelly, K. Claringbold, C. Jordan, R. Meehan and M. Hudson.* Geological Survey of Ireland (GSI), 60pp.

20) Barnes, R. P., Anderson, T. B. and McCurry, J. A. 1987. Along-strike variation in the stratigraphic and structural profile of the Southern Uplands Central Belt in Galloway and Down. *Journal of the Geological Society, London,* **146,** 807-16.

21) Stone, P. (editor) 1996. *Geology in south-west Scotland; an excursion guide.* Keyworth, Nottingham: British Geological Survey.

22) McCurry, J. A. and Anderson, T. B. 1989. Landward vergence in the Lower Palaeozoic Southern Uplands-Down-Longford terrane. *Geology,* **17,** 630-33.

23) Cameron, T. D. J. 1981. The history of Caledonian deformation in East Lecale, County Down. *Journal of Earth Sciences: Royal Dublin Society,* **4,** 53-74.

24) Anderson, T. B. 1987. The onset and timing of Caledonian sinistral shear in County Down. *Journal of the Geological Society, London,* **144,** 817-25.

25) Stringer, P. and Treagus, J. E. 1980. Non-axial planar S1 cleavage in the Hawick rocks of the Galloway area, Southern Uplands, Scotland. *Journal of Structural Geology,* **2,** 317-31.

26) Barnes, R. P., Lintern, B. C. and Stone, P. 1989. Timing and regional implications of deformation in the Southern Uplands of Scotland. *Journal of the Geological Society, London,* **146,** 905-8.

27) Anderson, T. B. 1969. The geometry of a natural orthorhombic system of kink bands. *In:* Baer, A. J. and Norris, D. K. (eds.). *Proceedings, Conference on research in Tectonics (Kink bands and brittle deformation),* Geological Survey of Canada Paper, **68-52,** 200-28.

28) Oliver, G. J. H., Smellie, J. L., Thomas, L. J., Casey, D. M., Kemp, A. E. S., Evans, L. J., Baldwin, J. R. and Hepworth, B. C. 1984. Early Palaeozoic metamorphic history of the Midland Valley, Southern Uplands-Longford-Down massif and the Lake District, British Isles. *Transactions of the Royal Society of Edinburgh: Earth Sciences,* **75,** 245-58.

29) Merriman, R. J. and Roberts, B. 2001 (for 2000). Low grade metamorphism in the Scottish Southern Uplands terrane: deciphering the patterns of accretionary burial, shearing and cryptic aureoles. *Transactions of the Royal Society of Edinburgh: Earth Sciences,* **91,** 521-37.

Chapter 5

Late Palaeozoic Intrusives

M. R. COOPER and T. P. JOHNSTON

Introduction

Late Palaeozoic intrusives are largely confined to the Southern Uplands-Down-Longford Terrane in Counties Down and Armagh (1). By far the largest, the Newry Igneous Complex, consists of late orogenic I-Type (Caledonian) granite rocks. Their intrusion at, or just before, 400Ma post-dated both the closure of the Iapetus Ocean and continental collision in the end Silurian-early Devonian period, but coincided with the onset of sinistral transpression in the Iapetus suture zone (2). The complex lies between Slieve Croob and Forkill and was emplaced in Silurian greywacke and mudstone (Figure 5.1). In addition to three overlapping granodiorite plutons there is an earlier intrusion of intermediate and ultramafic rocks at its northeastern end. The intrusion of the Newry Igneous Complex was

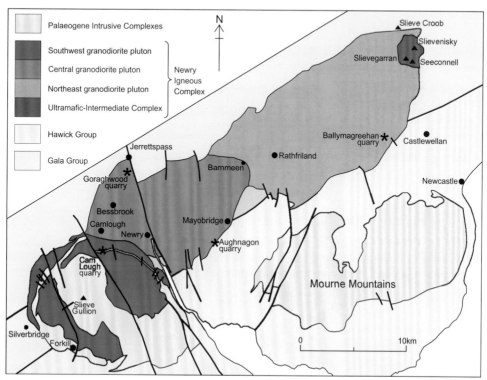

Figure 5.1
Geological map of the Newry Igneous Complex.

associated with the injection of dykes and sills of largely lamprophyric composition in two separate episodes. These minor intrusions are genetically related to the northeastern sector of the complex and are thus concentrated in Co. Down. To a much lesser extent lamprophyric intrusions are also found in the Midland Valley and Central Highlands (Grampian) terranes.

Newry Igneous Complex

A number of dates of intrusion have been published for the Newry Igneous Complex. While the oldest part of the Complex, the ultramafic-intermediate complex at Slievegarran gives an age of 403±3Ma, the southwestern pluton is dated at 399±21Ma based on whole-rock Rb-Sr isotope analysis (3). A granodiorite from the margin of the northeast pluton gives a Rb-Sr age of 399±3Ma (4).

In the mid-20th Century the origin of the Newry Igneous Complex was controversial and ranged from a magmatic origin (5) to an essentially non-magmatic 'transformist' model involving large-scale, *in situ* metasomatism of the Silurian country rocks (6). However, field, petrographic and geochemical evidence supports a magmatic origin for the complex. It is believed that the ultramafic rocks, and associated meladiorites originated by fractionation of intermediate magma of upper mantle origin. The layered nature of these rocks is probably the result of crystal accumulation in the magma chamber (4, 6). Thus the three granodiorite plutons, which form the bulk of the complex, represent a more evolved melt that may have resulted from this process operating on a larger scale at deeper crustal levels.

Photomicrograph No. 1
Biotite pyroxenite, composed mainly of biotite and augite with minor quartz, from the ultramafic-intermediate complex at the northeast end of the Newry Igneous Complex [J325 423]. (Crossed polars, field of view 5mm wide).

The Ultramafic-Intermediate Complex

Ultramafic rocks consisting of biotite pyroxenite and augite biotitite, and associated meladiorites are part of a layered intrusion that is confined to the northeast end of the Newry Igneous Complex in a close relationship with intermediate rocks. Petrologically they are composed of clinopyroxene, biotite and apatite as euhedral (cumulus) crystals (Photomicrograph 1) ± olivine with plagioclase the dominant cumulus phase in the meladiorites (Photomicrograph 2). The ultramafic rocks are mineralogically inhomogeneous, clinopyroxene-rich and biotite-rich varieties having sharp contacts. Massive biotite pyroxenite occurs in numerous exposures at Ardglass [J320 422] on the southeast flank of Slievegarran and is also intercalated as lenses in the 'laminated' meladiorite.

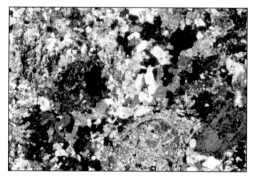

Photomicrograph No. 2
Meladiorite from the ultramafic-intermediate complex [J325 423] composed of a finer grained matrix of plagioclase feldspar with phenocrysts of pyroxene (augite) and masses of biotite. (Crossed polars, field of view 5mm wide).

The meladiorites are commonly heterogeneous with variable content of either biotite or clinopyroxene. The ultramafic and intermediate rocks are typically coarse-grained and have intricate contact relationships (Photograph 1).

Between the hills of Seeconnell [J328 420] and Slievegarran [J316 424] ultramafic rocks are closely associated with laminated meladiorites with a near vertical mineral layering of plagioclase crystals of calcic andesine to labradorite composition. In places the two rock types occur as centimetre-scale alternating layers. Between Slievegarran and Slievenisky [J324 444] the two main lithologies are interlayered with 'unlaminated', more leucocratic, intermediate rocks of monzonitic-dioritic composition.

Based on field evidence, the ultramafic rocks and associated meladiorites probably developed as crystal cumulates from an intermediate magma. There is no evidence that the ultramafic rocks were intruded into the associated intermediate rocks as a crystal mush, nor can they be construed as a marginal facies of an intermediate magma that developed against the Silurian country rocks. The mineralogical inhomogeneity and mineral layering in the meladiorites developed in the upper crust, in a convecting intermediate magma chamber that may have been connected to a Caledonian central volcano (4).

Intermediate rocks consisting of augite-hypersthene monzonite, monzodiorite and more rarely augite-biotite diorite are concentrated at the margin of the northeast granodiorite pluton in the vicinity of Slievegarran, Slievenisky and Seeconnell. Petrographically they contain clinopyroxene, large poikilitic orthopyroxene, biotite crystals up to 3cm long, minor amounts of quartz and plagioclase composed of sodic andesine. In the meladiorites, olivine can be abundant but quartz is usually absent. Rock types encountered along a 300m section from the northeast base of Slievegarran to its summit include laminated meladiorites interlayered with ultramafics and fine-grained, unlaminated quartz monzodiorite and diorite. Both the intermediate and ultramafic rocks are intruded and veined by granodiorite of the northeast pluton.

Photograph 1
Alternating dark biotite pyroxenite (ultrabasic composition) and light, meladiorite (intermediate composition), of the ultramafic-intermediate complex (Newry Igneous Complex). Ardglass [J320 422], southeast flank of Slievegarran, 7km NNW of Castlewellan, Co. Down. (Hammer head 16cm long).

At the margin of the Ultrabasic–Intermediate Complex, contact metamorphism has altered the Silurian country rock to a cordierite hornfels (Photograph 2) in which 'fusing' and remobilisation of the sediments may have destroyed bedding. Textures in these country rocks are extremely variable ranging from a rock resembling fine-grained biotite granite to a biotite-rich hornfels in which bedding is still preserved. The occurrence of the hornfels at the northeast end of the complex and at the outer contact of the granodiorite on Slieve Croob was historically viewed as confirmation of a metasomatic origin for the Newry Igneous Complex.

The Granodiorite Plutons
Granodiorite forms the largest part of the Newry Igneous Complex and occurs in three distinct plutons. It is likely that several

63

magma pulses were involved in the formation of each pluton (4). While the northeast and southwest plutons have more basic margins and relatively quartz-rich central portions, the rocks of the central pluton show an opposite trend. Mineralogically, the granodiorites are composed of zoned plagioclase, microcline, quartz, hornblende, biotite and accessory Fe-Ti oxide, apatite, zircon and titanite. At the margins of the plutons the granodiorite has a penetrative, steeply inclined mineral foliation that is sub-parallel to the Silurian envelope rocks (Photomicrograph 3). This deformation is not apparent towards the centre of the plutons (Photomicrograph 4). Evidence of diapiric strain was produced at the margins of the complex at both its northeast and southwest ends by the 'shouldering aside' of the country rocks (2).

The normally zoned **northeast pluton** (Figure 5.1) extends from Slieve Croob to Barnmeen [J173 327]. It is composed of medium- to coarse-grained granodiorite, with igneous and sedimentary xenoliths (enclaves) (Photograph 3), and is exposed in Ballymagreehan quarry [J305 354].

Photomicrograph No. 3
Granodiorite of the northeast pluton in Ballymagreehan quarry [J305 354]. A steeply inclined foliation at the margins of the pluton is reflected in the alignment of plagioclase feldspar.
(Crossed polars, field of view 5mm wide).

Photomicrograph No. 4
Unfoliated granodiorite composed of plagioclase and alkali feldspar, quartz, hornblende and biotite from the centre of the northeast pluton. Exposure [J205 355] 2km north of Rathfriland.
(Crossed polars, field of view 5mm wide).

Photograph 2
Silurian country rock of the Gala Group contact metamorphosed to cordierite hornfels ('fused' or mobilised) by the intrusion of the Newry Igneous Complex. Slieve Croob [J318 453], west and east of the summit, 10km NNW of Castlewellan, Co. Down. (Hammer head 16cm long).

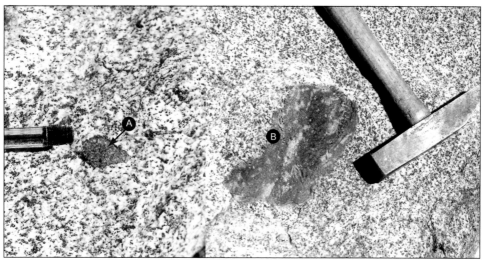

Photograph 3
Igneous enclave of ultramafic composition (A) and sedimentary enclave consisting of biotite hornfels of Silurian country rock (B) in the northeast granodiorite pluton of the Newry Igneous Complex. Ballymagreehan quarry [J305 354], east flank of Tullynasoo Mountain, 3.75km WSW of Castlewellan, Co. Down. (Pen 8mm wide and hammer head 16cm long).

The reversely zoned **central pluton** (Figure 5.1) extends from Barnmeen to Bessbrook and typical lithologies are exposed in Aughnagon quarry [J145 251]. At its exposed northern margin in Goraghwood quarry [J066 319], near Jerrettspass, an early-formed marginal facies of porphyritic 'rhyolite' intervenes between hornfelsed and mobilised Silurian rocks and medium- to coarse-grained unfoliated biotite-hornblende granodiorite. The marginal granodiorite is notably more acidic than the rock at the centre of the pluton.

Much of the area between Bessbrook and Silverbridge is underlain either by granodiorite of the normally zoned **southwest pluton** (Figure 5.1) or by the Palaeogene Slieve Gullion Complex (Chapter 15). Its margin is exposed in Cam Lough quarry [J037 246] and shows early microgranite, diorite and granodiorite (biotite granite) sheets intruding and hornfelsing Silurian country rock. A strong vertical fabric trending ENE, parallel to the pluton boundary, deforms the rocks in the quarry. The cross-cutting relationship between the southwest pluton and the Slieve Gullion ring dyke is also exposed here.

Lamprophyre Intrusions

Numerous lamprophyre dykes and subconcordant intrusions are mainly orientated parallel to the northeast-southwest structural grain of the Southern Uplands-Down-Longford Terrane. Two distinct phases of lamprophyre intrusion are recognised in Co. Down (8). An earlier 'crushed' series were cleaved, but are not seen folded, by the D1 deformation and occur mainly in the southern part of the Ards Peninsula, Co. Down (7), south of a west-east line (Figure 4.7) from Ringboy Point [J650 575] to Ringburr Point [J573 554]. A fine example (Photograph 4) occurs at Kearney Point [J646 512]. The implication is that intrusion of this earlier series of lamprophyres overlapped in time with intrusion of the Newry Igneous Complex and with the continuing D1 deformation. A later suite of unfoliated, post-tectonic lamprophyre intrusions (Photograph 5) are most numerous in north Co. Down (9), and on the east coast of the Ards Peninsula at Wallace's Rocks [J635 677], Black Rock [J633 712] and Ballyhalbert Pier [J660 633].

65

Photograph 4
Vertical 30cm thick older series lamprophyre dyke intruded parallel to bedding in the Kearney Siltstone Formation (Hawick Group). Dyke, seen below 33cm long hammer, is present only on the southern limb of the tight, upright F1 anticline so is not folded by F1 but is folded by F2. Whitehouse Port [J645 550], 1.5km southeast of Cloghy, Ards Peninsula, Co. Down.

66

Photograph 5
Horizontal lamprophyre sill (25cm thick) cross-cutting upright F1 anticline and syncline in Kearney Siltstone Formation (Hawick Group). Kearney Point [J646 512], 5km east of Portaferry, Ards Peninsula, Co. Down. (Hammer length 33cm).

The lamprophyres are divided petrographically on the basis of the main phenocrystic mineral and groundmass feldspar. The majority of the undeformed intrusions are identified as **vogesite** or **minette**, with hornblende and biotite/pyroxene respectively as the dominant phenocrysts, although **spessartite**, which contains phenocrystic hornblende in a plagioclase-dominated groundmass, is also recorded. All the lamprophyre dykes contain xenoliths, most commonly of greywacke or mudstone country rock, with very rare examples of igneous material of probable cognate origin (10). Although the majority of lamprophyres are recognised in coastal locations, examples also occur inland in Co. Armagh, north and west of the Newry Igneous Complex. In contrast to the Co. Down dyke swarm the orientation of the majority of inland intrusions is NNW-SSE, parallel to the Palaeogene basic dykes. While there is little doubt that the lamprophyres are Caledonian, the age of a few non-lamprophyric intrusions composed of pitchstone, felsite, microdiorite, quartz trachyandesite and quartz-hornblende trachyte is unclear but all are most likely late Palaeozoic (11). In Co. Armagh the lamprophyre suite is augmented by the presence of **kersantite**, a biotite lamprophyre with a plagioclase-rich groundmass. None of the inland intrusions are cleaved or folded but most are heavily altered to sericite, chlorite and carbonate.

References

1) Geological Survey of Northern Ireland 1997. Northern Ireland. Solid Geology (second edition). 1:250 000. (Keyworth, Nottingham: British Geological Survey).

2) Murphy, F. C. 1987. Late Caledonian granitoids and timing of deformation in the Iapetus suture zone of eastern Ireland. *Geological Magazine*, **124**, 135-42.

3) O'Connor, P. J. 1975. Rb-Sr whole-rock isochron for the Newry granodiorite, NE Ireland. *Scientific Proceedings of the Royal Dublin Society*, **A5**, 407-13.

4) Meighan, I. G. and Neeson, J. C. 1979. The Newry igneous complex, County Down. *In*: Harris, A. L., Holland, C. H. and Leake, B. E. (eds.). *The Caledonides of the British Isles—reviewed*. Special Publication of the Geological Society of London, **8**, 717-22.

5) Richey, J. E. and Thomas, H. H. 1932. The Tertiary ring complex of Slieve Gullion (Ireland). *Quarterly Journal of the Geological Society of London*, **88**, 776-847.

6) Reynolds, D. L. 1944. The south-western end of the Newry igneous complex. A contribution towards the petrogenesis of the granodiorites. *Quarterly Journal of the Geological Society of London*, **99**, 205-40.

7) Cameron, T. D. J. 1981. The history of Caledonian deformation in east Lecale, County Down. *Journal of Earth Sciences Royal Dublin Society*, **4**, 53-74.

8) Reynolds, D. L. 1931. The dykes of the Ards Penninsula. *Geological Magazine*, **65**, 97-111 and 145-65.

9) Anderson, T. B. and Cameron, T. D. J. 1979. A structural profile of Caledonian deformation in Down. In: Harris, A. L., Holland, C. H. and Leake, B. E. (eds.). *The Caledonides of the British Isles—reviewed*. Special Publication of the Geological Society of London, **8**, 263-67.

10) Smith, R. A., Johnston, T. P. and Legg, I. C. 1991. Geology of the country around Newtownards. *Memoir of the Geological Survey of Northern Ireland*, Sheet 37 and part of sheet 38 (Northern Ireland).

11) Geological Survey of Northern Ireland 1984. Armagh, Northern Ireland Sheet 47. Solid Geology. 1:50,000. (Southampton: Ordnance Survey for the Geological Survey of Northern Ireland).

Chapter 6

Devonian

W. I. MITCHELL

Introduction

In Ireland and Britain there is evidence that fault-controlled uplift of the Caledonian mountains during the last stages of the Caledonian Orogeny in Early Devonian times was accompanied by rapid subsidence of non-marine sedimentary basins (Figure 6.1). Reconstructions envisage a mountain range of Himalayan proportions extending from western Ireland to Scotland, composed largely of metamorphic rocks located to the north of those basins (2). From its southern margin, which was bounded by the active Highland Boundary Fault, river systems, comparable in size to the present-day Ganges-Brahmaputra system of the Indian subcontinent, transported sediment southwards. The conglomerate and coarse-grained sandstone was deposited on alluvial fans banked up against the mountain front with finer sediment deposited to the south on alluvial floodplains and in lakes in the axial region of the basins. This reconstruction is applicable to western Ireland and Scotland (3) but is only partly supported in Northern Ireland.

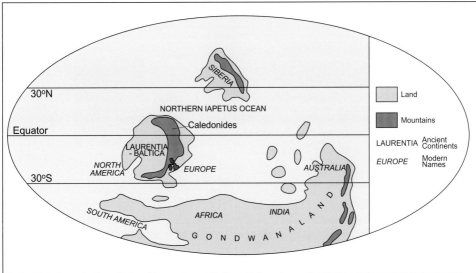

By the Early Devonian the collision of Laurentia and Baltica with the microcontinent of Avalonia resulted in the closure of the Iapetus Ocean and creation of a new, larger continental mass. Ireland and Britain lay on the southeastern margin of this new landmass in the rain shadow of the Caledonides mountain chain, which extended from northeastern America to Ireland, northern Britain and western Scandinavia. In the southern hemisphere all of the present continents were grouped together as Gondwanaland. In Northern Ireland the Devonian System is represented exclusively by rocks that were deposited in a continental, desert environment.

Figure 6.1
Position of the continents in the Early Devonian (*c.* 400Ma (1)).

Because of the absence of macrofossils in rocks of 'Lower' and 'Upper Old Red Sandstone' facies in Northern Ireland, their assignment to the Devonian was based on lithological comparisons with successions in the Midland Valley of Scotland. When those rocks were finally dated to the Early Devonian and Late Devonian-early Carboniferous respectively, the ages were applied indiscriminately to all 'Devonian' rocks in Northern Ireland (Figure 6.2). In 1938, the discovery of a fish ('pteraspid') fragment near Lisbellaw (4) was heralded as an affirmation of the long suspected Early Devonian age for the 'Old Red Sandstone' facies rocks. However, samples of green mudstone from the western half of the Fintona Block yielded Early Devonian to late Carboniferous miospore assemblages (5). They demonstrated a Carboniferous age for most of the conglomerates in the Fintona Block and prompted a revision of Devonian palaeogeography. Nevertheless, there was still no unequivocal evidence of Early Devonian strata in the Fintona Block and even the celebrated fish locality subsequently proved to be early Carboniferous (late Viséan) (5). Intriguingly, a reassessment of the fish fragment identified it as an indeterminate pteraspid of Early Devonian affinity and ranging from uppermost Silurian (Prídolí) to Middle Devonian (Givetian) (6). The specimen was probably reworked either from the Shanmullagh Formation (Figure 6.3) or from Devonian rocks long since eroded or now concealed.

Based on palynological data, the Shanmullagh Formation was originally assigned a Late Devonian (Frasnian-Famennian) age (7, 8) although there was still uncertainty as the palynomorph assemblages lacked Late Devonian zonal taxa. A further review (9) of the palynology now indicates an age ranging from the latest Lockhovian to early late Emsian (Table 6.1).

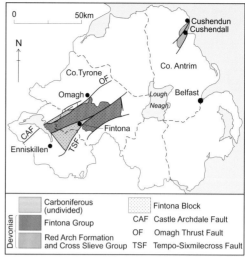

Figure 6.2
Distribution of Devonian and putative Devonian rocks in Northern Ireland.

	Stage	Tempo-Sixmilecross Fault	
		North	South
Devonian — Late	Famennian		
	Frasnian		Raveagh Sst Fm / Gortfinbar Cong. Fm / Barrack Hill Andesite Mbr
Middle	Givetian		Shanmaghery Sandstone Fm
	Eifelian		
	Emsian		
Early	Pragian	Shanmullagh Formation	
	Lockhovian	Tedd Fm	

Table 6.1
Subdivisions and age of the Fintona Group in Northern Ireland.

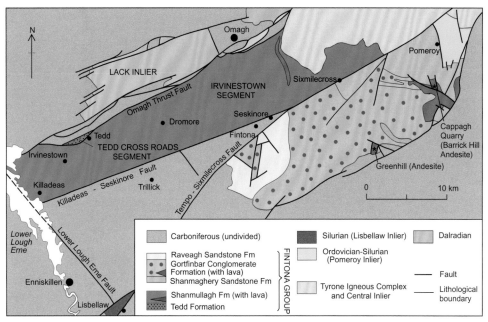

Figure 6.3
Geological setting of the Fintona Group.

Stratigraphy
Fintona Group

Fintona Block
Devonian strata in the Fintona Block (Figure 6.3) are assigned to the **Fintona Group**.
North of the Tempo-Sixmilecross Fault the Fintona Block is divided into fault-bounded
segments (5) with Devonian rocks confined to the Tedd Cross Roads Segment **(Tedd
Formation)** and the Irvinestown Segment **(Shanmullagh Formation)**. South of the Tempo-
Sixmilecross Fault the Fintona Group comprises three formations (10).

Tedd Cross Roads Segment
This fault-bounded lenticle (Figure 6.3) includes about 500m of red beds of the **Tedd
Formation** (8). They consist in the lower part of fining-upwards, pebbly and coarse-grained
sandstone, and in the top 200m are thin, fine-grained sandstone, siltstone and reddish
brown mudstone. Green mudstone (0.4m thick), with assemblages of indeterminate
palynomorphs, occurs at one locality in Cloghfin Townland [H259 615].

Irvinestown Segment
The lowest strata in the widespread Shanmullagh Formation (Figure 6.3) are brown,
coarse-grained pebbly sandstone, thin purplish grey fine-grained sandstone and mudstone
(10, 7). However, much of the formation consists of massive purplish grey sandstone
(Photograph 1) and mudstone laminae with ripples and desiccation cracks. Sandstone
also occurs in channels with dimensions varying from shallow washout structures
(Photograph 2) to features up to 2m deep and is associated with sandy siltstone, reddish
brown mudstone and palaeosols with calcrete nodules. Thin green mudstone contains
palynomorphs.

Photograph 1
The Shanmullagh Formation of the Fintona Group in the stratotype comprising about 10m of purple-brown, fine- to medium-grained feldspathic sandstone with mudstone clasts, ripples, laminae of coarse, angular quartz grains and thin layers of chocolate-brown mudstone. Disused quarry [H250 604], Drumduff Townland, 2.4km NNE of Irvinestown, Co. Fermanagh.

Photograph 2
Roadside cutting in red beds of the Shanmullagh Formation consisting of grey to purplish brown, fine- to medium-grained sandstone, siltstone and thin mudstone with sandstone channel 9m wide and 23cm deep. North side of the A32 Irvinestown Road [H348 627], 300m southwest of Dromore, Co. Tyrone. (Hammer 46cm long).

Fossils 1, 2 and 3
Early Devonian (latest Lockhovian-early late Emsian) miospores from the Shanmullagh Formation:
1 *Dictyotriletes* cf. *gorgoneus* (x 600)
2 *Emphanisporites rotatus* (x 630)
3 *Dictyotriletes emsiensis* (x 600)

Composition and age of the palynomorph assemblages

Green, colour-banded, mudstones contain palynomorphs and black phytoclast material. Miospores are dark brown and usually poorly preserved. The miospore assemblage includes *Acinosporites* cf. *apiculatus*, *Apiculiretusispora plicata*, *Dibolisporites* cf. *gibberosus*, *Dictyotriletes* cf. *gorgoneus* (Fossil 1), *Emphanisporites rotatus* (Fossil 2) and *Dictyotriletes emsiensis* (Fossil 3), a zonal taxon for the Pragian *Verrucosisporites polygonalis-Dictyotriletes emsiensis* Biozone (11), indicating a late Lockhovian to early late Emsian age. The absence of monolete spores and large spores with grapnel-tipped processes suggests a pre-late Emsian age (9).

South of the Tempo-Sixmilecross Fault

The Fintona Group hereabouts (Figure 6.3) is unfossiliferous and is divided into three formations about 3450m thick in total (Table 6.2). Palaeocurrent data in the **Shanmaghery Sandstone Formation** (12) indicate bimodal current flow from the northeast, deriving clasts from the Tyrone Inlier (13), and from the southwest. Rounded clasts of andesitic volcanic rock in the **Gortfinbar Conglomerate Formation** were derived from the east by erosion of the **Barrack Hill Andesite Member**.

Ferro-magnesian minerals in the andesitic lavas are commonly altered to haematite and groundmass plagioclase is kaolinised or chloritised. Vesicles are commonly infilled with calcite, chlorite, quartz or iron oxide. The best exposure of the Barrack Hill Andesite Member (Figure 6.3) is in Cappagh quarry [H696 674]. Radiometric dating of fresh lava (K-Ar whole-rock) records an extrusive event at 375±2Ma (Givetian to Frasnian), (Table 6.1) and a date of 275±6Ma for reddish coloured lava which indicates an Early Permian resetting event induced by hydrothermal alteration during the Variscan Orogeny. The Raveagh Sandstone Formation is poorly exposed.

Formation	Member	Lithology
Raveagh Sandstone (350m)		Sandstone, reddish brown, fine-grained, silty, clay matrix; abundant ripple marks and desiccation cracks
Gortfinbar Conglomerate (2500m)	Greenhill Andesite Barrack Hill Andesite	Conglomerate, purplish brown, clasts boulder and pebble-sized, volcaniclastic, rare vein quartz, quartzite and greywacke; sandstone, coarse-grained. Lava, trachyte or trachy-andesite, vesicular, flow-banded
Shanmaghery Sandstone (600m)		Sandstone, purplish brown, red and green stained, coarse-grained, calcareous, micaceous, fining upwards, with thin siltstone and mudstone intercalations; parallel, cross and ripple laminations and desiccation cracks. Basal conglomerate with pebbles of vein quartz, quartzite, biotite granite, tuff, jasper and mica schist

Table 6.2
The Fintona Group south of the Tempo-Sixmilecross Fault (10).

Photograph 3A
Cliff-forming conglomerates of the Cushendun Formation of the Cross Slieve Group. Cushendun Caves [D252 325], 300m ESE of Cushendun, Co. Antrim.

Cross Slieve Group and Red Arch Formation
Northeast Co. Antrim

The supposed Devonian rocks of northeast Co. Antrim (Figure 6.2) are assigned (Table 6.3) to the **Cross Slieve Group** and the **Red Arch Formation** (14, 15). However, because they are unfossiliferous and undated it is only certain that they were deposited sometime after the Dalradian and before the Middle Triassic (Table 6.3).

The Cross Slieve Group consists of about 1300m of red beds divided into three formations (Table 6.4). The thin basal breccia that rests on the Dalradian is schist-rich but the conglomerates in the remainder of the **Cushendun Formation** have mostly well-rounded quartzite clasts and are exposed on the coast at Cushendun (Photographs 3A, 3B). Southeast of Cave House [D252 324] the conglomerate and coarse sandstone (Photograph 4) is interbedded with laminae of green mudstone with

Photograph 3B
Detail of the conglomerate with clasts mainly of quartzite and pinkish red sandstone. (Hammer 46cm long).

74

		Wilson (1953)	Simon (1984)	Turner et al. (2000)
Triassic	Late			
Triassic	Middle			
Triassic	Early	New Red Sandstone		
Permian				Red Arch Formation (Old Red Sandstone)
Carboniferous				
Devonian	Late	Upper Old Red Sandstone	Red Arch Formation	
Devonian	Middle			
Devonian	Early	Lower Old Red Sandstone	Cross Slieve Group	Cross Slieve Group

Table 6.3
Proposed correlation of the Cross Slieve Group and Red Arch Formation in northeast Co. Antrim.

desiccation cracks. The upper half of the formation is composed mainly of finer grained sandstone and mudstone with thin beds of conglomerate. The quartzite clasts are probably of polycyclic origin and were derived from the northwest (14). In contrast the sandstone matrix is a lithic arenite composed of single cycle detritus with minor quartz and abundant fragments of welded tuff, schist and quartzite. The **Ballyagan Formation** is exposed on the beach and in low cliffs at Port Obe [D247 289]. North of Port Obe, the transition to the overlying **Cushendall Formation** is marked by the introduction of volcaniclastic conglomerate with clasts, up to 1m, of pilotaxitic andesite that was derived from contemporaneous lavas.

Photograph 4
Interbedded sandstone and conglomerate of the Cushendun Formation showing the predominance of quartzite pebbles and large cobbles. Coastal exposure [D252 324], 120m southeast of Cave House and 500m southeast of Cushendun, Co. Antrim. (Hammer 46cm long).

Formation	Subdivision	Lithology	Palaeoenvironment
Cushendall (600m)		Conglomerate, and very coarse and pebbly sandstone; clasts almost exclusively of volcanic origin	Alluvial fans derived from southwest and south; possible aeolian influence
Ballyagan (160m)		Sandstone, pinkish brown, fine- to coarse-grained; cross stratified, thin mudstone intercalations	Braided rivers flowing to the east and northeast
Cushendun	Upper (290m)	Sandstone, coarse-grained, parallel and cross laminated; thin and mudstone; conglomerate layers one clast thick	Mid-fan braided stream deposits from non-erosive sheet flow; mudstone with desiccation cracks
	Lower (320m)	Conglomerate, laterally persistent beds, clast supported, very well rounded clasts, mainly of quartzite; sandstone is lithic arenite; thin mudstone intercalations	Conglomerate, proximal to mid-fan sheetflood deposits; sandstone deposited by braided streams, derived from northwest and west
	Basal breccia (5-10m)	Angular clasts of schist and vein quartz in coarse sand matrix	

Table 6.4
Lithostratigraphy of the Cross Slieve Group (14).

Photograph 5
Boulder conglomerate and pebbly sandstone of Unit 1 of the Red Arch Formation. Coastal exposure [D244 249], at the Lifeboat House slipway, 1km southeast of Cushendall, Co. Antrim. (Hammer 46cm long).

Table 6.5 — Lithostratigraphy of the Red Arch Formation (15).

Unit	Thickness	Lithology	Palaeo-environment
5	165m	Conglomerate and sandstone, fining upwards, laminated mudstone, calcrete nodules	Alluvial fan; streamflood to playa lake
4	28m	Conglomerate, very thick beds	Alluvial fan; sheetflood
3	60m	Conglomerate, thin and pebbly sandstone	Alluvial fan; streamflood with gravel bars
2	c.20m	Conglomerate, small boulder to pebbles	Alluvial fan; sheetflood
1	170m	Boulder conglomerate, pebbly sandstone	Alluvial fan; proximal sheetflood to braided stream

(Red Arch Formation — unit column label alongside table)

Table 6.5
Lithostratigraphy of the Red Arch Formation (15).

At Cushendall, the **Cushendall Porphyry** outcrops between the Cross Slieve Group and Red Arch Formation. The dacitic lava flows are younger than the Cross Slieve Group and did not contribute clasts to the Cushendall Formation (14). At Limerick Point [D244 278] sedimentary clasts in the base of the porphyry were incorporated during lava flow. Its contact with the Red Arch Formation at the Lifeboat House slipway [D243 269] south of Cushendall is concealed and probably faulted.

The **Red Arch Formation** consists of 440m of unfossiliferous polymict conglomerate (Photograph 5) and pebbly sandstone and is divided (15) into five units with two intra-formational unconformities (Table 6.5). There is an angular discrepancy of 20° at the lower unconformity [D244 268] which was considered by Wilson (16) to represent the base of the Triassic System in northeast Co. Antrim, hence his assignment of the succeeding rocks to the 'New Red Sandstone' (Table 6.3). However, Simon (15) subsequently concluded that both unconformities were of minor importance, having probably developed on one alluvial fan, and regarded all of the Red Arch Formation as belonging to the 'Upper Old Red Sandstone' facies with a Late Devonian to early Carboniferous age. Later palaeomagnetic studies of sandstone from the Red Arch Formation have demonstrated a pole position consistent with a late Carboniferous-Early Permian age (17). However, without supporting biostratigraphical evidence the true age of the Cross Slieve Group and Red Arch Formation will remain unknown.

References

1) Osborne, R. and Tarling, D. H. 1995. *The Historical Atlas of the Earth (A Visual Exploration of the Earth's Physical Past)*. Viking. Penguin Books Ltd., London.

2) Simon, J. B. and Bluck, B. J. 1982. Palaeodrainage of the southern margin of the Caledonian mountain chain in the northern British Isles. *Transactions of the Royal Society of Edinburgh*, **73**, 11-15.

3) Graham, J. R., Richardson, J. B. and Clayton, G. 1983. Age and significance of the Old Red Sandstone around Clew Bay, NW Ireland. *Transactions of the Royal Society of Edinburgh*, **73**, 245-49.

4) Harper, J. C. and Hartley, J. J. 1938. The Silurian Inlier of Lisbellaw, County Fermanagh, with a note on the age of the Fintona beds. *Proceedings of the Royal Irish Academy*, **45B**, 73-87.

5) Mitchell, W. I. and Owens, B. 1990. The geology of the western part of the Fintona Block, Northern Ireland-evolution of Carboniferous basins. *Geological Magazine*, **127**, 407-26.

6) Blieck, A. 1991. Reappraisal of the heterostracans (Agnathan vertebrates) of Northern Ireland. *Irish Journal of Earth Sciences*, **11**, 65-69.

7) Geological Survey of Northern Ireland, 1996. Kesh, Northern Ireland Sheet 32. Solid Geology. 1:50,000. (Keyworth, Nottingham: British Geological Survey).

8) Geological Survey of Northern Ireland, 1996. Omagh, Northern Ireland Sheet 33. Solid Geology. 1:50,000. (Keyworth, Nottingham: British Geological Survey).

9) Stephenson, M. H. and Mitchell, W. I. 2002. Definitive new palynological evidence for the early Devonian age of the Fintona Group, Northern Ireland. *Irish Journal of Earth Sciences*, **20**, 41-52.

10) Geological Survey of Northern Ireland 1979. Pomeroy, Northern Ireland Sheet 34. Solid Geology. 1:50,000. (Southampton: Ordnance Survey for the Geological Survey of Northern Ireland).

11) Richardson, J. B. and McGregor, D. C. 1986. Silurian and Devonian spore zones of the Old Red Sandstone continent and adjacent regions. *Bulletin of the Geological Survey of Canada*, **364**, 1-79.

12) Simon, J. B. 1984a. Sedimentation and tectonic setting of the Lower Old Red Sandstone of the Fintona and Curlew Mountain districts. *Irish Journal of Earth Sciences*, **6**, 213-28.

13) Geological Survey of Northern Ireland, 1995. Draperstown, Northern Ireland Sheet 26. Solid Geology. 1:50,000. (Keyworth, Nottingham: British Geological Survey).

14) Simon, J. B. 1984b. Provenance and depositional history of the Lower Old Red Sandstone of northeast Antrim. *Irish Journal of Earth Sciences*, **6**, 1-13.

15) Simon, J. B. 1984c. Sedimentation of a small complex alluvial fan of possible Upper Old Red Sandstone age, northeast County Antrim. *Irish Journal of Earth Sciences*, **6**, 109-19.

16) Wilson, H. E. 1953. The petrography of the Old Red Sandstone rocks of the north of Ireland. *Proceedings of the Royal Irish Academy*, **55**, 283-320.

17) Turner, P., Shelton, R., Ruffell, A. and Pugh, J. 2000. Palaeomagnetic constraints on the age of the Red Arch Formation and associated sandstone dykes (Northern Ireland). *Journal of the Geological Society, London*, **157**, 317-25.

Chapter 7

Carboniferous

W. I. MITCHELL

Introduction

At the end of the Devonian, Ireland lay on the southern margin of Laurentia that stretched from the Appalachians, northeast across Britain into Fennoscandia (1) (Figure 7.1). Coastal alluvial plains merged into shallow tropical waters at the edge of an inhospitable desert landscape. Although marine conditions had reached the southern tip of Ireland at the Devonian-Carboniferous boundary (c.355Ma) the succeeding 10Ma passed before the transgression reached the north of Ireland in the late Tournaisian (2). This is only the first event in the turbulent 65Ma history of the Carboniferous in Northern Ireland (c.355-290Ma). Throughout the succession there is evidence of intermittent tectonic activity. Northern Ireland was not an area of quiet sedimentation, as previously envisaged, but straddled a zone of dextral strike-slip comparable to the Midland Valley of Scotland and the Maritimes Basin in Atlantic Canada (3). Thus, by the end of the Carboniferous, when the Variscan Orogeny had reached a maximum intensity, all of Ireland was now land and the Variscan Mountains stretched across the northern part of the country (Figure 8.9).

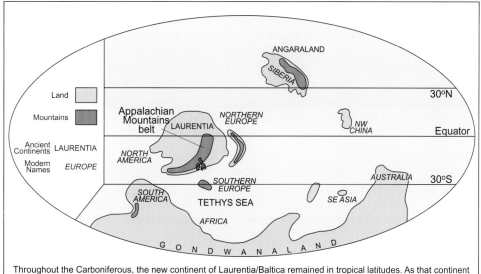

Throughout the Carboniferous, the new continent of Laurentia/Baltica remained in tropical latitudes. As that continent turned anti-clockwise it collided with Gondwanaland along the Appalachian Mountains belt. The huge continent of Gondwanaland was formed by the joining together of the present southern continents. At this time Ireland lay on the southern edge of the Laurentian landmass and was influenced by repeated transgression of the sea and periods of regression associated with tectonic episodes resulting from that on-going continental collision.

Figure 7.1
Position of the continents in the early Carboniferous (*c.* 350Ma (1))

79

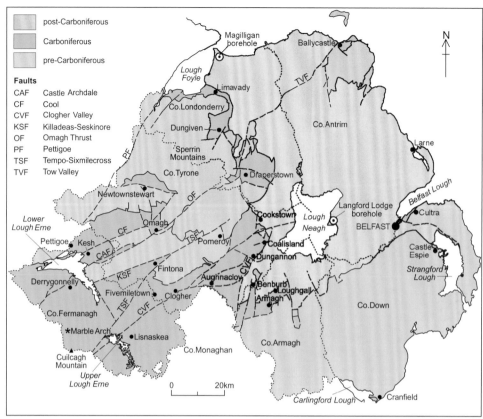

Figure 7.2
Geological map of Northern Ireland showing the Carboniferous outcrop.

Carboniferous rocks in Northern Ireland were deposited close to the northern margin of the "Northern Province" (4) and reflect the proximity of land at all times. Their cumulative thickness of 7000m is represented mainly by Lower Carboniferous (Tournaisian, Viséan and early Namurian) rocks in Co. Fermanagh, the Fintona Block, peripheral sections at Coalisland and isolated basins such as Newtownstewart (Table 7.1). The most continuous outcrop and succession extends from Co. Fermanagh and south Co. Tyrone into north Co. Armagh (Figure 7.2). The Carboniferous outcrop in the eastern part of Northern Ireland is reduced to outliers at Ballycastle, Cultra, Castle Espie and Carlingford Lough.

Litho- and biostratigraphy
The first Carboniferous lithostratigraphy for the north of Ireland was erected in Co. Sligo in the 19th Century by the Geological Survey. In 1955, a geographical name was attributed to each of the original units and thus laid the foundation for the current lithostratigraphical framework (5).

This description of the Carboniferous rocks starts with the four outliers in the eastern part of Northern Ireland at Ballycastle, Cultra, Castle Espie and Carlingford (Figure 7.2). This is followed by a north-south traverse covering the outcrop in Co. Londonderry, east Co. Tyrone, the Newtownstewart outlier and Co. Armagh. Although the largest Carboniferous outcrop is in the southwest part of Northern Ireland the description of those rocks concludes this section and immediately precedes the palaeogeographical section which is based on that continuous succession for its detailed reconstruction of events.

80

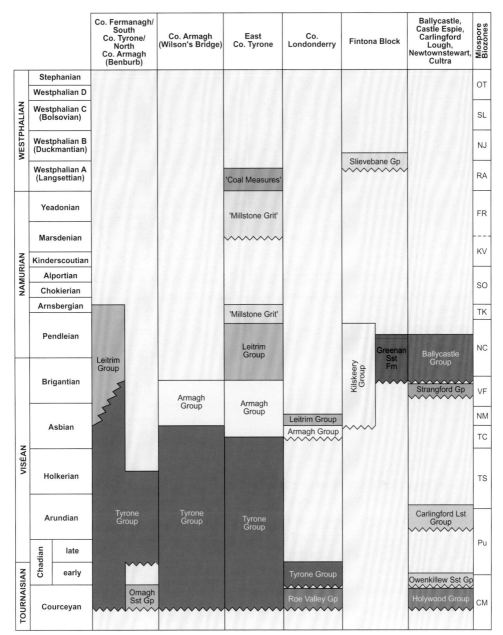

Table 7.1
Distribution and classification of Carboniferous rocks in Northern Ireland.

Ballycastle

The Ballycastle area (Figure 7.2) is the only coastal location of Carboniferous coal seams in Ireland (6). Coal mining is recorded in the 13th Century and continued until 1967 producing between 10-15,000 tons annually in the 18th Century (see Chapter 21). Spectacular cliffs between Pans Rock [D133 415] and Carrickmore [D163 426] expose the upper part of the succession (Chapter 21, Photograph 12). Strata become older from west to east due to minor faults that downthrow to the west (7). Lithostratigraphical details for the lower part of the succession are from boreholes.

The lowest unit of the Ballycastle Group (Table 7.2), the **Eglish Sandstone Formation**, rests unconformably on the Dalradian and is exposed at Murlough Bay. Grey mudstones 55m above the base in the stream [D147 387] at Ballyberidagh North contain the miospores *Spelaeotriletes arenaceus* and *Grandispora spinosa* which first appear in the VF Biozone (Brigantian).

The **Carey River Basalt Formation** is exposed in the north-facing, roadside cliff [D130 411] opposite Pans Rock. At Murlough Bay [D198 420] two, crudely columnar, flows are exposed on the shore. At least 10m of the **Glenshesk Tuff Formation** exposed in rock platforms on the shore [D168 433] west of Fair Head include fireclay with plant remains and lycopod stumps with root systems (Photograph 1). Black mudstone (oil shale) of the **Murlough Shale Formation** is exposed in rock platforms at Portnaloub [D166 430].

Formation	Lithology	Age
Ballyvoy Sandstone (*c.* 350m)	Sandstone, purple or brown, weathering red, pink, greyish white, fine- to coarse-grained, pebbly, planar and trough cross-bedding, pebble lags, channel bedforms. Mudstone, purple, rarely grey with hematite and limonite nodules; blackband ironstone. **Main Limestone Member**, fossiliferous mudstone and thin limestone. Coal seams of variable quality, seat earth and mudstone. **Carrickmore** and **McGildowney's Shale members** consist of fossiliferous dark grey mudstone, sandy with thin limestone	Pendleian / Brigantian
Murlough Shale (46m)	Mudstone, dark grey, plant debris, ostracods, fish and coprolites, ironstone and phosphatic nodules; 10 coal seams up to 1.3m thick	Brigantian
Glenshesk Tuff (61m)	Mudstone, reddish brown to grey, dolomitic; greenish grey vitric and lithic tuffs; tuffaceous sandstone; fireclay; plant fossils	
Carey River Basalt (*c.* 40m)	Lava flows, subaerial, micro-porphyritic olivine basalt, spheroidal weathering, crudely columnar	
Eglish Sandstone (*c.* 215m)	Conglomerate, reddish brown, yellow-stained; sandstone, grey, white and yellow, coaly streaks; grey mudstone with miospores	

Table 7.2
Lithostratigraphy of the Ballycastle Group at Ballycastle.

Photograph 1
Lycopod tree stumps with roots in thick bedded sandstone. Glenshesk Tuff Formation at Portnalaub, 4.7km ENE of Ballycastle, Co. Antrim. (Red portion of staff is 50cm long).

The **Ballyvoy Sandstone Formation** is exposed in cliffs between Ballycastle and Fair Head. Although few coal seams are visible their stratigraphical position is well documented (Figure 21.6). The **Carrickmore Shale Member** consists of 13m of grey mudstone with thin, banded ironstone and limestone and is exposed above the cliff-top waterfall [D165 426] 250m southeast of Carrickmore. The 20m thick **Main Limestone Member** consists of mudstone and thin limestone. The limestone component, which consists of two or three closely spaced beds with a combined thickness of up to 2.4m, is an important marker horizon and contains the Brigantian brachiopod *Gigantoproductus giganteus*. Exposures are confined to headlands between the North Star Colliery and Carrickmore and to the rock platform west of the North Star Dyke [D148 419]. An ammonoid fauna including *Sudeticeras adeps*, of the late Brigantian P2b Biozone, occurs in calcareous sandstone 1.3m above the top of the Main Limestone Member in cliffs [D142 417] 250m NNE of Corrymeela. **McGildowney's Shale Member** is 20m thick, of which 15m is lenticular sandstone that forms Pans Rock. The Viséan-Namurian boundary is located at the base of the **Main Coal**.

Cultra

The Holywood Group (Table 7.3), which is exposed between Cultra and Craigavad (Figure 9.3) rests unconformably on Ordovician strata and is overlain by the Permian (8). Late Courceyan-early Chadian miospores in the Ballycultra Formation (9) include *Schopfites claviger* and *Auroraspora macra*, of the late Tournaisian CM Biozone.

Castle Espie

The **Strangford Group** (Table 7.1) comprises pink limestone with greenish and purplish red mudstone and was formerly exposed in quarries at Castle Espie (Figure 7.2). The quarries are flooded but blocks of grainstone on the shore [H489 675] contain brachiopods, corals and trilobites. Their Brigantian age is based on the presence of foraminifera including *Loeblichia paraammonoides*.

Carlingford

The **Carlingford Limestone Group** comprises silty limestone and calcareous siltstone (Figure 7.2). East of Soldiers Point [J261 105] the rocks are bioturbated with crinoid debris filling scour structures. The rocks contain numerous fossils including the brachiopod *Delepinea carinata*, corals *Michelinia megastoma*, *Siphonodendron martini* and

Formation	Lithology	Depositional Environment
Ballycultra (140m)	Mudstone, dark grey to greenish grey, calcareous, rare brachiopods, miospores; thin siltstone, sandstone; algal (cyanobacterial) laminated limestone; evaporites	Sabkha and hypersaline tidal flats; arid climate, high rates of evaporation; brackish water with restricted bivalve, ostracod, annelid fauna; cyclical sedimentation
Craigavad Sandstone (140m)	Sandstone, red and yellow, coarse-grained, pebbles of vein quartz and greywacke, unfossiliferous, layers of calcrete nodules, ripples; rare micritic limestone; greyish red calcareous mudstone at top	Near-shore, high energy, shallow brackish water to non-marine environment; high sediment influx from nearby land; gradational top into the Ballycultra Formation

Table 7.3
Lithostratigraphy of the Holywood Group at Cultra.

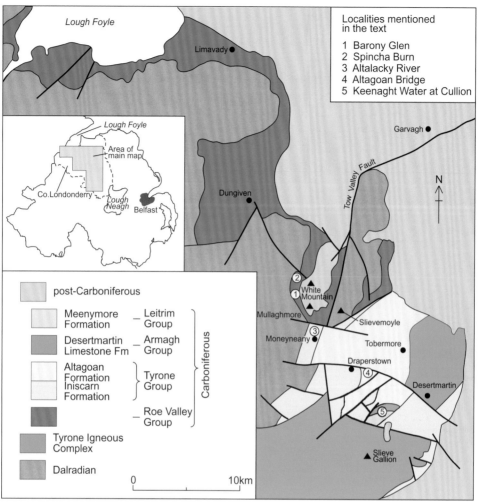

Figure 7.3
Geological map of the Carboniferous rocks in Co. Londonderry.

Siphonophyllia garwoodi and foraminifera *Glomodiscus* and *Paraarchaediscus* at *involutus* stage, of mid- to late Arundian age. Calcareous sandstone, and sandy and oolitic limestone with ripple, parallel and cross-laminations, also contain pebbles of locally derived underlying rocks.

Co. Londonderry

The outcrop of the Roe Valley Group and the Tyrone Group is separated by the Tow Valley Fault (Figure 7.3).

The **Roe Valley Group** (Table 7.4) crops out on the west side of White Mountain and Mullaghmore (Figure 7.3) and along the south side of Lough Foyle. The **Spincha Burn Conglomerate Formation** rests on the Dalradian and the lower part (Photograph 2) of the succeeding **Barony Glen Formation** in Barony Glen [C731 016] is dominated by calcrete, mudstone and siltstone, interpreted as pedogenic and lacustrine deposits. The upper part consists of grey mudstone and thin limestone deposited in a marginal marine environment. The Roe Valley Group contains the miospores *Schopfites claviger* and *Auroraspora macra* (Fossils 1 and 2), of late Tournaisian (CM Biozone) age.

84

Photograph 2
The Barony Glen Formation in the stratotype. Barony Glen [C731 016], 9km WNW of Draperstown,
Co. Londonderry.

	Formation		Lithology	Age
Leitrim Group	Meenymore (*c.* 20m)		Sandstone, brown; micritic limestone; mudstone, grey with sparse marine fauna of corals, brachiopods and nautiloids	late Asbian
Armagh Group	Desertmartin Limestone		Limestone, sandy and pebbly grainstone; conglomerate, fawn to grey, small pebbles, fossiliferous	
Tyrone Group	Altagoan	Mormeal Member (*c.* 250m)	Sandstone and siltstone, pale grey to greenish-grey; mudstone, grey, miospores; laminated (cyanobacterial) limestone, evaporites	early Chadian
		Drumard Member (*c.* 300m)	Sandstone, siltstone and mudstone, purplish red to brown, unfossiliferous; fining upward	
	Iniscarn (400m)		Breccia, purplish red to brown, poorly sorted, angular clasts Conglomerate, purplish brown, coarse sand matrix, well rounded boulders to pebbles	
Roe Valley Group	Barony Glen (150-200m)		Upper section of mudstone, grey, miospores; laminated (cyanobacterial) limestone Lower section of mudstone, siltstone and sandstone, purplish red to brown and greenish grey; calcrete, palaeosols	Courceyan
	Spincha Burn Conglomerate (25-100m)		Conglomerate, rounded pebbles only of vein quartz and green quartzite; sandstone, very coarse-grained, unfossiliferous	

Table 7.4
Lithostratigraphy of the Carboniferous rocks in Co. Londonderry.

The outcrop of the **Tyrone Group** occurs in the Draperstown district. The basal **Iniscarn Formation** crops out in the Altalacky River (Figure 7.3). At its base [H746 981], boulder conglomerates representing half the Formation contain rounded clasts up to 2m long. The upper part is exposed on Slievemoyle and consists of feldspathic breccias. It fines up into the succeeding **Altagoan Formation** with the **Drumard** and **Mormeal members** (Table 7.4). The Mormeal Member, seen south of Altagoan Bridge [H799 944], consists of mudstone and channelised sandstone (10). It includes five evaporite beds up to 0.43m thick with halite and gypsum or anhydrite now pseudomorphed by calcite (11). Grey mudstone with a macrofauna of bivalves and ostracods also contains the miospores *Auroraspora macra, Schopfites claviger* and rare *Lycospora pusilla* (Fossil 3) indicating the basal Pu Biozone and an early Chadian age.

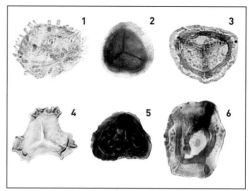

Fossils 1-6
Early Carboniferous miospores:
1-3: (Courceyan and early Chadian) from the Roe Valley and Tyrone groups in Co. Londonderry.
1 *Schopfites claviger* (x 275)
2 *Auroraspora macra* (x 250)
3 *Lycospora pusilla* (x 625)

4-6: (Brigantian-Pendleian) from the Kilskeery Group in the Fintona Block, Co. Tyrone:
4 *Tripartites vetustus* (x 350)
5 *Savitrisporites nux* (x 300)
6 *Reticulatisporites carnosus* (x 225)

Formation	Lithology	Palynology	Zone	Stage
Ballinamallard Mudstone (1000m)	Mudstone and siltstone, greyish red, rarely greyish green, miospores. **Corkill Sandstone, Errington** and **Coa Sandstone members** consist mainly of sandstone	*Reticulatisporites carnosus*	NC	Pendleian
Ballyreagh Conglomerate (350m)	Conglomerate, pebbly sandstone, sandstone, thin siltstone and mudstone; purplish brown to grey, fining upward; unfossiliferous; pebbles mainly of greywacke		VF	Brigantian
Topped Mountain Sandstone (1000m)	Sandstone, grey, weathering reddish brown, fine- to coarse-grained; mudstone, greyish red, purple and green with calcrete nodules and mud-flake conglomerates. **Glen Mbr** (20m) is unfossiliferous grey, calcareous siltstone, mudstone and thin sandstone. **Coolcran Conglomerate Mbr** (40m) is sandstone, pebbly sandstone and conglomerate with lamina of green mudstone with miospores	*Savitrisporites nux Tripartites vetustus* *Knoxisporites stephanephorus* *Schulzospora* sp. cf. *elongata* *Vallatisporites ciliaris*	NM	Asbian

Table 7.5
Litho-, bio- and chronostratigraphy of the Kilskeery Group of the Fintona Block.

86

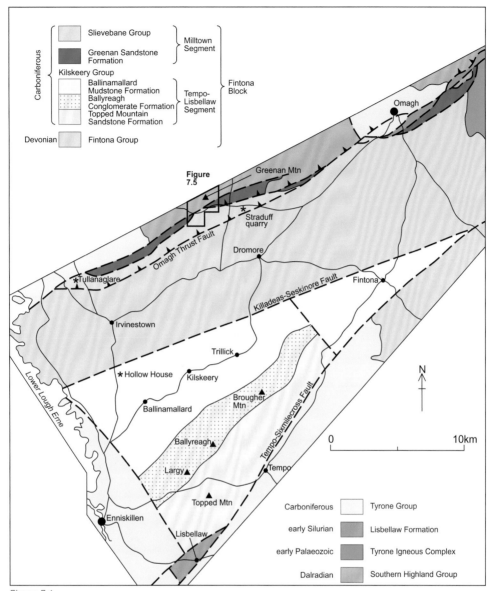

Figure 7.4
Geological map of the western part of the Fintona Block.

The local unconformity between the Tyrone and Armagh groups (Table 7.4) is equivalent to 2000m of early Chadian to late Asbian strata in Co. Fermanagh and south Co. Tyrone. Sandy limestone of the **Desertmartin Limestone Formation** contains corals and the late Asbian brachiopod *Gigantoproductus* cf. *semiglobosus* in the exposure at Cullion [H813 909] (Figure 7.3). Exposures of the **Meenymore Formation** (Leitrim Group) occur some 400m to the south.

Fintona Block

The Carboniferous rocks are restricted (12) to the fault-bounded and lithostratigraphically distinctive Milltown and Tempo-Lisbellaw segments (Figure 7.4) (13, 14).

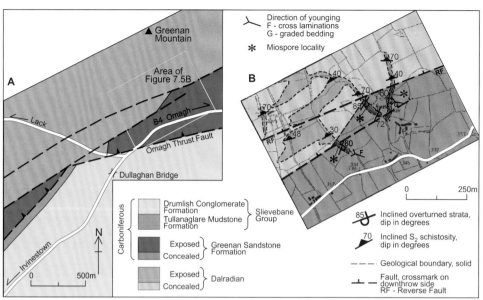

Figure 7.5
Location (A) and detailed geological map (B) of the stratotype of the Greenan Sandstone Formation.

Tempo-Lisbellaw Segment
Kilskeery Group (Table 7.5)
Green mudstones near the top of the basal **Topped Mountain Sandstone Formation**
exposed on the east flank of Brougher Mountain [H355 531] contain miospores of the VF
Biozone (Brigantian) including the index taxon *Tripartites vetustus* and *Savitrisporites nux*
(Fossils 4, 5). The hills of Largy, Ballyreagh and Brougher Mountain (316m) are formed of the
Ballyreagh Conglomerate Formation (Figure 7.4). Interbedded sandstone and conglomerate
occur in Largy quarry [H298 475], 5km west of Tempo and are associated with ripple marks
and desiccation cracks. The **Ballinamallard Mudstone Formation** is exposed in the
Ballinamallard River [H268 529]. Miospores, recovered from green mudstones in the stream
(Figure 7.4) at the Hollow House [H251 552], include *Reticulatisporites carnosus* (Fossil 6) an
index taxon of the NC Biozone (Table 7.5).

Milltown Segment
Greenan Sandstone Formation (Table 7.1)
The basal unconformity with the Dalradian is exposed [H316 668] on Greenan Mountain
(Figures 7.4 and 7.5). Green mudstone laminae in the sandstone contains miospores
diagnostic of the VF and possibly NC biozones. Rhyolitic lava occurs towards the top of the
Formation east of Omagh.

Slievebane Group (Table 7.6)
The outcrop of this Group is fault-bounded (Figure 7.4) (12). At the best exposure [H218 616]
of the **Tullanaglare Mudstone Formation** at Tullanaglare, green mudstones contain
miospore assemblages (Fossils 7-10) with index taxa of the RA and NJ biozones
(Westphalian A/B). The **Drumgivery Limestone Member** marks the top of the formation.
The **Drumlish Conglomerate Formation** is exposed [H343 666] in Straduff Quarry (Figure 7.4,
Photograph 3). Volcanic rocks (12) in the Omagh Thrust Fault zone [H432 712] may be the
source of the lava clasts in the conglomerate.

88

Formation	Lithology	Palynology	Zone	Stage
Drumlish Conglomerate (c. 1000m)	Conglomerate, greyish purple, volcaniclastic clasts up to 0.5m of trachybasalt and trachyandesite, minor metamorphic content; sandstone, very coarse- to fine-grained, upward fining; mudstone, green, miospores	*Crassispora kosankei* *Laevigatosporites medius*	NJ	Westphalian B (Duckmantian)
Tullanaglare Mudstone (c. 80m)	**Drumgivery Limestone Mbr,** 0.3-0.5m of pink calcrete Mudstone, siltstone, sandy palaeosol, mottled purplish brown and greenish grey, calcareous, calcrete nodules	*Endosporites globiformis* *Microreticulatisporites nobilis* *Vestispora pseudoreticulata* *Dictyotriletes bireticulatus* *Schulzospora rara* *Laevigatosporites desmoinesensis*	RA	Westphalian A (Langsettian)

Table 7.6
Litho-, bio- and chronostratigraphy of the Slievebane Group of the Fintona Block.

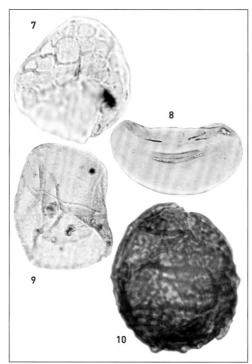

Fossils 7-10
Late Carboniferous (Westphalian A-B) miospores from the Slievebane Group in the Fintona Block, Co. Tyrone:
7 *Dictyotriletes bireticulatus* (x 550)
8 *Laevigatosporites desmoinesensis* (x 550)
9 *Endosporites globiformis* (x 400)
10 *Vestispora pseudoreticulata* (x 500)

Co. Armagh
In the Carboniferous outcrop between Co. Fermanagh and north Co. Armagh (Figure 7.2) the component formations of the Tyrone Group (Table 7.1) maintain their lithological integrity. However, in the rest of Co. Armagh the Carboniferous succession is thinner and is divided into two groups. With the exception of the Killuney Conglomerate and Carganamuck Limestone formations (Figure 7.6) details are available from the 359m deep Wilson's Bridge borehole (15).

Tyrone Group
The unconformity with Ordovician rocks is exposed in the Killuney stream [H896 461]. Late Tournaisian strata at the base of the Tyrone Group were deposited before and during a marine transgression and comprise the **Killuney Conglomerate, Retreat Siltstone** and **Ballynahone Micrite formations** (Figure 7.6). Two significant biostratigraphical events occur in the latter formation. The appearance of the miospore *Lycospora pusilla* marks the early Chadian and the foraminiferan

Photogragh 3
The Drumlish Conglomerate Formation, Straduff quarry [H343 666], Co. Tyrone, 16km ENE of Kesh. Vertical bedding, youngs to the right.

Eoparastaffella simplex marks the base of the late Chadian and the Tournaisian-Viséan series boundary. The base of the TS Biozone in the **Milford Mills Formation** coincides with the appearance of the miospore *Knoxisporites stephanephorus* (Figure 7.6). The **Oulart Villa Limestone Formation** at Oulart Villa [H897 469] contains the coral *Dorlodotia pseudovermiculare* and early Arundian foraminifera at the base, with *D.* cf. *briarti* and *Siphonodendron martini* and mid- to late Arundian foraminifera at the top. The base of the **Drumman More Sandstone Formation** is probably Holkerian, based on the presence of *Lithostrotion* corals and the foraminifera *Paraarchaediscus* at *concavus* stage. Near the top of the Formation the miospore *Perotrilites tesselatus* indicates the TC Biozone and a Holkerian–early Asbian age.

Armagh Group

The Armagh Group consists almost exclusively of marine, shallow water limestones with palaeokarst surfaces and reddish brown clay palaeosols. Although their use as building stone has declined it is still quarried for aggregate between Loughgall and Armagh (Figure 7.2). It is represented by three formations of late Asbian to Brigantian age (Figure 7.6).

90

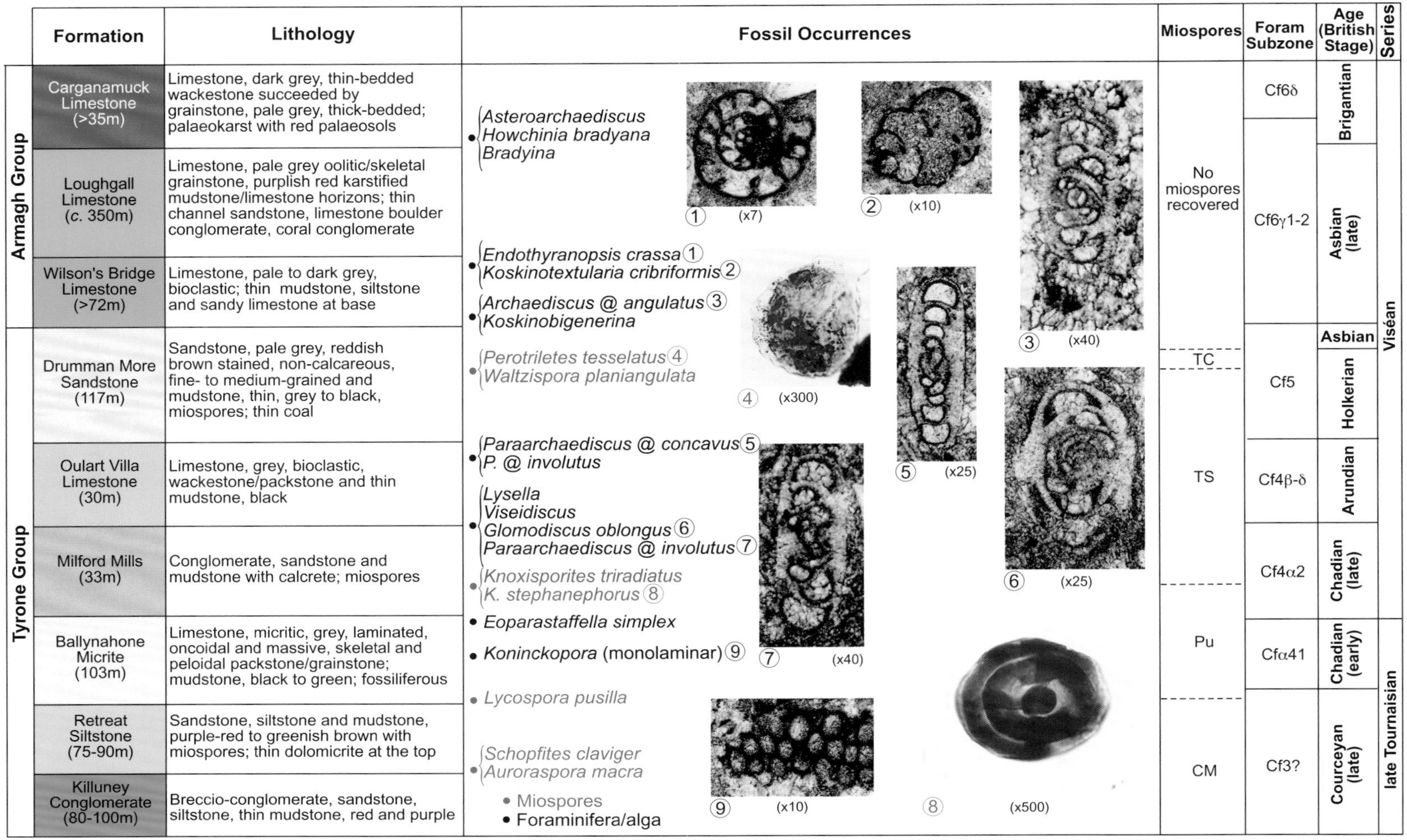

Litho-, bio- and chronostratigraphy of the Carboniferous rocks in the Armagh area.

Series	Age (British Stage)	Foram Subzone	Miospores	Formation	Lithology	Group
Viséan	Brigantian	Cf6δ		Carganamuck Limestone (>35m)	Limestone, dark grey, thin-bedded wackestone succeeded by grainstone, pale grey, thick-bedded; palaeokarst with red palaeosols	Armagh Group
Viséan	Asbian (late)	Cf6γ1-2	No miospores recovered	Loughgall Limestone (c. 350m)	Limestone, pale grey oolitic/skeletal grainstone, purplish red karstified mudstone/limestone horizons; thin channel sandstone, limestone boulder conglomerate, coral conglomerate	Armagh Group
Viséan	Asbian	Cf5	TC	Wilson's Bridge Limestone (>72m)	Limestone, pale to dark grey, bioclastic; thin mudstone, siltstone and sandy limestone at base	Armagh Group
Viséan	Holkerian	Cf5		Drumman More Sandstone (117m)	Sandstone, pale grey, reddish brown stained, non-calcareous, fine- to medium-grained and mudstone, thin, grey to black, miospores; thin coal	Tyrone Group
Viséan	Arundian	Cf4β-δ	TS	Oulart Villa Limestone (30m)	Limestone, grey, bioclastic, wackestone/packstone and thin mudstone, black	Tyrone Group
Viséan	Chadian (late)	Cf4α2		Milford Mills (33m)	Conglomerate, sandstone and mudstone with calcrete; miospores	Tyrone Group
Viséan	Chadian (early)	Cfα41	Pu	Ballynahone Micrite (103m)	Limestone, micritic, grey, laminated, oncoidal and massive, skeletal and peloidal packstone/grainstone; mudstone, black to green; fossiliferous	Tyrone Group
late Tournaisian	Courceyan (late)	Cf3?	CM	Retreat Siltstone (75-90m)	Sandstone, siltstone and mudstone, purple-red to greenish brown with miospores; thin dolomicrite at the top	Tyrone Group
late Tournaisian				Killuney Conglomerate (80-100m)	Breccio-conglomerate, sandstone, siltstone, thin mudstone, red and purple	Tyrone Group

Fossil Occurrences

- Asteroarchaediscus ①
- Howchinia bradyana
- ● Bradyina
- Endothyranopsis crassa ①
- ● Koskinotextularia cribriformis ②
- Archaediscus @ angulatus ③
- ● Koskinobigenerina
- Perotriletes tesselatus ④
- Waltzispora planiangulata
- Paraarchaediscus @ concavus ⑤
- ● P. @ involutus
- Lysella
- Viseidiscus
- ● Glomodiscus oblongus ⑥
- Paraarchaediscus @ involutus ⑦
- Knoxisporites triradiatus
- K. stephanephorus ⑧
- ● Eoparastaffella simplex
- ● Koninckopora (monolaminar) ⑨
- ● Lycospora pusilla
- Schopfites claviger
- Auroraspora macra
- ● Miospores
- ● Foraminifera/alga

Image magnifications: ① (×7), ② (×10), ③ (×40), ④ (×300), ⑤ (×25), ⑥ (×25), ⑦ (×40), ⑧ (×500), ⑨ (×10)

Figure 7.6 Litho-, bio- and chronostratigraphy of the Carboniferous rocks in the Armagh area.

The **Wilson's Bridge Limestone Formation** in Rock Road quarry [H871 434] shows evidence of reworking of soft sediment and benthic faunas as a 2m bed of conglomerate composed of the colonial corals *Lithostrotion* and *Michelinia* and *Siphonophyllia benburbensis*. Limestone intraclast conglomerate and lenticular sandstone are exposed in a lane section at Annacramph [H886 494]. Most limestone quarries in the area are developed in the **Loughgall Limestone Formation** using the distinctive pale grey to creamy white, coarse-grained bioclatic and oolitic grainstone.

The quarry section [H878 498] in the **Carganamuck Limestone Formation** (Figure 7.6) contains Brigantian corals including *Actinocyathus floriformis* and *Diphyphyllum lateseptatum* (15) and the brachiopod *Gigantoproductus* (Fossils 11-15).

East Co. Tyrone

The succession in east Co. Tyrone (Table 7.1) rests unconformably on the Tyrone Igneous Complex (10) and on Devonian rocks of the Fintona Block and is concealed in the east by Mesozoic and Cenozoic rocks (16). Coal mines operated at Coalisland from at least 1672 until the early 1960s. Lithostratigraphical details were largely obtained from boreholes drilled in search of coal (17) and from quarries in Viséan limestone and Westphalian mudstone used in the manufacture of cement and bricks, respectively.

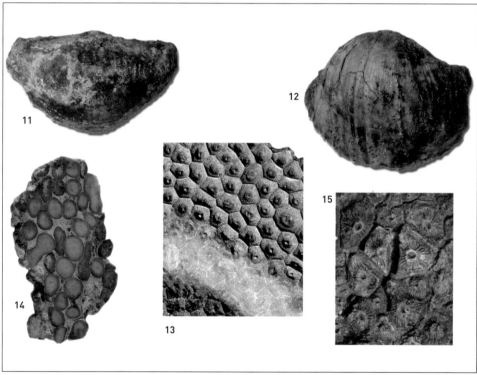

Fossils 11-15
Early Carboniferous (Brigantian) fossils from the Carganamuck Limestone Formation (Armagh Group) in Co. Armagh:
Brachiopods:
11 *Gigantoproductus* sp. (latissimoid x 0.4), **12** *Gigantoproductus elongatus* (x 0.5)
Corals:
13 *Lithostrotion vorticale* (x 0.7), **14** *Siphonodendron pauciradiale* (x 1.3),
15 *Actinocyathus floriformis* (x 1).

Photograph 4
Palaeo-doline at least 15m deep excavated in late Asbian limestones of the Rockdale Limestone Formation infilled with reddish brown clay and silt. Ballysudden quarry, 3km SSW of Cookstown, Co. Tyrone.

Tyrone Group (Table 7.7)

The lowest units of the Tyrone Group east of Pomeroy are the Chadian **Ballyness** and **Clogher Valley formations**. Succeeding limestones are correlated (17) with the **Ballyshannon Limestone Formation**. The **Carland Sandstone Formation**, exposed in Carland quarry [H792 668] 4km NNW of Dungannon (16), contains the miospore *Perotrilites tesselatus*, and is Holkerian to early Asbian.

Armagh Group

The late Viséan Armagh Group is exposed in Ballysudden quarry [H801 748], 3km SSW of Cookstown (Figure 7.2). The **Derryloran Grit Formation** consists of non-marine sandstone with channel bedforms up to 5m deep and fossiliferous marine sandstone. The **Rockdale Limestone Formation** consists mainly of packstone and oolitic, oncoidal and pisolitic grainstone, sandstone and thin mudstone (Figure 7.7). Purplish to reddish brown palaeosols occur above palaeokarst surfaces that, at one horizon, include a 15m deep doline (Photograph 4). Abundant fossils including foraminifera, brachiopods and corals identify the early-late Asbian and Asbian-Brigantian boundaries (Figure 7.7).

93

Leitrim Group

The **Rossmore Mudstone Formation** in Derraghadoan quarry [H793 644] consists of dark grey mudstone, thin siltstone and fine-grained sandstone (17) (Photograph 5). The lower part contains the ammonoid *Sudeticeras crenistriatus*, indicating the Brigantian P2a Biozone, but the upper part is undated and may be Pendleian.

Millstone Grit

Exposures of the Millstone Grit consist mainly of coarse-grained sandstone but the lithological variability of the succession (Figure 21.5) was defined in boreholes (17). Palynological data confirm the presence of a mid-Carboniferous hiatus (18) (Table 7.1).

Coal Measures

The only exposure of Westphalian Coal Measures in Northern Ireland is in the brick pit [H834 662] at Coalisland. Boreholes (17) show the rocks consist of 275m of grey mudstone, silty mudstone, fine-grained sandstone, fireclay and coal seams (Figure 21.5). The Coalisland Marine Band contains the ammonoid *Gastrioceras subcrenatum* that marks the base of the Westphalian Series.

Photograph 5
The Rossmore Mudstone Formation with three thin beds of very hard calcareous siltstone.
Pit at Derraghadoan [H793 644], 2km north of Dungannon, Co. Tyrone.

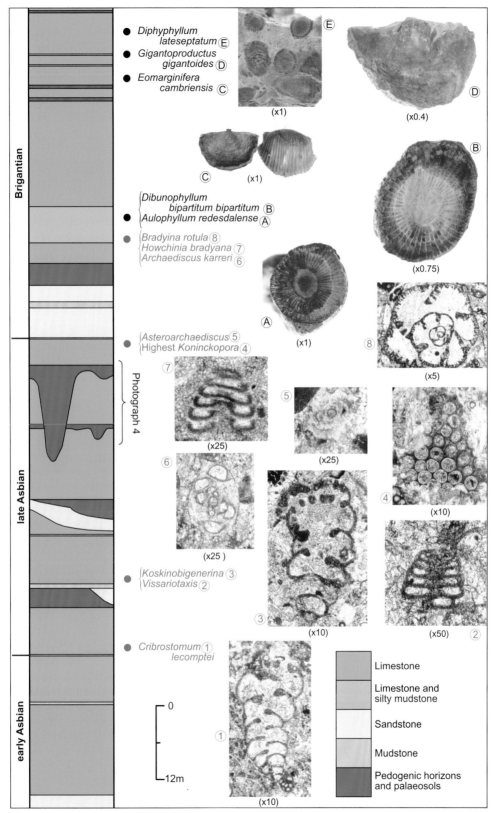

Figure 7.7
Litho- and biostratigraphy of the Armagh Group (Viséan) in Ballysudden quarry near Cookstown.

95

Newtownstewart Outlier

The **Owenkillew Sandstone Group** (Table 7.1) makes up the outlier of Carboniferous rocks located north of Newtownstewart, Co. Tyrone (Figure 7.2). It rests unconformably on the Dalradian and comprises about 1500m of predominantly non-marine strata. Lithologies exposed in Middletown Burn [H492 879] consist of greenish grey and purplish red sandstone and siltstone with thin beds of algal laminated (cyanobacterial) limestone. Dark grey mudstones contain miospores including rare *Lycospora* indicating an early Chadian age. Current indicators suggest a sediment source located to the north.

Co. Fermanagh-south Co. Tyrone

This large outcrop of Carboniferous strata (Figure 7.2) is divided into four regions (Figure 7.8). All the early Carboniferous rocks are assigned to the Tyrone and Leitrim groups with the Omagh Sandstone Group restricted to the Kesh-Omagh area (Table 7.1). Although the standard Tyrone Group succession (5) extends across this area with few variations (Table 7.7) many new members have been identified.

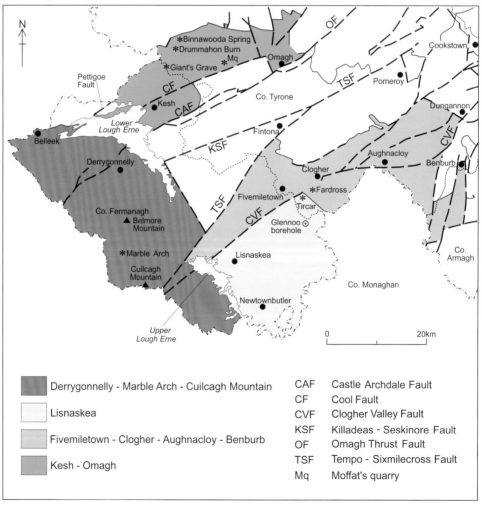

Legend:

- Derrygonnelly - Marble Arch - Cuilcagh Mountain
- Lisnaskea
- Fivemiletown - Clogher - Aughnacloy - Benburb
- Kesh - Omagh

CAF	Castle Archdale Fault
CF	Cool Fault
CVF	Clogher Valley Fault
KSF	Killadeas - Seskinore Fault
OF	Omagh Thrust Fault
TSF	Tempo - Sixmilecross Fault
Mq	Moffat's quarry

Figure 7.8
Distribution of Carboniferous rocks in Co. Fermanagh - south Co. Tyrone.

96

Derrygonnelly-Marble Arch-Cuilcagh Mtn	Lisnaskea	Fivemiletown-Clogher-Aughnacloy-Benburb	Kesh-Omagh	Age
		Blackwater Lst		Brigantian
		Carrickaness Sst		Asbian
		Blackstokes Lst		
Dartry Limestone	Dartry	Maydown Lst		
Glencar Lst	Glencar			
		Aughnacloy Sst		Holkerian
Benbulben Shale	Benbulben	Benbulben	Tubbrid Sst	
			Benbulben	
Mullaghmore Sst	Mullaghmore	Mullaghmore	Drumchorick Siltstone	Arundian
			Mullaghmore	
Bundoran Shale	Bundoran	Bundoran	Bundoran	
			Ballyshannon	late Chadian
			Bin Mountain Sst	
		Ballyshannon	Termon River Limestone	
Ballyshannon Limestone	Ballyshannon		Claragh Sandstone	
	?			
	?	Clogher Valley		early Chadian
	?			
Kilbryan Limestone	?			
	?	Ballyness		
Keenaghan Shale				
Twigspark	Ballysteen			Courceyan
Boyle Sst	Ulster Canal		Omagh Sst Group	
Kilcoo Sst	Cooldarragh			
	Fearnaght			

Table 7.7
Lithostratigraphy of the Tyrone Group in the four regions of Co. Fermanagh-south Co. Tyrone.

Derrygonnelly-Marble Arch-Cuilcagh Mountain

Tyrone Group

Tyrone Group rocks are about 2500m thick (19) and are depicted on geological maps of the Derrygonnelly (20) and Kesh (21) areas. Beneath the oldest exposed unit, the Ballyshannon Limestone Formation, the Courceyan-early Chadian succession of four formations (Table 7.7) is recorded in boreholes. The CM-Pu biozonal boundary is located near the base of the Kilbryan Limestone Formation.

West of the Pettigoe Fault (Figure 7.8), the sub-Carboniferous unconformity with the Moinian Lough Derg Group and the **Keenaghan Shale Formation** are exposed at Keenaghan Lough [G973 600]. Black mudstones of early Chadian age contain miospores including rare

Lycospora pusilla of the Pu Biozone. At the base of the **Ballyshannon Limestone Formation**, Waulsortian mud-mound facies limestone and mudstone of the **Magherameena Limestone Member**, exposed in Magherameena quarry [G980 597] 4km east of Belleek, contain *Eotextularia diversa* and *Tetrataxis* of early Chadian age.

Waulsortian facies limestone also occurs in Bellanaleck quarry [H235 389], 12km ENE of Marble Arch and contains brachiopods, rare solitary corals and the trilobites *Bollandia* cf. *rugiceps* and *Cummingella* sp. nov. of uppermost early Chadian age.

The lower and middle 'members' of the **Ballyshannon Limestone Formation** are exposed in quarries on the south shore of Lower Lough Erne at Blaney [H167 525] and Carrickreagh [H174 521]. They contain a late Chadian microfauna including *Eoparastaffella simplex* and monolaminar *Koninckopora* (19). The highest limestones of the upper 'member', exposed at Inisway [H163 518], 4.5km east of Derrygonnelly, consists of grainstone and contain

Formation	Lithology
Dartry Limestone (130-280m)	Limestone, dark grey, spicular, bluish black chert, fine-grained, fossiliferous; thin mudstone
Glencar Limestone (18-170m)	Limestone and mudstone in equal proportions; black chert nodules
Benbulben Shale (90-365m)	Mudstone, grey, calcareous, fossiliferous; thin lenticular limestone and sandstone
Mullaghmore Sandstone (200m)	Sandstone, pale grey, orange-weathering, calcareous, fine- to medium-grained, subarkose; thin siltstone and mudstone
Bundoran Shale (60-555m)	Mudstone, dark grey, calcareous; siltstone, thin limestone; fossiliferous; basal sandstone
Dowra Sandstone Member (0-53m)	Pebble conglomerate, sandstone, mudstone, micritic 'limestone'
Ballyshannon Limestone (200-345m)	Limestone, lower and upper members are dark grey packstone and thin mudstone; middle member is pale fawn grainstone; fossiliferous
Magherameena Limestone Member (0-15m)	Waulsortian limestone
Keenaghan Shale (20m)	Mudstone, black, silty, rare miospores; thin sandstone; stromatolitic and micritic limestone

Table 7.8
Lithostratigraphy of the Tyrone Group in the Derrygonnelly - Marble Arch - Cuilcagh Mountain area.

Arundian foraminifera including *Glomodiscus, Uralodiscus* and *Paraarchaediscus* at *involutus* stage. The **Dowra Sandstone Member** at the base of the Arundian **Bundoran Shale Formation** (Table 7.8) consists of up to 53m of sandstone and silty mudstone. Dark to medium grey calcareous mudstone, with a fauna dominated by solitary corals, is the main component of the Bundoran Shale Formation and crops out at Claragh [H148 528], 3km ENE of Derrygonnelly.

The contact between the **Mullaghmore Sandstone** and **Benbulben Shale formations** is exposed in a road cutting [H123 512] near Derrygonnelly where the top bed of the former consists of 0.25m of oncolitic limestone with *Glomodiscus, Paraarchaediscus* and *Uralodiscus* of mid- to late Arundian age. Higher parts of the Benbulben Shale Formation contain an Asbian macrofauna including the brachiopod *Gigantoproductus*, solitary coral *Siphonophyllia benburbensis* and fasciculate coral *Siphonodendron pauciradiale* (19). The junction between the Benbulben Shale and **Glencar Limestone Formation** crops out in the Tullyhona stream [H153 338], east of Marble Arch. The top of the Glencar Limestone in the Cladagh River [H121 346], 100m northwest of Marble Arch, consists of calcareous sandstone, siltstone and thin limestone and is succeeded abruptly by the Knockmore Limestone Member of the Dartry Limestone Formation.

The **Dartry Limestone Formation** comprises (19) limestone with chert, and at the top a bed with *in situ* colonies of the coral *Siphonodendron irregulare* (Photograph 6). Poorly and unbedded limestones of the mudmound facies are referred to the **Knockmore Limestone Member**. The succeeding members, the **Cloghan Hill, Carrickmacsparrow,** and **Cloghany**

98

Photograph 6
Top bed of cherty facies limestones of the Dartry Limestone Formation with *in situ* colonies of *Siphonodendron irregulare*. Gortalughany, east side of Cuilcagh Mountain, Co. Fermanagh. (Hammer head 20cm long).

Limestone members are only developed in the Marble Arch-Cuilcagh Mountain area (20). The Cloghany Limestone Member contains *angulatus* stage archaediscids and *Howchinia bradyana* and is of late Asbian age. At the top of the Dartry Limestone Formation on Cuilcagh Mountain the **Carn Limestone Member** is separated from the Meenymore Formation, at the base of the Leitrim Group, by an erosional gap (19).

In Cashel quarry [G979 474], 14.5km WSW of Derrygonnelly, mudstone near the top of the Dartry Limestone Formation contains the B_2 Biozone (late Asbian) ammonoids *Beyrichoceras, Bollandites, Bollandoceras, Entogonites borealis* and *Nomismoceras*.

Formation	Lithology	Age
Lackagh Sandstone (36m)	Sandstone, pebbly, coarse-grained, fawn to white	Arnsbergian (pars)
Gowlaun Shale (55m)	Mudstone, calcareous, dark grey, fossiliferous	
Briscloonagh Sandstone (52m)	Sandstone, beds coarsening and thickening upwards; siltstone and mudstone	Pendleian
Dergvone Shale (130m)	Mudstone, dark grey to bluish black, fissile, ferruginous, siderite nodules; calcareous mudstone with ammonoids; sandstone in thin beds and dykes	
Carraun Shale (55m)	Mudstone, dark bluish grey, fossiliferous in lower half; five thin limestone members; sandstone dykes, bentonites, carbonate bullions	Brigantian
Bellavally (45m)	Cyclical sediments of mudstone, subordinate siltstone, sandstone and stromatolitic and fossiliferous marine limestone	
Glenade Sandstone (75-300m)	Sandstone, pebbly, fawn to white; thin siltstone	Asbian (pars)
Meenymore (100-240m)	Non-cyclical mudstone, siltstone, sandstone and limestone	

Table 7.9
Lithostratigraphy of the Leitrim Group on Cuilcagh Mountain.

Leitrim Group

The Leitrim Group consists of mudstone and sandstone with thin limestone and is characterised by major and minor cyclicity and the lateral persistence of individual beds across a wide region (22). In Northern Ireland, the most complete section of the Leitrim Group (Table 7.9) on Cuilcagh Mountain is 560m thick (19, 20).

The **Meenymore Formation** (23) is generally poorly exposed but on the south side of Belmore Mountain in the Lurgan River [H087 413] almost the full thickness of 48m is present (20). The ammonoids *Bollandoceras micronotum, Goniatites* sp. *maximus* group and *Nomismoceras vittigerum* indicate the late Asbian B_2a Subzone. The **Glenade Sandstone Formation** is widely exposed in the Fermanagh Highlands but only on Cuilcagh Mountain is there evidence of coarsening-upwards cycles, each one about 10m thick. Basal pebbly, coarse-grained sandstone succeeds algal laminated carbonates of the Meenymore Formation in the Lurgan River.

The contact between the Glenade Sandstone Formation and the **Bellavally Formation** (Table 7.9) is only exposed (19) in the Sruh Croppa River at Tromogagh [H104 317]. Ammonoids recorded in the sequence give the ages of the various members (19). A miospore assemblage of the VF Zone (24) in the Doobally Sandstone Member locates the Asbian-Brigantian boundary either at its base or in the underlying Drummangarvagh Member. The contact between the top of the Bellavally Formation (Corry Member) and the Derreens Limestone Member, the basal unit of the **Carraun Shale Formation** (Table 7.9), is also exposed in the Sruh Croppa River [H098 307]. In the middle of this Formation the distinctive Tawnyunshinagh Limestone Member is commonly exposed on Cuilcagh Mountain. Sandstone dykes intruding the mudstones are a feature of this part of the

Visean-Namurian Boundary

b

b

b

b

cm

Photograph 7
Contact between the Carraun Shale Formation (below) and Dergvone Shale Formation (Viséan-Namurian boundary). (b—bentonite, cm—Camderry Member of the Carraun Shale Formation). Altvenagh [H129 289], Cuilcagh Mountain, Co. Fermanagh.

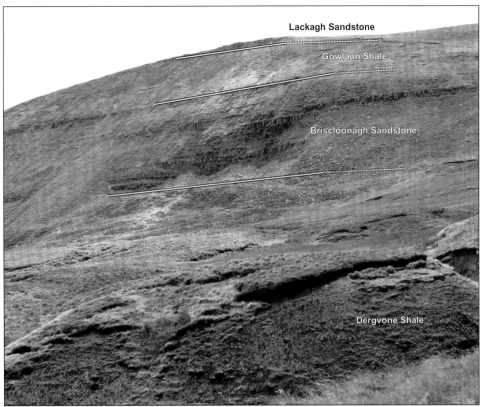

Lackagh Sandstone

Gowlaun Shale

Briscloonagh Sandstone

Dergvone Shale

Photograph 8
Northeast face of Cuilcagh Mountain below the summit (665m) showing the highest formations of the Leitrim Group, Co. Fermanagh.

succession. At least eight thin K-bentonites (volcanic ash beds) are located mostly above the Sranagross Member. The Viséan-Namurian boundary coincides with the contact between the Carraun Shale and Dergvone Shale formations, 6.5m above the Camderry Member (Photograph 7).

A stream section at Altvenagh [H120 293] exposes 70m of the Leitrim Group from below the Tawnyunshinagh Limestone Member into the Pendleian **Dergvone Shale Formation** (19). The north face of Cuilcagh Mountain (Photograph 8) exposes the three highest formations of the Leitrim Group.

Lisnaskea
Tyrone Group
The outcrop of the Tournaisian (Courceyan-early Chadian) section of strata is located mainly in Counties Cavan and Monaghan in Ireland (25, 26). The basal **Fearnaght Formation** (Table 7.7) rests unconformably on Ordovician rocks (26).

Despite the absence of the Mullaghmore Sandstone and Glencar Limestone formations in the area between Lisnaskea and Newtownbutler, Tyrone Group strata between the Ballyshannon Limestone and lower Dartry Limestone formations (Table 7.7) are 1400m thick compared to 1300m in the Glennoo Borehole (Figure 7.8).

Loose blocks, and a small exposure, of the **Ballyshannon Limestone Formation** on the shore of Upper Lough Erne at Derryvore [H341 229] are rich in corals including *Clisiophyllum spissum, Koninckophyllum fragile, Siphonodendron martini* and *S. sociale* and the brachiopod

Pustula pyxidiformis. The upper 'member' of the Formation crops out at Mullynagowan [H425 265] 1km northeast of Newtownbutler. They are overlain by 20m of grey to fawn grainstone of the **Newtownbutler Limestone Member** (27), the highest part of the Ballyshannon Limestone Formation in this area. Above the exposed conformable base [H426 266] of the succeeding **Bundoran Shale Formation** the lowest beds belong to the **Mullynagowan Sandstone Member** and consist of 2m of calcareous silty sandstone containing *Chondrites* and *Rhizocorallium* burrows. A coral fauna from near the base of the **Benbulben Shale Formation** is dominated by the solitary species *Clisiophyllum vesiculosum, Koninckophyllum cyathophylloides, Siphonophyllia garwoodi* and *S. caninioides*, and is associated with *Lithostrotion* and Holkerian foraminifera including *concavus* stage *Paraarchaediscus*. This coral fauna is more typically found in the Bundoran Shale Formation where it is associated with mid- to late Arundian foraminifera. In the Lisnaskea-Newtownbutler area the contact between the **Dartry Limestone Formation** and Benbulben Shale Formation is exposed in a road cutting [H362 337] at Lisnaskea. The Dartry Limestone consists of bedded, fine-grained limestone with thin mudstone and grey-black chert. Near the top of the Formation the **Ballagh Limestone Member** consists of 6m of crinoidal grainstone and is exposed [H404 310] in Rockfield quarry.

Leitrim Group

The disconformable contact between the Dartry Limestone Formation and overlying **Meenymore Formation** is exposed at the top of Rockfield quarry. Near the middle of the Meenymore Formation the **Carnmore Sandstone Member** (27) comprises about 75m of pale greyish fawn, very coarse-to medium-grained pebbly sandstone. The youngest, **Alderwood Mudstone Formation**, crops out (13) in the stream at Tircar [H486 470], 4.3km ESE of Fivemiletown (Figure 7.8). It consists of fossiliferous mudstone, laminated (stromatolitic) limestone, peritidal limestone, bioclastic limestone and calcareous siltstone. The early Brigantian age is based on the occurrence of the trilobite *Paladin bakewellensis*.

Fivemiletown-Clogher-Aughnacloy-Benburb

The Carboniferous rocks of this region are divided into three separate areas around Fivemiletown-Clogher, near Aughnacloy and at Benburb (Figure 7.8).

Fivemiletown-Clogher
Tyrone Group

The **Ballyness** and **Clogher Valley formations** (Table 7.7) are exposed in conformable contact in the Cole Bridge River [H443 523], 4km north of Fivemiletown. The unfossiliferous **Ballyness Formation** comprises about 300m of red and purplish red sandstone and conglomerate with clasts mainly of white quartz pebbles. The **Clogher Valley Formation** (400m) is divided into lower and upper parts separated by a sandstone unit. The lower part is fenestral micrite, siltstone, sandstone, evaporite beds and grey mudstone with miospores indicating an early Chadian age. The upper part crops out [H424 516] at Moysnaght, 4km NNW of Fivemiletown, and consists of fossiliferous mudstone, siltstone, sandstone and thin crinoidal limestone with the early Chadian solitary coral *Siphonophyllia cylindrica*. The lower 'member' of the **Ballyshannon Limestone Formation** is exposed in Mullaghsillogagh quarry [H424 504] 3km northwest of Fivemiletown and contains corals such as *Sychnoelasma konincki* and is late Chadian.

The Fardross section (Figure 7.8) [H523 486] (28), exposes five formations of the Tyrone Group (Figure 7.9). Mid- and late Arundian foraminifera including *involutus* stage *Paraarchaediscus, Glomodiscus* and *Uralodiscus* occur in the **Bundoran Shale Formation,**

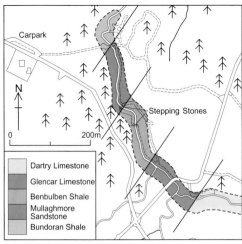

Figure 7.9
Geology of the Fardross stream section.

Mullaghmore Sandstone Formation and lower part of the **Benbulben Shale Formation**. Higher strata in the latter Formation contain the brachiopod *Gigantoproductus* sp. cf. *semiglobosus* and coral *Lithostrotion decipiens* (I. Somerville pers. comm.) and are early Asbian as are the succeeding **Glencar Limestone** and **Dartry Limestone formations**.

Aughnacloy

The stratigraphy of the Tyrone Group east and southeast of Aughnacloy is not defined accurately because of poor exposure (Table 7.7). The oldest rocks of the **Bundoran Shale Formation** are exposed (28) in Drummond quarry [H690 519], 2.5km east of Aughnacloy. In the Oona Water [H777 565] the **Benbulben Shale Formation** contains an Asbian macrofauna of corals and brachiopods. Thin mudstones in the succeeding **Aughnacloy Sandstone Formation** contain Holkerian-early Asbian miospores including *Schulzospora campyloptera*, an index taxon of the TC Biozone. Calcareous sandstone in Carricklongfield quarry [H716 545] contains rare early Asbian corals and brachiopods. The Formation is equated with the Carland Sandstone Formation of east Co. Tyrone and Drumman More Sandstone Formation in Co. Armagh (Figure 7.6). The **Maydown Limestone Formation** exposed in Plaister quarry [H676 539], 2.3km NNE of Aughnacloy, contains an early Asbian macrofauna including *Gigantoproductus* sp. *maximus* group and *Siphonophyllia benburbensis*.

Benburb

Despite the proximity of rocks of the Armagh Group in Co. Armagh the late Viséan succession at Benburb (29, 30) lithostratigraphically more closely resembles the Tyrone Group succession in Co. Fermanagh and south Co. Tyrone. In the River Blackwater, 230m of Asbian and Brigantian strata are exposed (Table 7.7).

The **Maydown Limestone Formation** contains abundant Asbian corals and brachiopods and is exposed in Maydown quarry [H817 518]. It includes lithologies that are typical in Co. Fermanagh of the change between the upper part of the Benbulben Shale, the Glencar Limestone and Dartry Limestone formations (Table 7.8). Mudstones in the **Carrickaness Sandstone Formation** contain miospores of the late Asbian NM Biozone including the index taxa *Raistrickia nigra* and *Triquitrites marginatus*. The Asbian-Brigantian boundary is placed at the contact between the Glenview and Drumflugh limestone members in the **Blackwater Limestone Formation** (29). Diagnostic Brigantian elements are rare in higher members but the typical bivalve *Posidonia becheri* is present.

Kesh-Omagh

Carboniferous rocks in this area rest unconformably on the Dalradian to the north and in the south are faulted (Figure 7.8) (14, 31). The Omagh Sandstone Group and Tyrone Group (Tables 7.1 and 7.7) are separated by an unconformity. Newly described formations and clastic members in the Tyrone Group help resolve the cause, effect and timing of marine transgression and regression and reflect the proximity of the northern shoreline in early and mid-Viséan times.

Omagh Sandstone Group

Uplift, folding and erosion in the late Courceyan and early Chadian reduced the outcrop of the **Omagh Sandstone Group** which consists of strata deposited prior to, and during, a marine transgression. The basal unconformity in Killyclogher Burn [H473 744] is overlain by 100m of unfossiliferous red sandstone with calcrete nodules and pebbles of white quartz. The section in the Glendurragh River [H275 671] near Lack includes channel sandstone and siltstone and mudstone with Courceyan-early Chadian (CM Biozone) miospores. Thin algal (cyanobacterial) limestone, evaporite replacement textures, serpulid worm traces and crinoidal sandstone with rare brachiopods are also present. A small outlier [H559 807] of unfossiliferous and undated reddish brown conglomerate and coarse-grained sandstone, overlying the Dalradian of the Central Highlands (Grampian) Terrane in the hanging wall of the Omagh Thrust Fault, may belong to this Group (32) (Figure 7.2).

Tyrone Group

In the north of this area the sub-Tyrone Group unconformity and Claragh Sandstone Formation (Table 7.7) overstep the Omagh Sandstone Group westwards and rest on the Dalradian. Coarse-grained, pebbly lithic arkose of the **Claragh Sandstone Formation**, with channels and planar cross-laminations, form the twin ridges [H213 740] 250m southwest of Scraghy quarry. Its late Chadian age is confirmed by miospores including *Lycospora pusilla* in mudstones and of mono- and bilaminar *Koninckopora* in an oncolitic boundstone near the top of the Formation. The succeeding Termon River Limestone and Bin Mountain Sandstone formations (Table 7.7) are partly contemporaneous (Figure 7.10).

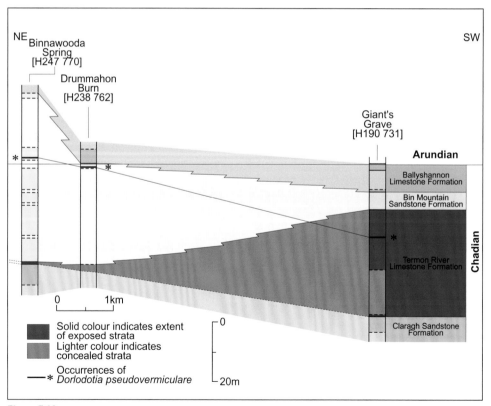

Figure 7.10
Correlation of early Carboniferous (Chadian – Arundian) rocks in the Kesh - Omagh area.

The upper part of the **Termon River Limestone Formation** is exposed in the Giants Grave section [H190 731] (Figure 7.8) and contains the late Chadian foraminifera *Eoparastaffella* but no archaediscids and the coral *Dorlodotia pseudovermiculare*. At Binnawooda Spring [H247 769] the Formation comprises 1.2m of mudstone, siltstone and peritidal limestone (Figure 7.10). The overlying **Bin Mountain Sandstone Formation** is bioturbated with a similar micro- and macrofauna and is late Chadian, except in the upper part where the early Arundian foraminifera *Glomodiscus*, *Uralodiscus* and *Viseidiscus umbogmaensis* are present. Scattered pebbles of vein quartz occur in the lowest 12m of strata but at Tullyard [H301 764] 5.5km to the east, are restricted to the 4m thick **Tullyard Conglomerate Member** (14). The **Rushindoo Oolite Member** crops out at the western end of the Formation outcrop [H159 719], 8km north of Kesh, and consists of 6m of oolitic limestone and calcareous sandstone (Table 7.10).

In Drummahon Burn [H238 762] (Figure 7.8) 5m of strata at the contact between the Bin Mountain Sandstone Formation and **Ballyshannon Limestone Formation** contain foraminifera and the corals *Dorlodotia pseudovermiculare, Dorlodotia* cf. *briarti* and *Siphonodendron martini* which define the position of the Chadian-Arundian and early to mid-Arundian boundaries. The upper 60m of the Ballyshannon Limestone Formation (Table 7.10) is exposed in Moffatt's quarry [H316 717], 3km southwest of Drumquin (Figure 7.8), overlain by 40m of the Bundoran Shale Formation (Photograph 9). The **Crockanaver Limestone Member** is exposed in quarries at the west end of the ridge at Carn [H222 635], 1.5km south of Ederney (Table 7.10). In contrast, the laterally equivalent **Drumowen Sandstone Member** is only developed near Drumquin. The **Ederny Limestone Member** represents the top of the Ballyshannon Limestone Formation and outcrops widely in the Kesh-Omagh area (14, 21).

Photograph 9
Contact between the Ballyshannon Limestone Formation and succeeding Bundoran Shale Formation. (BAL—Ballyshannon Limestone Formation and ELM—Ederny Limestone Member, BUNS—Bundoran Shale Formation). Moffat's quarry [H317 718], 3km SSW of Drumquin, Co. Tyrone.

Formation	Lithology	Member	Age
Tubbrid Sandstone (c. 20m)	Sandstone, grey, rusty weathering, calcareous, medium- to coarse-grained, fossiliferous		Holkerian
Benbulben Shale (75m)	Mudstone, silty, dark grey, calcareous; limestone, thin to lenticular, fossiliferous		Holkerian
Drumchorick Siltstone (100m)	Siltstone, mudstone and thin sandstone; limestone turbidites, fossiliferous		Arundian
Mullaghmore Sandstone (220m)	Sandstone, siltstone, mudstone, thin limestone, red beds, thin coal	Drumskinny Sandstone Dromore Sandstone	Arundian
Bundoran Shale (40-100m)	Mudstone, dark grey, yellow staining; siltstone, calcareous; limestone, thin to thick beds, fossiliferous Thin basal multicoloured clay	Skea Sandstone	Arundian
Ballyshannon Limestone (120-150m)	Limestone, dark bluish grey, silty mudstone, fossiliferous; rare chert	Ederny Limestone Drumowen Sandstone Crockanaver Limestone	Arundian
Bin Mountain Sandstone (0-53m)	Sandstone, grey, calcareous; limestone, sandy, pale grey with ooliths and coated grains, fossiliferous; thin micrite	Rushindoo Oolite	late Chadian
Termon River Limestone (0-35m)	Limestone, bluish grey packstone with radial spar ooliths, oncolites, coated grains and peloids; poorly fossiliferous; thin mudstone	Tullyard Conglomerate	late Chadian
Claragh Sandstone (325-500m)	Sandstone, very coarse-grained, fine conglomerate, fawn and grey, arkosic; thin limestone; grey mudstone with miospores		late Chadian

Table 7.10
Lithostratigraphy of the Tyrone Group in the Kesh-Omagh area.

The **Bundoran Shale Formation** (Table 7.10) thins northwards from 100m in the Kesh-Ederney area to 40m at Drummahon Burn. At its base the **Skea Sandstone Member** thickens northwards from 1.4m of sandy, bioclastic limestone in Ederney quarry [H224 640], to 4.5m of sandstone at Shanvin [H212 733] and at least 20m of conglomerate at Drummahon Lane [H227 761], 13km NNE of Kesh. The conglomerate consists of vein quartz and quartzite clasts in an orange-stained, coarse-grained feldspathic sand matrix. Dolomitised limestone clasts contain mid- to late Arundian corals. The sandstone is absent in Moffatt's quarry and 3m of mudstone, siltstone and fenestral micrite with rhizoliths mark the base of the Bundoran Shale Formation.

The basal beds of the **Mullaghmore Sandstone Formation** (Table 7.10) in contact with the Bundoran Shale Formation in White Glen [H292 731] are orange-stained sandstone of the **Dromore Sandstone Member** (30m). The Member is also exposed in the nearby roadside quarry [H293 731] as 12m of green to fawn micaceous sandstone with parallel laminations. The southerly inclined dip-slope at Tullynashammer [H187 713] represents the top surface of this Member, overlain by black mudstone and algal limestone of sabkha and lagoonal environments. The **Drumskinny Sandstone Member** (40m) consists of fawn to white

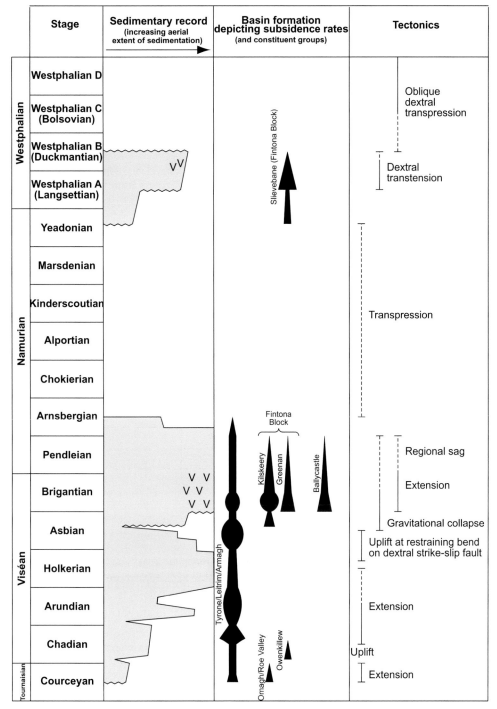

Figure 7.11
Summary of the principal events in the Carboniferous history of Northern Ireland.
V - contemporaneous volcanism

sandstone with rare brachiopods and burrows. The upper part of the Formation in the Bannagh River [H169 675] includes thin limestones with the late Arundian foraminifera *Eoparastaffella*, *Eotextularia* and *Paraarchaediscus* at *involutus* stage.

The basal bed of the overlying **Drumchorick Siltstone Formation** (Table 7.10) in the Bannagh River [H169 675] is a bioturbated calcareous silty sandstone with brachiopods. Higher limestones with corals possessing features of both *Siphonodendron* and *Lithostrotion*, a 'cerioid tendency', and foraminifera including *Eotextularia* and *Paraarchaediscus* at *involutus* and possibly *concavus* stages, occupy a position just below the Arundian-Holkerian boundary (33). Crinoidal limestone turbidites are exposed at Drumkeeran [H207 670], 2.5km northwest of Ederney.

A rich macrofauna in the **Benbulben Shale Formation** includes brachiopods and colonial and solitary corals. A limestone bed located 4m above the base in a stream [H209 675] 4.3km northeast of Kesh contains the coral *Lithostrotion portlocki* and late Arundian foraminifera *Pararchaediscus* at *involutus* stage. Higher strata contain Holkerian foraminifera. The youngest formation, the **Tubbrid Sandstone Formation**, is probably Holkerian (Table 7.10).

Palaeogeographical and Environmental Reconstruction

There is abundant evidence in the outcrop in Co. Fermanagh, south Co. Tyrone and Co. Armagh with which to reconstruct the palaeogeographical evolution of Northern Ireland

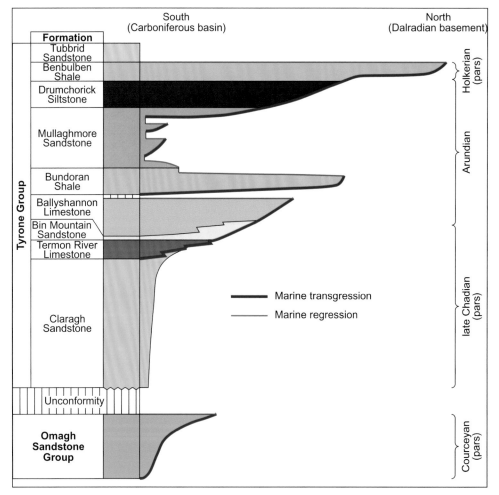

Figure 7.12
Generalised sea-level curve for the early Carboniferous Omagh Sandstone Group and Tyrone Group in the Kesh - Omagh area.

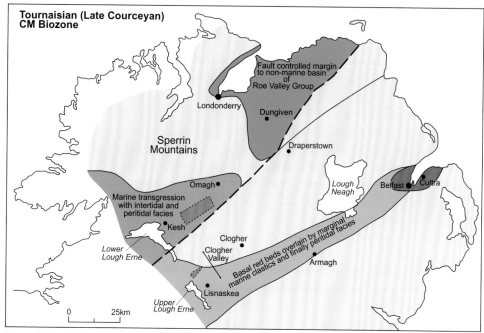

Figure 7.13
Palaeogeography of Northern Ireland in the late Courceyan.

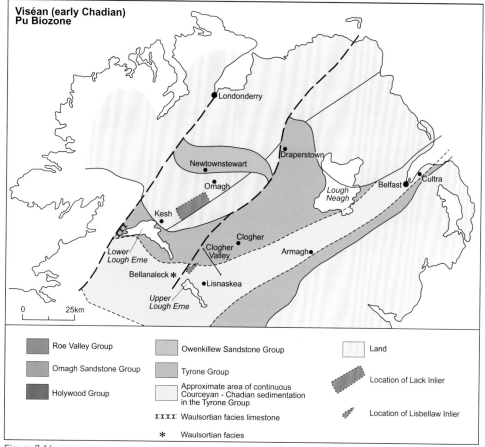

Figure 7.14
Palaeogeography of Northern Ireland in the early Chadian.

during the early Carboniferous. This is not the case however, in the eastern part of Northern Ireland where isolated outliers hint at other events but provide little evidence. The recognition of Carboniferous rocks in the Fintona Block helped resolve aspects of the geological evolution of Northern Ireland (12). It particularly revealed the importance of strike-slip faulting in the dismembering of the three non-marine basins (Figure 7.11). Deformation styles in the Carboniferous tectonic collage between the Castle Archdale Fault-Omagh Thrust Fault zone and the Clogher Valley Fault resulted from serial strike-slip overprinted by end-Variscan transpression and southeasterly-directed thrusting.

The detailed synthesis presented here of early Carboniferous transgression and regression is based on the Tyrone Group (Courceyan to late Asbian) succession in Co. Fermanagh-south Co. Tyrone (Table 7.1) and in the Kesh-Omagh area (Figure 7.12).

Late Courceyan (CM Biozone)

The most extensive deposits in Northern Ireland associated with the late Courceyan (CM Biozone) transgression occupy a 25km wide and more than 125km long, northeast-southwest trending trough at the northern edge of the Southern Uplands-Down-Longford Terrane (Figure 7.13). They occur in the **Holywood Group** on Belfast Lough and as continental, peritidal and shallow marine sediments of the **Tyrone Group** in Co. Armagh (Table 7.1) and at Lisnaskea (Table 7.7). In the succession the early continental sediments which developed at fault scarps were buried by later peritidal sediments deposited during the earliest northwards transgression (2). That transgression ultimately failed due to tectonic uplift but is recorded in the **Omagh Sandstone Group** in the Kesh-Omagh area. North of the Sperrin Mountains, the **Roe Valley Group** was deposited initially by rivers and as soil profiles in a late Courceyan inter-montane basin with marine sediments at the top. Courceyan sediments are absent north of the present position of the Clogher Valley.

Chadian (Pu Biozone)

Chadian time in Northern Ireland was a period when the marine transgression spread northwards and southeastwards from the early-formed trough (Figure 7.14). Tyrone Group sequences that contain evidence of the Courceyan-early Chadian boundary (CM to Pu biozones) occur in Co. Armagh and at Lisnaskea. In the Clogher Valley, both the continental **Ballyness Formation** and peritidal and shallow marine **Clogher Valley Formation** (Table 7.7) are early Chadian. Contemporaneous rocks at Draperstown in Co. Londonderry (**Altagoan Formation**) were also deposited by this transgression (Table 7.4). There, however, localised uplift halted the early Chadian transgression and the break in sedimentation extends into the late Asbian. Minor regression and deposition of the continental late Chadian **Milford Mills Formation** demonstrates the pulsed nature of the transgression in Co. Armagh (Figure 7.6).

There is no record of early Chadian deposits in the Kesh-Omagh area (Figure 7.12). The **Claragh Sandstone Formation** was largely deposited in a non-marine environment. Succeeding sediments deposited during the ensuing late Chadian transgression, the **Bin Mountain Sandstone** and **Termon River Limestone formations**, gradually submerged the wedge of clastic sediments of the Claragh Sandstone Formation. As the transgression progressed northwards and the sea deepened southwards, shallow marine sand and gravel gave way to peritidal carbonates of the Termon River Limestone and then, in the latest Chadian and early Arundian, to coral-rich, open marine platform carbonate and mudstone of the basal **Ballyshannon Limestone Formation** (Figure 7.12). The **Owenkillew Sandstone Group** at Newtownstewart was deposited in an intra-cratonic basin (Table 7.1).

Arundian

During the early and mid-Arundian, the transgression continued and the sea expanded northwards onto the Dalradian and submerged more of the Southern Uplands-Down-Longford Terrane at Lisnaskea and Carlingford (Figure 7.15). Arundian sediments are 840m thick at Derrygonnelly, 600m at Kesh-Omagh and 30m in Co. Armagh.

Evidence of regression is apparent in Arundian strata of the Tyrone Group across the southwest part of the Carboniferous outcrop. Shallow water sediments occur at the top of the **Ballyshannon Limestone Formation** (Table 7.10). In the Kesh-Omagh area the **Ederny Limestone Member** is the product of emergence and micritisation of semi-consolidated carbonate of that formation by groundwater brine. At both Derrygonnelly and Lisnaskea the top of the formation was not exposed but the highest strata are represented by shallow water, oolitic grainstones. The base of the **Bundoran Shale Formation** is represented by a thin, possibly volcaniclastic, clay in the Kesh-Omagh area. The **Skea Sandstone Member** succeeds the clay. That detritus was eroded from Dalradian and Carboniferous rocks and funnelled southwards in a palaeovalley, incised into the top surface of the Ballyshannon Limestone. This episode corresponds to a localised period of emergence prior to the transgression in which mudstone of the Bundoran Shale Formation (Figure 7.12) was deposited. At Lisnaskea, the **Mullynagowan Sandstone Member** is the contemporary of the Skea Sandstone Member, and has a southerly provenance. Both sandstones formed as a result of regional eustatic sea-level fall.

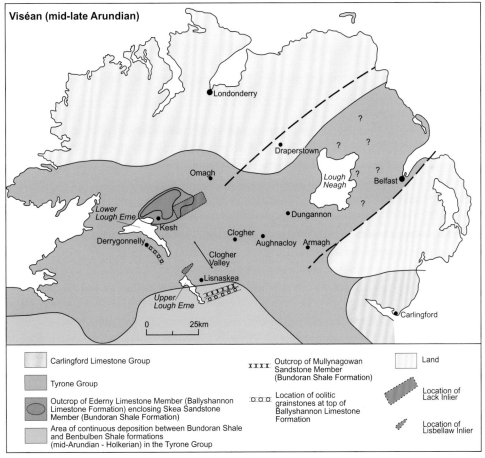

Figure 7.15
Palaeogeography of Northern Ireland in the mid- to late Arundian.

The late Arundian **Mullaghmore Sandstone Formation** (Table 7.8) was deposited at a time of marine regression and of increased erosion of land to the north of the Carboniferous basin. It is 220m thick in the Kesh-Omagh area, at Derrygonnelly and in the Glennoo borehole but thins southwards and is absent at Lisnaskea and in Co. Armagh (Figure 7.8). In the former area, the basal **Dromore Sandstone Member** is a marine deposit that was followed by the formation of a sabkha. Succeeding shallow marine and intertidal sediments were deposited on a delta with periods of intermittent exposure leading to the formation of palaeosols and thin coals. The arrival of a renewed transgression in the late Arundian is evident in the brackish to marine sediments in the upper part of the Mullaghmore Sandstone Formation. By latest Arundian-early Holkerian times (Table 7.7) the shoreline and sediment source lay far to the north. Water depths had increased from shallow marine with corals (**Drumchorick Siltstone Formation**), to a deeper shelf, slope setting with turbiditic limestone (**Drumchorick Siltstone and Benbulben Shale formations**).

Holkerian

Throughout much of Northern Ireland, the Holkerian is represented by the **Benbulben Shale Formation**. However, coarse detritus of the **Carland Sandstone Formation** at Dungannon, **Drumman More Sandstone Formation** (Figure 7.6) in Co. Armagh and **Aughnacloy Sandstone Formation** (Table 7.7) at Aughnacloy accumulated at the eastern and southern margins of the rising basement block that included the Lack and Lisbellaw inliers. Almost 2000m of older Dinantian strata were stripped from the basement block exposing the Dalradian and early Palaeozoic rocks respectively.

Early Asbian

Asbian time in the north of Ireland was a period of syn-sedimentary fault movement, of basin formation (34, 35) and of continued uplift of the Lisbellaw Inlier and erosion of early Dinantian cover rocks.

While early Asbian basins were fault-controlled, there is no evidence of transgression onto either the Central Highlands (Grampian) or Southern Uplands-Down-Longford terranes or of near-shore depositional environments in the **Benbulben Shale, Glencar Limestone** or **Dartry Limestone formations** (Table 7.8). The absence of the Glencar Limestone Formation, for example at Lisnaskea, is believed to indicate deep water conditions. While cherty limestones are a major part of the Dartry Limestone Formation they are impoverished in faunal and floral remains and are deep water facies. Near the top of the Dartry Limestone Formation shallow water grainstones of the Ballagh Limestone (27) (Lisnaskea) and Carrickmacsparrow Limestone (19) (Derrygonnelly) members show evidence of slumping and channels and represent shallow water sediments that moved downslope to deeper water. Carbonate 'buildups' of the Knockmore Limestone Member (19) accumulated on the southwesterly inclined ramp in Co. Fermanagh in shallower water than the cherty limestones. In Co. Armagh (Figure 7.6) the early Asbian was a period of non-deposition.

Late Asbian

The late Asbian was a time of uplift and marine regression and subsidence of the non-marine Kilskeery Group basin (Fintona Block). Over much of Co. Fermanagh and Co. Sligo the erosional gap between the Dartry Limestone Formation (Tyrone Group) and **Meenymore Formation** (Leitrim Group) was the result of regional uplift. It separates deep-water marine carbonates from shallow marine, intertidal, sabkha and fluvial sediments respectively.

The Meenymore Formation accumulated on tidal flats some 40km wide that stretched for 120km from Draperstown to Co. Sligo, but is replaced in the Armagh-Cookstown area by the Armagh Group (Figure 7.16).

At the southern margin of the subsiding **Kilskeery Group** basin, the Lisbellaw Inlier was the source of greywacke pebbles in the **Ballyreagh Conglomerate Formation** (Table 7.5). Subsidence probably resulted from gravitational collapse in the centre of an uplifted and arched orogenic belt (Figure 7.16).

Deposition of the **Glenade Sandstone Formation** (Table 7.9) occurred in a half-graben with the northern faulted margin defining a clastic source area that included Courceyan-Chadian strata. Minor faulting continued during deposition of the lowest two members of the **Bellavally Formation** which were overlapped southwards by younger members onto the

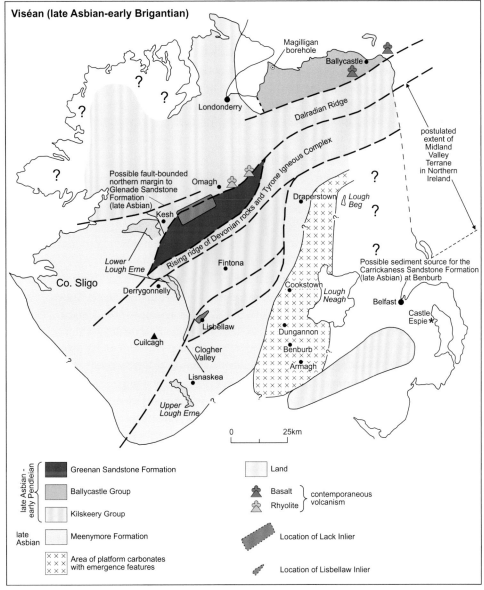

Figure 7.16
Palaeogeography of Northern Ireland in the late Asbian–early Brigantian.

top surface of the Glenade Sandstone Formation. Deposition of the Doobally Sandstone Member coincides with the early Brigantian subsidence event.

Between Co. Armagh and Draperstown the **Armagh Group** developed on a north-south orientated carbonate platform (Figure 7.16). Deposition was affected by oscillating sea levels, exposure and by pedogenesis and resulted in the formation of solution features filled with red clay of continental origin. The development of Asbian emergence surfaces is believed to indicate a glacio-eustatic control on sea levels and on emergence (36).

Brigantian–Arnsbergian

During the Brigantian, Northern Ireland experienced bimodal volcanism, development of new, non-marine basins and marine sedimentation in quiet basinal settings.

Extensional faulting in the early Brigantian at the margins of the Central Highlands (Grampian) Terrane led to the development of two new sedimentary basins (Figure 7.16). At Ballycastle the **Ballycastle Group** was deposited in a fault-controlled basin associated with basalt volcanism. Similar sediments occur in the Magilligan borehole and were deposited in shallow marine, fluviodeltaic and coal swamp environments with limestones only developed during brief transgression. Deposition of the **Greenan Sandstone Formation** (Table 7.1) in a new basin was associated with rhyolitic volcanism. Sandstone composition is constant and indicates a low topographic contrast between the basin and sediment source areas. Subsidence of the **Kilskeery Group** basin continued from Brigantian into Pendleian times when alluvium of the **Ballinamallard Mudstone Formation** was deposited in axial parts of the basin and in playa lakes.

Early Brigantian sediments at Armagh-Cookstown, Benburb and Castle Espie were deposited in shallow marine, lagoonal and carbonate platform environments and all contain evidence of shallowing upwards cycles, emergence, palaeokarsts and fluvial channels. Their occurrence at Benburb and Cookstown may be related to the proximity of a shoreline to the east, marking the edge of a basement block beneath Lough Neagh that is now concealed by Mesozoic and Cenozoic rocks (Figure 7.2).

In Co. Fermanagh, basinal mudstone and deltaic sandstone with a northerly provenance succeed the Bellavally Formation (Table 7.9). In the late Brigantian, anaerobic bottom conditions prevailed and the rich benthic community of the lower **Carraun Shale Formation** disappeared in the upper part and in the Pendleian **Dergvone Shale Formation**. The K-bentonites in the Carraun Shale Formation represent distal ashfall deposits of volcanic eruptions. The relative tectonic quiescence of late Brigantian and early Pendleian times is ascribed to regional thermal subsidence (12, 34).

The late Pendleian and Arnsbergian was a time of marine transgression and delta progradation. In the Dergvone Shale Formation the Lacoon Sandstone Member (19) is a forerunner of the **Briscloonagh Sandstone** delta with its upward coarsening and increasingly proximal succession. Marine transgression at the base of the Arnsbergian drowned the delta and deposited the **Gowlaun Shale Formation**. Thin coals in the succeeding **Lackagh Sandstone Formation** testify to intermittent exposure of the delta top. Across Northern Ireland, Carboniferous sedimentation ceased in the mid-Arnsbergian and renewed uplift created the mid-Carboniferous hiatus.

In east Co. Tyrone, the Leitrim Group comprises the **Rossmore Mudstone Formation** which was deposited during the mid-Brigantian transgression and faunally resembles the Carraun Shale Formation. The lower part of the **Millstone Grit** was deposited in times of fluctuating sea-levels and subaerial exposure and of deposition in shallow marine, deltaic, fluvial and coal swamp environments.

Late Namurian-Westphalian A/B

Coal Measures in east Co. Tyrone accumulated in poorly drained swamps as alluvium and peat of the alluvial plain facies association. In the Fintona Block the **Tullanaglare Mudstone Formation** was also deposited on this alluvial plain but at a higher topographic level with improved drainage (Table 7.6). The bed of calcrete (**Drumgivery Limestone Member**) at the top of the formation indicates a period of sediment starvation in early Westphalian B times corresponding to the onset of dextral strike-slip, uplift of Dalradian basement and rapid subsidence of a pull-apart basin to the south. The upwards-fining, volcaniclastic, alluvial fan sediments of the **Drumlish Conglomerate Formation** reflect either decreasing rate of subsidence and gradual lowering of the clastic source area or of depocentre migration to the southwest.

Late Carboniferous-Early Permian

In Northern Ireland the late Carboniferous and early Permian was a time of maximum Variscan deformation in a zone of convergent dextral strike-slip faulting and orogenic shortening along the Omagh Thrust Fault. The severity of strike-slip faulting and southeasterly-directed thrusting may be gauged from the virtual destruction of the original sedimentary basin of the early Westphalian Slievebane Group.

References

1) Osborne, R. and Tarling, D. H. 1995. *The Historical Atlas of the Earth (A Visual Exploration of the Earth's Physical Past)*. Viking. Penguin Books Ltd., London.

2) Clayton, G. and Higgs, K. 1979. The Tournaisian marine transgression in Ireland. *Journal of Earth Sciences of the Royal Dublin Society* **2**, 1-10.

3) Calder, J. H. 1998. The Carboniferous evolution of Nova Scotia. *In*: Blundell, D. J. and Scott, A. C. (eds.). *Lyell: the Past is the Key to the Present*. Publication of the Geological Society, London, No. **143**, 261-302.

4) Sevastopulo, G. D. and Wyse Jackson, P. N. 2001. Carboniferous (Dinantian). *In*: Holland, C. H. (ed.). *The Geology of Ireland*. Dunedin Academic Press, Edinburgh.

5) Oswald, D. H. 1955. The Carboniferous rocks between the Ox Mountains and Donegal Bay. *Quarterly Journal of the Geological Society of London*, **111**, 167-83.

6) Geological Survey of Northern Ireland 2002. Ballycastle, Northern Ireland Sheet 8. Solid Geology (second edition). 1:50,000. (Keyworth, Nottingham: British Geological Survey).

7) Wilson, H. E. and Robbie, J. A. 1966. *Geology of the country around Ballycastle*. Memoir of the Geological Survey of Northern Ireland, Sheet 8 (Northern Ireland).

8) Griffith A. E. and Wilson, H. E. 1982. *Geology of the country around Carrickfergus and Bangor*. Memoir of the Geological Survey of Northern Ireland, Sheet 29 (Northern Ireland).

9) Clayton, G. 1986. Late Tournaisian miospores from the Ballycultra Formation at Cultra, County Down, Northern Ireland. *Irish Journal of Earth Sciences*, **8**, 73-79.

10) Geological Survey of Northern Ireland 1983. Cookstown, Northern Ireland Sheet 27. Solid Geology. 1:50,000. (Southampton: Ordnance Survey for the Geological Survey of Northern Ireland).

11) Cameron, I. B. and Old, R. A. 1997. *Geology of the country around Cookstown, Co. Tyrone. Geological Sheet 27 (Cookstown)*. Geological Survey of Northern Ireland. Technical Report GSNI 97/7.

12) Mitchell, W. I. and Owens, B. 1990. The geology of the western part of the Fintona Block, Northern Ireland-evolution of Carboniferous basins. *Geological Magazine*, **127**, 407-26.

13) Geological Survey of Northern Ireland 1982. Enniskillen, Northern Ireland Sheet 45. Solid Geology. 1:50,000. (Southampton: Ordnance Survey for the Geological Survey of Northern Ireland).

14) Geological Survey of Northern Ireland 1995. Omagh, Northern Ireland Sheet 33. Solid Geology. 1:50,000. (Keyworth, Nottingham: British Geological Survey).

15) Somerville, I. D., Strogen, P., Mitchell, W. I., Higgs, K. and Somerville, H. E. A. Stratigraphy of Dinantian rocks in a borehole from Co. Armagh, N. Ireland. *Irish Journal of Earth Sciences*, **19** (2001), 51-78.

16) Geological Survey of Northern Ireland 1960. Dungannon, Northern Ireland Sheet 35. Solid Geology. 1:63,360 (Southampton: Ordnance Survey for the Geological Survey of Northern Ireland).

17) Fowler, A. and Robbie, J. A. 1961. *Geology of the country around Dungannon*. Memoir of the Geological Survey of Northern Ireland, Sheet 35 (Northern Ireland).

18) Ramsbottom, W. H. C., Calver, M. A., Eagar, R. M., Hodson, F., Holliday, D. W., Stubblefield, C. J.and Wilson, R. B. 1978. *A correlation of Silesian rocks in the British Isles*. Geological Society, London, Special Report, **10**.

19) Legg, I. C., Johnston, T. P., Mitchell, W. I. and Smith, R. A. 1998. *Geology of the country around Derrygonnelly and Marble Arch*. Memoir of the Geological Survey of Northern Ireland, Sheet 44, 56 and 43. (Northern Ireland).

20) Geological Survey of Northern Ireland 1991. Derrygonnelly, Northern Ireland Sheet 44, 56 and 43. Solid Geology. 1:50,000. (Keyworth, Nottingham: British Geological Survey).

21) Geological Survey of Northern Ireland 1994. Kesh, Northern Ireland Sheet 32. Solid Geology. 1:50,000. (Keyworth, Nottingham: British Geological Survey).

22) Brandon, A. and Hodson, F. 1984. The Stratigraphy and Palaeontology of the late Viséan and early Namurian rocks of North-east Connaught. *Geological Survey of Ireland Special Paper* No. **6**.

23) Brandon, A. 1977. *The Meenymore Formation – an evaporitic intertidal formation in the Upper Viséan (B2) of northwest Ireland*. Institute of Geological Sciences Report No. 77/23.

24) Higgs, K. 1984. Stratigraphic palynology of the Carboniferous rocks in northwest Ireland. *Geological Survey of Ireland Bulletin*, **3**, 171-202.

25) Geological Survey of Northern Ireland 2004. Lisnaskea, Northern Ireland Sheet 57 and 58. Solid Geology. 1:50,000. (Keyworth, Nottingham: British Geological Survey).

26) Geraghty, M. 1997. *A geological description of Monaghan - Carlingford to accompany the Bedrock Geology 1:100 000 Scale Map Series, sheet 8 and 9, Monaghan and Carlingford, with contributions by J. Farrelly, K. Claringbold, C. Jordan, R. Meehan and M. Hudson*. Geological Survey of Ireland (GSI), 60pp.

27) Mitchell, W. I. 1995. *Geological description of the area around Lisnaskea and Newtownbutler, Co. Fermanagh. Part of 1:50 000 Geological Sheet 57 (Lisnaskea)*. Geological Survey of Northern Ireland. Technical Report GSNI 95/8.

28) Geological Survey of Northern Ireland 1982. Clogher, Northern Ireland Sheet 46. Solid Geology. 1:50,000. (Southampton: Ordnance Survey for the Geological Survey of Northern Ireland).

29) Mitchell, W. I. and Mitchell, M. 1983. *The Lower Carboniferous (Upper Viséan) succession at Benburb, Northern Ireland*. Institute of Geological Sciences Report No. 82/12.

30) Geological Survey of Northern Ireland 1984. Armagh, Northern Ireland Sheet 47. Solid Geology. 1:50,000. (Southampton: Ordnance Survey for the Geological Survey of Northern Ireland).

31) Geological Survey of Northern Ireland 1997. Northern Ireland. Solid Geology (second edition). 1:250,000. (Keyworth, Nottingham: British Geological Survey).

32) Geological Survey of Northern Ireland, 1995. Draperstown, Northern Ireland Sheet 26. Solid Geology. 1:50,000. (Keyworth, Nottingham: British Geological Survey).

33) Riley, N. J. 1993. Dinantian (Lower Carboniferous) biostratigraphy and chronostratigraphy in the British Isles. *Journal of the Geological Society, London*, **150**, 427-46.

34) Mitchell, W. I. 1992. The origin of Upper Palaeozoic sedimentary basins in Northern Ireland and relationships with the Canadian Maritime Provinces. In: Parnell, J. (ed.). *Basins on the Atlantic Seaboard: Petroleum Geology, Sedimentology and Basin Evolution*. Special Publication of the Geological Society, London, No. **62**, 191-202.

35) Philcox, M. E., Baily, H., Clayton, G. and Sevastopulo, G. D. 1992. Evolution of the Carboniferous Lough Allen Basin, Northwest Ireland. *In*: Parnell, J. (ed.). *Basins on the Atlantic Seaboard: Petroleum Geology, Sedimentology and Basin Evolution*. Special Publication of the Geological Society, London, No. **62**, 203-15.

36) Horbury, A. D. 1989. The relative roles of tectonism and eustacy in the deposition of the Urswick Limestone in south Cumbria and north Lancashire. *In*: Arthurton, R. S., Gutteridge, P. and Nolan, S. C. (eds.). *The role of tectonics in Devonian and Carboniferous sedimentation in the British Isles*. Yorkshire Geological Society, Occasional Publication No. **6**, 153-69.

Chapter 8

Variscan (Hercynian) Orogenic Cycle

W. I. MITCHELL

Introduction

Carboniferous basin development is attributed to extensional reactivation of Caledonian basement faults in a north-south tensional field (1). The driving force creating the tension probably resulted from the Bretonic subduction event far to the south of Ireland and Britain. In different parts of Ireland and Britain the sequence of tectonic events was never consistent throughout Carboniferous time. In northern Britain the sequence of events commenced with an early Carboniferous rifting event which was followed by thermal sag in the late Carboniferous, the transition being represented by sedimentation in the early to mid-Namurian period. Detailed analysis of the Carboniferous history of the Midland Valley of Scotland recognised both of the main events. However, the important and persistent influence of dextral strike-slip during alternating episodes of transtension and transpression superimposed on this structural pattern, particularly during the Namurian (2) was also recognised. In Ireland (Figure 8.1), intense deformation associated with the Variscan Orogenic Cycle is primarily confined to Zone 1, the area of Devonian and early Carboniferous rocks between Dingle and Dungarvan (3). In Zone 1, which lay close to the northern edge of the Variscan tectonic front, the rocks were folded and cleaved and finally subjected to thrusting. Elsewhere in Ireland, the intensity of deformation declines northwards in Zone 2 and by Zone 3, including Northern Ireland (Figure 8.1), structures are gentle folds and major faults (Figure 8.2).

The principal set of faults in Northern Ireland are orientated northeast-southwest and are probably reactivated basement structures (4). A suite of shorter northwest-southeast lineaments may also represent basement features, whose reactivation was controlled by motion on the bounding northeast-

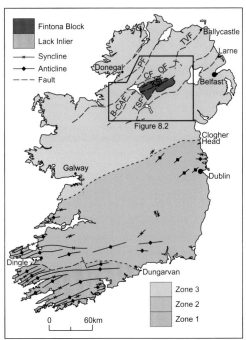

Figure 8.1
Variscan deformation zones and major structures in Ireland (3)

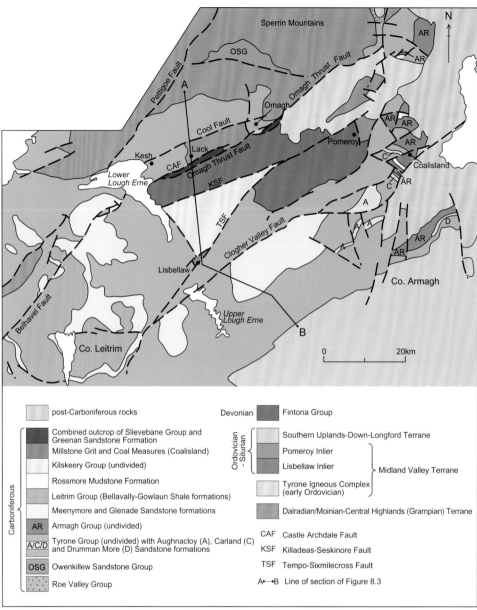

Figure 8.2
Simplified geological map of part of northwest Ireland showing the location of the principal Variscan faults.

southwest structures. The final set of lineaments has an ESE-WNW orientation.

The principal faults show both dip slip and strike-slip movement and the Carboniferous basins formed in a dextral transtensional shear system in a regional north-south tensional field. In some parts of Northern Ireland it is evident that intra-Carboniferous faulting was responsible for the development of non-sequences and unconformities (5, 6, 7). The dating (K-Ar modal ages) of samples of fault gauge affecting the Dalradian rocks of the southern Sperrin Mountains at 327±13Ma indicates early Carboniferous movement (8). Therefore the main episode of basin inversion, which was responsible for the expulsion of basinal brines, may correlate with late Holkerian-early Asbian dextral transpression and uplift of basement rocks between the Lack and Lisbellaw inliers. Movement of the basinal brine was associated with the precipitation of late gold-bearing quartz in the fault gauge (8). These effects herald the major, and final, phase of deformation in the end Carboniferous to Early Permian period.

It is evident that subsidence of early and late Carboniferous basins in the Fintona Block was a response to recurring episodes of intra-Carboniferous tectonic activity of varying intensity (9, 10). The dismembering and juxtaposition of those non-marine basins was largely the result of end-Carboniferous instability. Depending on the severity of each tectonic event the impact on sedimentary processes varied from minimal, in marine facies of the Tyrone and Leitrim groups, to profound resulting in marine regression, regional uplift and deposition of continental alluvium in non-marine basins. In Northern Ireland there is little resemblance between the present Carboniferous outcrop and the configuration of the original sedimentary basins.

The focus of deformation during the Variscan Orogenic Cycle in Northern Ireland was located on, and between, two major faults. In the north is the northern-bounding fault of the Midland Valley Terrane (Figure 1.3), the Castle Archdale Fault-Omagh Thrust Fault zone, while in the south is the Clogher Valley Fault. Carboniferous rocks located between these faults were affected by strike-slip, associated with intermittent dextral transpression and transtension. Between the Clogher Valley Fault and the Southern Upland Fault, the southern bounding fault of the Midland Valley Terrane, the Carboniferous rocks are relatively undeformed (Figure 8.3).

In Northern Ireland, significant disruption to the Carboniferous lithostratigraphy is related to seven separate episodes of tectonic activity that define important stages in the evolution of the area and illustrate the variability of Variscan deformation.

Late Tournaisian-early Viséan extension
The propagation of back-stepping faults aided the northward migration of the first marine transgression (Figure 8.4). Southeast of Upper Lough Erne and in Co. Armagh, basal Carboniferous red-beds of the Tyrone Group rest unconformably on Ordovician rocks of the Southern Uplands-Down-Longford Terrane and are succeeded by late Courceyan marginal marine sediments. In the Kesh-Omagh area, 50km to the northwest, the basal clastic rocks of the Tyrone Group are late Chadian (Figure 8.2). In the latter area, late Chadian and early Arundian peritidal and shallow marine sediments are overlapped northwards by late Arundian-Holkerian sediments of the outer shelf slope environment (Table 7.10).

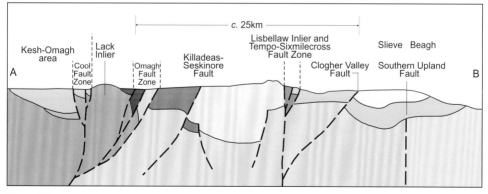

Figure 8.3
Simplified present structural cross-section of the Midland Valley Terrane and the Fintona Block (see Figure 8.2 for approximate line of section and Figure 8.4 for the index of colours).

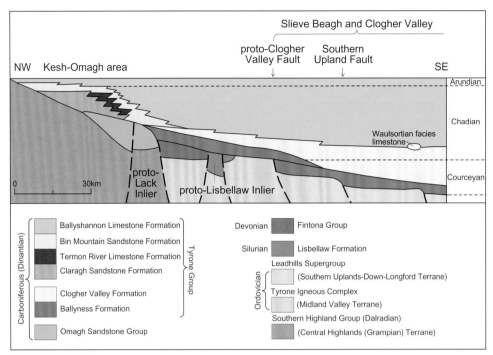

Figure 8.4
Simplified cross-section of the northern margin of the Carboniferous despositional basin in Courceyan-early Arundian times.

Late Holkerian-early Asbian

Reactivated early Palaeozoic faults acted as strike-slip faults in a zone of dextral transpression induced by WNW compression. Structural control was exercised by converging basement blocks at a restraining bend in a wide zone of dextral strike-slip (Figure 8.5). Crustal shortening occurred between the Belhavel Fault-Castle Archdale Fault-Omagh Thrust Fault Zone in the north and the Clogher Valley Fault to the south. Uplift of basement rocks between these faults was accommodated in a positive flower structure (11) in which major faults developed at a relatively gentle angle and with an important thrust component (Figure 8.6). Those basement rocks included the Dalradian (Lack Inlier) of the Central Highlands (Grampian) Terrane, in the Midland Valley Terrane the Tyrone Igneous Complex and cover sequence rocks that are now restricted to the Lisbellaw Inlier, and Devonian red-beds.

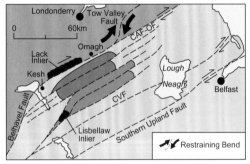

Figure 8.5
Simplified map showing the distribution of basement terranes and the main structural elements in late Holkerian-early Asbian times (colour scheme as for Figure 8.4). Castle Archdale Fault-Omagh Thrust Fault (CAF-OF), Clogher Valley Fault (CVF).

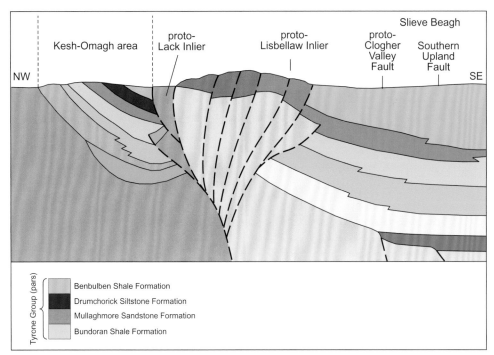

Figure 8.6
Simplified cross-section of the Carboniferous depositional basin in the late Holkerian-early Asbian.

At least 1800m of pre-late Holkerian Carboniferous strata were eroded and marine and continental basins developed in close proximity.

The detritus produced by erosion of the older Carboniferous strata was deposited to the east and southeast (Figure 8.2) as the Carland Sandstone, Aughnacloy Sandstone and Drumman More Sandstone formations. Although the original dimensions of the basement block between the Castle Archdale Fault-Omagh Thrust Fault Zone and the Clogher Valley Fault are not known it certainly exceeded the present 25km between the Lack and Lisbellaw inliers. The ensuing marine regression in the late Holkerian and early Asbian resulted in a permanent cessation to sedimentation in the Kesh-Omagh area.

Late Asbian

A change in the style of deformation from strike-slip to extension caused rifting and collapse of the domed axial region of the basement block (Figure 8.6) and resulted in the subsidence of the basin in which the continental Kilskeery Group was deposited (Figure 8.7). Southwest and south of this land area the Meenymore Formation (Leitrim Group) was deposited on a coastal plain of supratidal and intertidal flats fringing the Kilskeery Group basin. In the marine realm, this period of late Asbian extension is marked by the disconformity between the Tyrone Group (Dartry Limestone Formation) and the succeeding Leitrim Group (Meenymore Formation). In Counties Armagh and Tyrone a carbonate platform (Armagh Group) developed seaward of this coastal plain. Reactivated faults at the southern margin of the Central Highlands (Grampian) Terrane defined a new half-graben which received coarse sediment of the late Asbian Glenade Sandstone Formation. This sandstone thins from 300m at Lower Lough Erne to 4m in Co. Leitrim, 45km to the south (12).

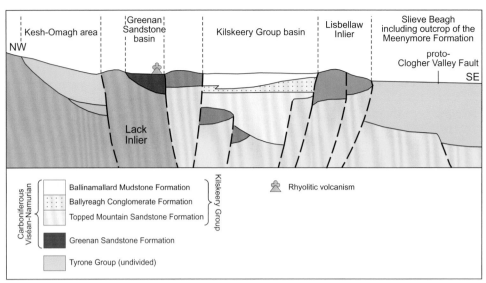

Figure 8.7
Simplified cross-section of the Carboniferous depositional basin in the late Viséan (Brigantian)-early Namurian (Pendleian). (Colours as in Figure 8.4)

Late Asbian-Brigantian
Cyclical sediments of the Bellavally Formation were deposited on the top surface of the Glenade Sandstone in shallow marine, evaporitic and deltaic environments. Until mid-Arnsbergian time, deposition of the remainder of the Leitrim Group (Carraun Shale to Gowlaun Shale formations and the Rossmore Mudstone Formation in Co. Tyrone) was influenced by thermal subsidence. This is exemplified by the persistence of thin limestone and mudstone members beyond the present outcrop of 1400km² (12, 13). In the Carraun Shale and Dergvone Shale formations, sandstone dykes injected into incipient fractures provide evidence of contemporaneous seismicity (13).

Late Viséan-early Namurian
On-going tectonic activity prolonged the subsidence history of the Kilskeery Group sedimentary basin in the Fintona Block and initiated subsidence of a separate basin in which the Greenan Sandstone Formation was deposited. The mid-Carboniferous break in Nova Scotia was the result of dextral transpression and converging basement terranes along a single fault complex (14). It is also evident in Carboniferous sequences offshore west of Ireland (15), in the Midland Valley of Scotland (16), parts of northwest England and in Northern Ireland (10) where it represents a period of regional uplift and non-deposition extending from the mid-Arnsbergian (E2b1 Ammonoid Biozone) to the late Marsdenian.

Late Namurian-Westphalian B (early Duckmantian)
After the mid-Carboniferous break, sediments of the coal-bearing and alluvial plain red-bed facies associations accumulated at Coalisland and in the Fintona Block respectively. Renewed strike-slip on the Omagh Thrust Fault induced uplift and erosion of the Central Highlands (Grampian) Terrane. South of the fault a new pull-apart basin (Figure 8.8) received at least 1200m of alluvial fan volcaniclastic boulder conglomerate and coarse-grained sandstone of the Drumlish Conglomerate Formation. An identical sequence of events in northeast Canada was produced by a combination of dextral transtension and transpression (14).

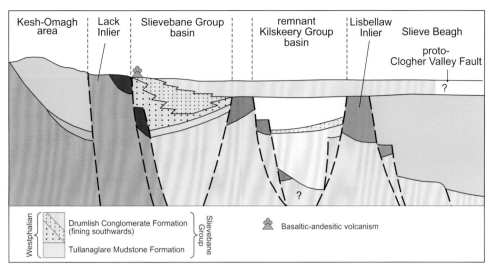

Figure 8.8
Simplified cross-section of the Carboniferous depositional basin in the Westphalian A/B.

Post-Westphalian B

Carboniferous rocks of this age are unknown in Northern Ireland. The dating of unfossiliferous clastic rocks that rest unconformably on the Carboniferous in Co. Tyrone as 'early Permian' is based only on their occurrence below the Late Permian 'Magnesian Limestone'. Nevertheless the end-Variscan deformation occurred in the 15Ma period between the late Carboniferous (post-Duckmantian) and Early Permian and gave rise to the Variscan Mountain chain (Figure 8.9).

The strongest Variscan deformation affected the Greenan Sandstone Formation and Slievebane Group (Figure 8.2), adjacent to the Castle Archdale Fault-Omagh Thrust Fault Zone (18). The destruction of the original sedimentary basins of both units, in particular the

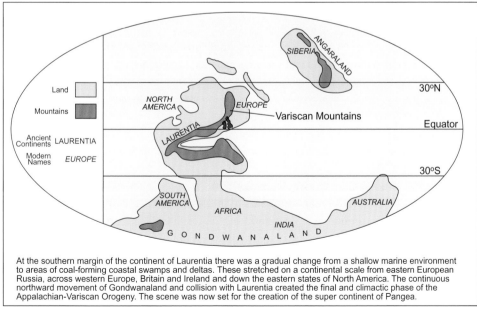

At the southern margin of the continent of Laurentia there was a gradual change from a shallow marine environment to areas of coal-forming coastal swamps and deltas. These stretched on a continental scale from eastern European Russia, across western Europe, Britain and Ireland and down the eastern states of North America. The continuous northward movement of Gondwanaland and collision with Laurentia created the final and climactic phase of the Appalachian-Variscan Orogeny. The scene was now set for the creation of the super continent of Pangea.

Figure 8.9
Position of the continents in the late Carboniferous (c. 300Ma (17)).

Westphalian basin, occurred late in the Variscan Orogenic Cycle with the result that the strata remaining in their respective outcrops are only about 550m and 1200m thick. During the end-Variscan period of dextral transpression the remaining strata of both the Greenan Sandstone Formation and the Slievebane Group were located in the footwall of the Omagh Thrust Fault. Clockwise rotation of bedding to the vertical was the result of footwall drag induced by oblique, dextral overthrusting to the southeast on the Omagh Thrust Fault (Figure 8.3). It is estimated that Dalradian rocks located at the southern margin of the Central Highlands (Grampian) Terrane were thus transported at least 10km to the southeast over the Midland Valley Terrane (Tyrone Igneous Complex). Southeasterly-directed thrusting also affects strata in the footwall of the Clogher Valley Fault (Figure 8.2).

By the Early Permian, a change in the regional stress system in Northern Ireland produced northwest-southeast trending rift basins. Permian rocks below the 'Magnesian Limestone' are always thin at outcrop indicating deposition marginal to the main depocentres. In contrast, the Larne No. 2 borehole encountered over 1000m of Early Permian sedimentary and contemporaneous volcanic rock (19).

References

1) Leeder, M. R. 1982. Upper Palaeozoic basins of the British Isles - Caledonian inheritance versus Hercynian plate margin processes. *Journal of the Geological Society* (London), **139**, 481-94.

2) Read, W. A. 1988. Controls on Silesian sedimentation in the Midland Valley of Scotland. *In*: Besley, B. M. and Kelling, G. (eds.). *Sedimentation in a synorogenic basin complex: the Upper Carboniferous of Northwest Europe.* Blackie, Glasgow and London, 222-41.

3) Gill, W. D. 1962. The Variscan foldbelt in Ireland. *In*: Coe, K. (ed.). *Some aspects of the Variscan Foldbelt*, 49-64.

4) Millar, G. 1990. Fracturing style in the Northwest Carboniferous Basin, Ireland. Unpublished Ph.D thesis, Queens University, Belfast.

5) Wilson, H. E., 1972. Regional Geology of Northern Ireland. Geological Survey of Northern Ireland. Belfast: Her Majesty's Stationery Office.

6) Sevastopulo, G. D., 1981. Hercynian structures. *In*: Holland, C. H. (ed.). *A Geology of Ireland*. Edinburgh: Scottish Academic Press, 189-99.

7) Philcox, M. E., 1989. The mid-Dinantian unconformity at Navan, Ireland. *In*: Arthurton, R. S., Gutteridge, P. and Nolan, S. C. (eds.). *The role of tectonics in Devonian and Carboniferous sedimentation in the British Isles.* The Yorkshire Geological Society, 67-81.

8) Earls, G., Hutton, D. W., Wilkinson, J., Moles, N., Fallick, A. and Boyce, A. 1996. The Gold Metallogeny of Northwest Northern Ireland. Geological Survey of Northern Ireland Technical Report GSNI/96/6.

9) Mitchell, W. I. and Owens, B. 1990. The geology of the western part of the Fintona Block, Northern Ireland-evolution of Carboniferous basins. *Geological Magazine*, **127**, 407-26.

10) Mitchell, W. I. 1992. The origin of Upper Palaeozoic sedimentary basins in Northern Ireland and relationships with the Canadian Maritime Provinces. *In*: Parnell, J. (ed.). *Basins on the Atlantic Seaboard: Petroleum Geology, Sedimentology and Basin Evolution*. Special Publication of the Geological Society, London, **62**, 191-202.

11) Woodcock, N. H. and Fischer, M. 1986. Strike-slip duplexes. *Journal of Structural Geology*, **8**, 725-35.

12) Brandon, A. and Hodson, F. 1984. *The Stratigraphy and Palaeontology of the late Viséan and early Namurian rocks of north-east Connaught*. Geological Survey of Ireland Special Paper, **6**.

13) Legg, I. C., Johnston, T. P., Mitchell, W. I. and Smith, R. A. 1998. Geology of the country around Derrygonnelly and Marble Arch. *Memoir of the Geological Survey of Northern Ireland*, Sheet 44, 56 and 43 (Northern Ireland).

14) Calder, J. H. 1998. The Carboniferous evolution of Nova Scotia. *In*: Blundell, D. J. and Scott, A. C. (eds.). *Lyell: the Past is the Key to the Present*. Special Publication of the Geological Society, London, **143**, 261-302.

15) Tate, M. P. and Dobson, M. R. 1989. Pre-Mesozoic geology of the western and northwestern Irish continental shelf. *Journal of the Geological Society, London*, **146**, 229-41.

16) Read, W. A. 1989. The interplay of sedimentation, volcanicity and tectonics in the Passage Group (Arnsbergian, E_2 to Westphalian A) in the Midland Valley of Scotland. *In*: Arthurton, R. S., Gutteridge, P. and Nolan, S. C. (eds.). *The role of tectonics in Devonian and Carboniferous sedimentation in the British Isles*. The Yorkshire Geological Society, 143-52.

17) Osborne, R. and Tarling, D. H. 1995. *The Historical Atlas of the Earth (A Visual Exploration of the Earth's Physical Past)*. Viking. Penguin Books Ltd., London.

18) Geological Survey of Northern Ireland 1995. Omagh, Northern Ireland Sheet 33. Solid Geology. 1:50,000. (Keyworth, Nottingham: British Geological Survey).

19) Penn, I. E., Holliday, D. W., Kirby, G. A., Kubala, M., Sobey, R. A., Mitchell, W. I., Harrison, R. K.and Beckinsale, R. D. 1983. The Larne No. 2 Borehole: discovery of a new Permian volcanic centre. *Scottish Journal of Geology*, **19**, 333-46.

Chapter 9

Permian

W. I. MITCHELL

Introduction

After continental collision during the Variscan Orogeny, northwest Europe lay in equatorial latitudes within the Pangean supercontinent (Figure 9.1A) during the Permian and Triassic (1). In Northern Ireland, while Carboniferous stress fields were influenced by northeast-southwest-trending Caledonian structures, the Early Permian is the first time that the effects of North Atlantic rifting can be detected. Permian rocks only crop out south of the Highland Border Ridge (Figure 9.2). The succession consists of the **Enler Group** at the base, consisting of coarse, clastic rocks, overlain by the **Belfast Group**, which is divided into a calcareous unit ('Magnesian Limestone') and the succeeding unit of fine-grained clastic rocks with evaporites (Table 9.1).

In the western part of Northern Ireland near Cookstown, the exposed, but attenuated, Permian basal clastic sequence represents a regolith that developed in an area of relative uplift. Beneath the Antrim Plateau in Co. Antrim, the discovery of a thick Permian volcanogenic succession in deep boreholes demonstrated the existence of contemporaneous

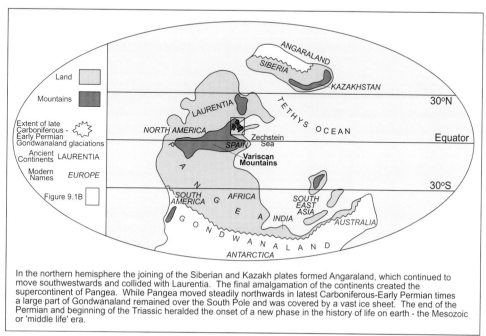

In the northern hemisphere the joining of the Siberian and Kazakh plates formed Angaraland, which continued to move southwestwards and collided with Laurentia. The final amalgamation of the continents created the supercontinent of Pangea. While Pangea moved steadily northwards in latest Carboniferous-Early Permian times a large part of Gondwanaland remained over the South Pole and was covered by a vast ice sheet. The end of the Permian and beginning of the Triassic heralded the onset of a new phase in the history of life on earth - the Mesozoic or 'middle life' era.

Figure 9.1A
Position of the continents in the Late Permian (c. 260Ma (1)).

discrete, fault-bounded, basins, separated by areas of higher ground. The Late Permian **'Magnesian Limestone'** occurs in all outcrops and deep boreholes and has been formally renamed the Belfast Harbour Evaporite Formation in Northern Ireland. It was deposited during a marine transgression (Figure 9.1B) which signified the end of the erosion and rapid peneplanation of the Variscan Mountains and of earlier episodes of basin subsidence. Based on the abundance of gastropods and bivalves, a tentative correlation has been proposed (2) with the 'Lower Magnesian Limestone' EZ1 Cycle in eastern England (3).

In the Early Permian, sedimentation in Northern Ireland occurred primarily in an arid, hot, desert environment. However, in the Late Permian (Figure 9.1B) a southwards migrating transgression created the Bakevellia Sea in which the 'Magnesian Limestone' was deposited (4). Palaeontological evidence from Co. Tyrone indicates two cycles of marine transgression causing a reintroduction of a benthic assemblage (5). However, at Cultra (Figure 9.2) despite evidence of up to three carbonate-evaporite cycles, Late Permian sedimentation patterns are variable due to the proximity of contemporary shorelines, the migration of marginal marine facies and influence of local tectonism (6).

Stratigraphy
Belfast Lough
The Permian outcrop at Cultra (Figure 9.3), the most extensive in Northern Ireland, comprises about 13m of strata (7) with the Permian section in the Belfast Harbour borehole (6) nearly 135m thick (Table 9.2). Fossils are rare in the **Belfast Harbour Evaporite Formation** in the borehole. At Cultra, the Magnesian Limestone consists of 9m of yellow, coarse-grained dolomite but cannot be assigned to one particular member in the Belfast

Figure 9.1B
Palaeogeographic reconstruction of Ireland and Britain in the Late Permian (4).

		Stage	Lithostratigraphy
Jurassic	Early	Pliensbachian	Waterloo Mudstone Formation
		Sinemurian	
		Hettangian	
Triassic	Late	Rhaetian	Penarth Group
		Norian	Mercia Mudstone Group
		Carnian	
	Mid-	Ladinian	
		Anisian	
	Early (Scythian)	Olenekian	Sherwood Sandstone Group
		Induan	? ?
Permian	Late / Lopingian	Changhsingian	Belfast Group
		Wuchiapingian	? ?
	Middle / Guadalupian	Capitanian	
		Wordian	
		Roadian	? ?
	Early / Cisuralian	Kungurian	Enler Group
		Artinskian	? ?
		Sakmarian	
		Asselian	
	Carboniferous (Stephanian)		

Table 9.1
Litho- and chronostratigraphy of the Permian, Triassic and Jurassic rocks.

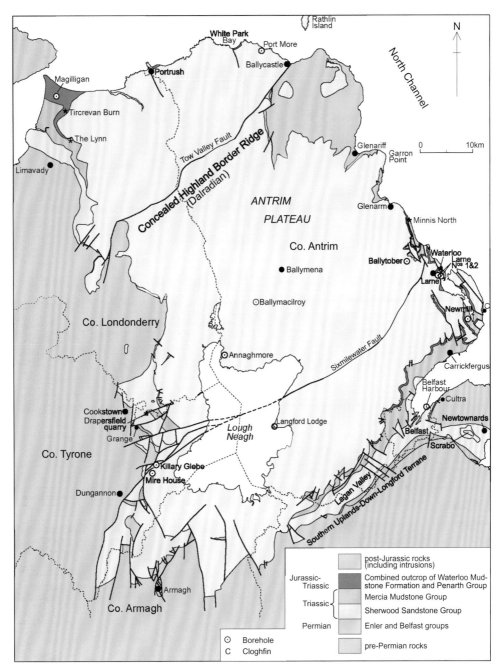

Figure 9.2
Distribution of Permian, Triassic and Jurassic rocks in northeast Northern Ireland.

Harbour Evaporite Formation (Table 9.2). At Cultra, shells are either dispersed or occur in layers up to 0.3m thick composed of the bivalve *Bakevellia (B.) binneyi* and gastropods. The junction with the succeeding **Connswater Marl Formation** is sharp and conformable (Photograph 1).

During the Early Permian, rivers draining high ground on the Southern Uplands-Down-Longford Terrane (Figure 1.4) deposited clastic detritus (Enler Group) on alluvial fans. The overlapping Late Permian marine transgression initially deposited fine-grained sandstone and siltstone of the **Musgrave Clastic Member**. Succeeding carbonate beds accumulated on

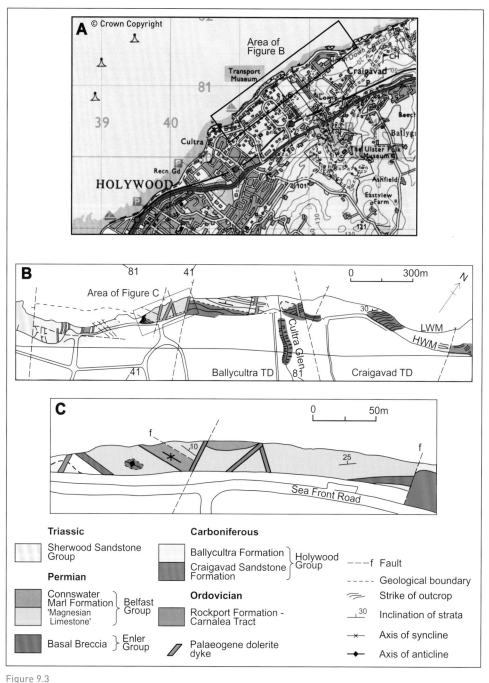

Figure 9.3
Geology of the Cultra foreshore, north Co. Down; **A.** location map (1:50 000 Ordnance Survey sheet 15),
B. geological map of the Carboniferous and Permian outcrop (7),
C. detailed geological map of the Permian outcrop.

a coastal fringe with fluctuating water depths and salinity. Near-shore shoals of oolitic and
shelly carbonate sands protected areas of algal mat and laminated micrite mud on a
sabkha. Hot, evaporitic climatic conditions resulted in the crystallisation of primary
anhydrite, gypsum and halite. Sediment of the Connswater Marl Formation washed from
the early Palaeozoic landmass that still basked in a hot arid climate.

128

Photograph 1
The Permian outcrop at Cultra and the contact between the 'Magnesian Limestone' (foreground) and the Connswater Marl Formation ('Permian Upper Marls'). Southeast side of Belfast Lough [J412 809] at Cultra, Co. Down. (Hammer 36cm long).

Newtownards

Permian rocks are exposed at only one locality in this area but the succession is established in boreholes (8). The rocks were deposited in the Newtownards trough and show lithological differences with the adjacent Belfast area (9). The rocks consist entirely of coarse clastic and argillaceous lithologies and, in the absence of a correlative of the Magnesian Limestone, are undated (Figure 9.4).

				Previous Nomenclature (2,6)	Belfast Harbour Borehole (6)	
					Formation	Member (and lithology)
Permian	Late	Lopingian	Belfast Group	'Permian Upper Marls'	Connswater Marl (95m)	Siltstone and mudstone, red, calcareous, thin evaporites at base
				'Magnesian Limestone'	Belfast Harbour Evaporite (36m)	'B' Anhydrite Member
						Refinery Breccia Member
						'A' Anhydrite Member
						Airport Oolite Member
						Jetty Banded Limestone Member
						Shorts Micrite Member
						Harland Micrite Member
						Wolff Micrite Member
				'Silty Dolomite'		Musgrave Clastic Member
	Early?	?	Enler Group	'Basal Breccia'	Carnamuck (3.5m)	Sandstone, pink brown and yellow, medium- to coarse-grained; thin breccia; thin siltstone and mudstone, dark red-brown
					Coolbeg Breccia (3.5m)	Angular fragments of greywacke, siltstone, rare vein quartz and micrite; sandstone, red-brown, coarse-grained

Table 9.2
Divisions of the Permian rocks in the Belfast area.

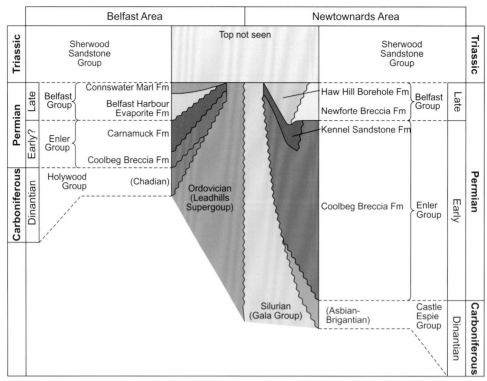

Figure 9.4
Comparative vertical sections of the Permian rocks in the Belfast and Newtownards areas of Co. Down (9).

East Co. Tyrone

The poorly exposed Permian outcrop at Grange (Figure 9.2) is better known from boreholes and consists of three units (10). The **'Basal Sands'**, 0.1-7.8m of reddish brown pebbly sandstone, the fossiliferous (bivalves, gastropods and bryozoa) **'Magnesian Limestone'** (18-23m) with a lower dolomitic siltstone overlain by dolomitic and oolitic limestone and the **'Permian Upper Marls'**, less than 10m thick.

Group		Formation	Lithology
Triassic	Sherwood Sandstone	Derrycreevy Sandstone	Sandstone, fine- to medium-grained, siltstone and mudstone, reddish brown; ripples, bioturbation
		Milltown Conglomerate	Conglomerate, grey, small pebbles and sandstone, reddish purple, coarse-grained, thin beds
Permian	Belfast	'Magnesian Limestone'	(Not exposed): "soft, grey, sandy limey rock"
	Enler	Dobbin Sandstone	(Not exposed): "sandstone, soft, red, fine-grained, micaceous"
		Drumarg Conglomerate	Conglomerate, pinkish purple, crudely bedded, clasts of local Carboniferous limestone, rare vein quartz and red sandstone, coarse-grained

Table 9.3
Lithostratigraphy of the Permian and Triassic rocks at Armagh (9).

Armagh

Information on the unfossiliferous Permian rocks in this outlier (Figure 9.2, Table 9.3), is mostly from boreholes (11). A Permian age is unsubstantiated and is based on the historical identification of the 'Magnesian Limestone'. The only exposure is of 3.5m of the **Drumarg Conglomerate Formation** on the west side of the Keady Road [H871 439], south of Armagh. The outcrop of presumed Triassic rocks is confined to the northern edge of the outlier but other exposures of the constituent formations do occur in the main Triassic outcrop in north Co. Armagh.

Larne No. 2 borehole

At least 1265m of Permian strata (12) are recorded in the borehole (Figure 9.5). The lowest strata of the Enler Group, the **Inver Volcanic Formation** (13), consist of about 60m of breccio-conglomerate and sandstone overlain by 554m of heavily altered lavas and tuffs. Though difficult to classify petrographically they range from basaltic to trachyandesitic and trachytic (14). It has been suggested (14) that the source of the Larne lavas, and the other trachyte-dominated lava centre within the Midland Valley of Scotland in East Lothian, are located over a sub-surface extension of the Southern Upland Fault. They are overlain by 440m of arenaceous sediments of the **Ballytober Sandstone Formation**.

The overlying Belfast Group is divided into the 'Magnesian Limestone Formation' (14m) that has a 6m bed of anhydrite at the top and **White Brae Mudstone Formation** (13), which includes a 113m thick halite at its base. A miospore assemblage (15) including *Lueckisporites virkkiae* (Fossil 1) and *Perisaccus granulosus* (Fossil 2) indicates a Wordian (Middle Permian, Guadalupian) to Late Permian (Lopingian) age (Table 9.1). The precise position of the Permian-Triassic system boundary in Northern Ireland is not known.

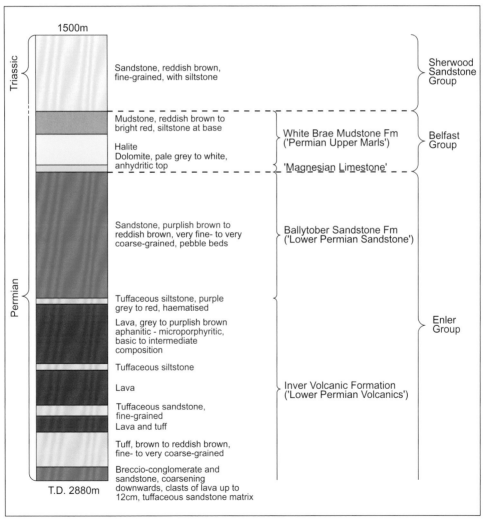

Figure 9.5
Detailed lithostratigraphy of the Permian section in the Larne No.2 borehole (12).

North Co. Antrim

At the base of the Portmore borehole, north of the Tow Valley Fault (Figure 10.2), unfossiliferous conglomeratic sandstone (51m) is succeeded by dolomitic mudstone and siltstone (14m). These rocks probably correlate with the Enler Group and may be Early Permian.

After the transitory marine transgression, in which the Belfast Group was deposited, continental conditions became the major control on Late Permian and Triassic climates in northwest Europe.

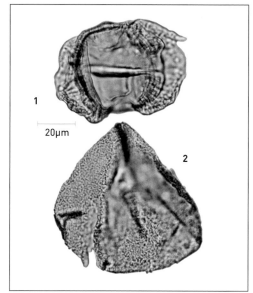

Fossils 1-2
Late Permian (Lopingian) miospores from the Larne No. 2 borehole:
1 *Lueckisporites virkkiae*
2 *Perisaccus granulosus*

References

1) Osborne, R. and Tarling, D. H. 1995. The Historical Atlas of the Earth (A Visual Exploration of the Earth's Physical Past). Viking. Penguin Books Ltd., London.

2) Smith, D. B., Brunstrom, R. G. W., Manning, P. I., Simpson, S. and Shotton, F. W. 1974. A correlation of Permian rocks in the British Isles. *Journal of the Geological Society of London*, **30**, 1-45.

3) Smith, D. B., Harwood, G. M., Pattison, J and Pettigrew, T. H. 1986. A revised nomenclature for Upper Permian strata in eastern England. *In*: Harwood, G. M and Smith, D. B. (eds.). *The English Zechstein and Related Topics.* Special Publication of the Geological Society, London, No. **22**, 9-17.

4) Ziegler, P. A. 1990. *Geological Atlas of Western and Central Europe. 2nd Edition* (completely revised), 239 pp + 54 enclosures. Shell Internationale Petroleum Maatschappij B. V, The Hague, Netherlands.

5) Pattison, J. 1970. A review of the marine fossils from the Upper Permian rocks of Northern Ireland and north-west England. *Bulletin of the Geological Survey of Great Britain*, **32**, 123-65.

6) Smith, R. A. 1986. Permo-Triassic and Dinantian rocks of the Belfast Harbour Borehole. *Report of the British Geological Survey*, **18**, No. 6.

7) Griffith A. E. and Wilson, H. E. 1982. *Geology of the country around Carrickfergus and Bangor.* Memoir of the Geological Survey of Northern Ireland, Sheet 29 (Northern Ireland).

8) Smith, R. A., Johnston, T. P. and Legg, I. C. 1991. Geology of the country around Newtownards. *Memoir of the Geological Survey of Northern Ireland*, Sheet 37 and part of sheet 38 (Northern Ireland).

9) Geological Survey of Northern Ireland 1989. Newtownards, Northern Ireland Sheet 37 and part of sheet 38. Solid Geology. 1:50,000. (Southampton: Ordnance Survey for the Geological Survey of Northern Ireland).

10) Fowler, A. and Robbie, J. A. 1961. Geology of the country around Dungannon. *Memoir of the Geological Survey of Northern Ireland*, Sheet 35 (Northern Ireland).

11) Geological Survey of Northern Ireland 1985. Armagh, Northern Ireland Sheet 47. Solid Geology. 1:50,000. (Southampton: Ordnance Survey for the Geological Survey of Northern Ireland).

12) Penn, I. E., Holliday, D. W., Kirby, G. A., Kubala, M., Sobey, R. A., Mitchell, W. I., Harrison, R. K. and Beckinsale, R. D. 1983. The Larne No. 2 Borehole: discovery of a new Permian volcanic centre. *Scottish Journal of Geology*, **19**, 333-46.

13) Geological Survey of Northern Ireland 2001. Ballymena, Northern Ireland Sheet 20. Solid Geology. 1:50,000. (Keyworth, Nottingham: British Geological Survey).

14) Harrison, R. K., Styles, M. T., Penn, I. E. and Davis, A. E. 1985. Petrology of Lower Permian volcanic rocks from the Larne No. 2 (Geothermal) Borehole, Co. Antrim, Northern Ireland. Report of the British Geological Survey, **17**, No. 6.

15) Warrington, G. 1995. The Permian, Triassic and Jurassic in Northern Ireland: a palynological study with special reference to the hydrocarbon prospectivity of the Larne-Lough Neagh Basin. *Geological Survey of Northern Ireland Technical Report* GSNI/95/7.

Chapter 10

Triassic

W. I. MITCHELL

Introduction

The supercontinent of Pangea continued to exist into the Triassic (Figure 10.1) (1).
Triassic rocks in Northern Ireland (Figure 9.2) overstep the Permian basin margins and rest
unconformably on older basement including the Dalradian and the early Palaeozoic rocks of
the Southern Uplands-Down-Longford Terrane. Sedimentation appears to have been
continuous across the Permian system boundary but the rocks are undated. Thus, for
convenience, the base of the Triassic is equated with the base of the Sherwood Sandstone
Group (Table 9.1). The Triassic rocks are divided into the Sherwood Sandstone Group
(formerly the 'Bunter Sandstone'), the Mercia Mudstone Group (formerly the 'Keuper Marl')
and the Penarth Group (formerly the 'Rhaetic'). The latter is succeeded conformably by the
Waterloo Mudstone Formation which, although largely Early Jurassic, is latest Triassic at
the base.

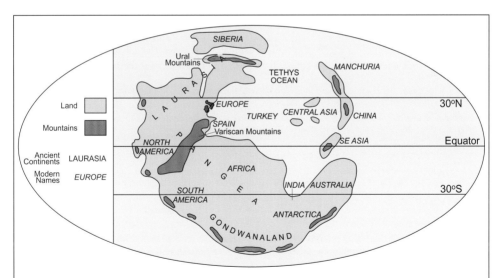

At this time all the major continents were locked together in the supercontinent of Pangea. Clockwise rotation of
Pangea moved eastern Gondwanaland, incorporating Australia, Antarctica and India, into southern latitudes while the
western part, including Africa and North America, moved into northern latitudes. This landmass remained above sea
level for most of the Triassic and was the site for the accumulation of red continental desert deposits. Transitory
marine incursions at its margins affected Ireland and Britain and were responsible for the formation of thick evaporite
deposits of salt. Towards the end of the Triassic Pangea had started to break-up and, for the first time, the new
arrangement of the continents began to resemble their present configuration.

Figure 10.1
Position of the continents in the Early Triassic (c. 250Ma (1))

Sherwood Sandstone Group

The Group consists of red-bed sediments, mainly pink to reddish brown sandstone and silty sandstone with brown mudstone accounting for up to one-third of the total thickness. Sedimentary structures include ripples, low to medium convolute and planar cross laminations (Photograph 1), mudflakes, rain pits and desiccation cracks. The common occurrence of well-rounded (millet seed) sand grains suggests the influence of aeolian deposition. The Group is up to 648m thick at Larne, about 300m in the Lagan Valley and east Co.Tyrone, thins northwards to about 30m on the Dalradian Highland Border Ridge and reaches over 500m in the north, at Ballycastle (Port More borehole) and in the Magilligan borehole. Near the base of the Group is a unit up to 9m thick consisting of pink, cross-bedded, oolitic limestone and calcareous sandstone which is interbedded in the red sandstones (Photograph 2). This is exposed in Drapersfield quarry [H841 767], east of Cookstown (2) but has also been encountered in many of the deep boreholes drilled in the Triassic succession in Northern Ireland. The oolitic rocks represent a fluviatile facies.

In the Ballycastle area of north Co. Antrim the Port More borehole (Figure 10.2) encountered over 500m of the Sherwood Sandstone Group consisting mainly of reddish sandstone and pebbly sandstone, layers up to 12m thick of brown mudstone and a 78m thick conglomerate (3). Across Northern Ireland a conglomerate usually represents the base of the Sherwood Sandstone Group where it rests unconformably on older basement rocks. In Co. Armagh, up to 25m of small pebble conglomerate rests unconformably on Carboniferous and early Palaeozoic rocks.

No stratigraphically useful macrofossils are found in the Sherwood

Photograph 1
Parallel and cross-stratified sandstones of the Sherwood Sandstone Group. Scrabo Hill [J477 727], 2km SSW of Newtownards, Co. Down. (Hammer length 33cm).

Photograph 2
Pink, cross-stratified, calcareous sandstone and oolitic limestone representing the lower part of the Sherwood Sandstone Group, overlain by reddish brown sandstone and siltstone. Drapersfield quarry [H841 767], 3km ESE of Cookstown, Co. Tyrone.

Photograph 3
East side of Scrabo Hill from the A21 Newtownards-Comber road, 1.5km south of Newtownards, Co. Down.

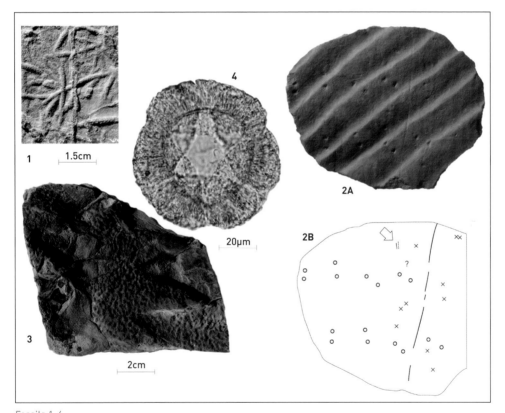

Fossils 1-4
Early to Mid-Triassic fossils from the Sherwood Sandstone Group at Scrabo in Co. Down (1-3) and from the Langford Lodge borehole (4):
(1) Ichnofauna: *Planolites beverleyensis*; horizontal, cross-cutting, endostratal burrows.
(2) Arthropod trackways: **A** Sandstone with asymmetric ripples and 'arthropod trackways';
B Explanatory sketch: crosses are of a Type 1 'large arthropod trackway', with imprints centred around a discontinuous sinuous groove, representing the movement of an arachnid, probably a scorpion; open circles are imprints from a Type 2 'large arthropod trackway' possibly produced by a scorpion. The arrow indicates a 'small arthropod trackway' of unknown affinity.
(3) Vertebrate footprint: *Chirotherium* sp.; of reptilian origin the tuburculated appearance of the print is of a secondary nature and does not represent hide markings.
(4) Miospore: *Stellapollenites thiergartii*

135

Sandstone Group. However, a diverse, non-marine ichnofauna has been reported (4) from Scrabo, near Newtownards (Photograph 3) (5) including invertebrate trace fossils (Fossil 1), 'small and large arthropod (scorpion) trackways' (Fossil 2) and the unique occurrence of a reptilian footprint, possibly of *Chirotherium* (Fossil 3). Near Dungannon in Co. Tyrone, the sandstones contain the crustacean *Euestheria* and, at one locality (6), examples of the fish *Palaeoniscus catopterus*.

The Triassic age of the Sherwood Sandstone Group is based on sparse miospore assemblages. In the Larne No. 2 borehole *Cycloverrutriletes presselensis* indicates a late Early Triassic (Olenekian) age for the middle and upper parts of the Group (Table 9.1). The presence of *Stellapollenites thiergartii* (Fossil 4) near the top of the Group in the Langford Lodge borehole indicates an early Mid-Triassic (Anisian) age (7).

Depositional environment

The Sherwood Sandstone Group was deposited in hot, continental conditions, mainly by fluviatile processes representing channel and overbank floodplain and lacustrine environments. Although the large-scale foresets at Scrabo developed as sand dunes dunefield sedimentary structures are relatively scarce elsewhere in the Group. Nevertheless aeolian conditions did prevail during deposition of the sandstones and provided the millet seed grains in fluviatile sediments. Conglomerates represent migrating channel deposits in a braided stream environment. The presence of desiccation cracks and breccias comprising curled flakes of mudstone is evidence for the existence of shallow lakes that periodically dried out.

Mercia Mudstone Group

The six formations of the Mercia Mudstone Group (Figure 10.2) were originally defined in the Port More borehole and overall consist of calcareous, reddish to brown mudstone and thin, laminated, micaceous siltstone that weather to a brick red colour (3). Sandstone is common only in the basal Lagavarra Formation, the transitional unit from the underlying Sherwood Sandstone Group. In higher formations sandstone is restricted to beds up to 2.5m thick, in the past called "skerries", such as the Suitcase Sandstone and Coolmaghra Skerry, which are typically hard, fine-grained, pale greenish white to buff and often dolomitic.

The maximum thickness of about 1030m attained by the Group in Northern Ireland is based on the combined sections recorded in the Larne No. 1 and No. 2 boreholes. At Larne (Figure 10.2) the Group includes 400m of halite beds (8) that are only 40m thick at Carrickfergus (Figure 9.2). Elsewhere the maximum thickness of the Group in boreholes is 620m at Port More (3, 9), 492m at Ballymacilroy, 315m at Langford Lodge and 122m at Killary Glebe (Figure 9.2). The presence of nodular anhydrite, gypsum and pseudomorphs after halite is evidence of an evaporitic depositional environment. Sedimentary structures in the lowest three formations and in the topmost Collin Glen Formation include rhythmic laminations, load casts, flame structures, oscillation ripples and desiccation cracks. In contrast, these structures are rare in the massive mudstones of the Knocksoghey and Port More formations. Although the main outcrop of this Group is on the north side of the Lagan Valley at Belfast, exposures also occur on the east coast of Co. Antrim as far north as Glenariff and, in Co. Londonderry, north and east of Limavady (10).

At the top of the Mercia Mudstone Group is the **Collin Glen Formation** (formerly the 'Tea Green Marls'). Alternating red and green mudstone about 1m thick at the base are succeeded by up to 10m of pale greyish green silty mudstone with thin beds of

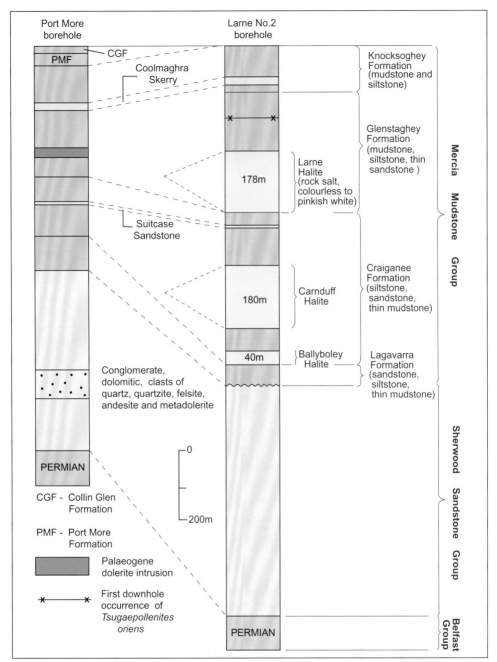

Figure 10.2
Comparative lithostratigraphy of the Triassic rocks in the Port More and Lame No.2 boreholes (for location of boreholes see Figure 9.2).

autobrecciated micrite. At Waterloo (Figure 9.2), the top 50m of mudstone of the Mercia Mudstone Group, including part of the Knocksoghey Formation and the Port More and Collin Glen formations, has been metasomatised and altered to a green colour with abundant pea-sized pseudo-pisoliths and pseudo-ooliths. The Mercia Mudstone Group is succeeded abruptly by grey and black mudstones of the Penarth Group.

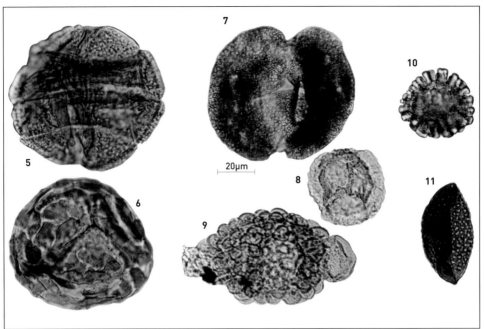

Fossils 5-11
Mid- to Late Triassic (Anisian-Carnian) miospores from the Mercia Mudstone Group in the
Larne No. 2 borehole: **5** *Guttulapollenites hannonicus*, **6** *Verrucosisporites thuringiacus*,
7 *Angustisulcites gorpii*, **8** *Perotriletes minor*, **9** *Tsugaepollenites oriens*, **10** *Echinitosporites iliacoides*,
11 *Retisulcites perforatus*.

The age of the Mercia Mudstone Group is determined from miospore assemblages
recorded from deep boreholes (Table 9.1). The assemblages (Fossils 5-11), of early Mid-
Triassic (Anisian) age, from the Larne No. 2 borehole (7) occur in the **Lagavarra, Craiganee**
and **Glenstaghey formations**. The top beds of the Glenstaghey Formation and the
Knocksoghey Formation also contain miospores (Fossils 10 and 11) of Ladinian (late Mid-
Triassic) to Carnian (early Late Triassic) age. The **Collin Glen Formation** contains rare fossils
including fish debris and the crustacean *Euestheria*.

Penarth Group

Regional uplift and erosion in the post-Early Jurassic and pre-Cretaceous confines the
Penarth Group to rare exposures at the margins of the Antrim Plateau (Figure 9.2).
Correlation has been made with similar sequences in England (Table 10.1). The Penarth
Group at Larne rests disconformably on rocks of the Mercia Mudstone Group (Photograph 4)
and is conformably succeeded by the Waterloo Mudstone Formation. In the Magilligan
borehole the contact between the Penarth Group and Waterloo Mudstone Formation is a
non-sequence. The thickness of the **Penarth Group** varies from 25.4m (11) in the Magilligan
borehole to 20m in the Larne No. 1 borehole (12).

In the Larne No. 1 borehole the **Westbury Formation** (Table 10.1) consists of about 8.5m
of black and dark grey shaley mudstone with silty laminae and a thin sandstone (12).
Identical rocks in the faulted lower part of the Waterloo section (13) (Figure 10.3) contain
diagnostic bivalves including *Rhaetavicula contorta* (Fossil 12). The base of this section is a
thin bed of sandstone and includes fish teeth and scales that occur through the rock
sequence. In the Larne No. 1 borehole the succeeding rocks of the **Lilstock Formation**
(Table 10.1) commence with the **Cotham Member** which consists of about 5m of

Photograph 4
The Waterloo foreshore near Larne showing the Collin Glen Formation (Mercia Mudstone Group) in foreground overlain by the Penarth Group.

	Group	Formation	Member
Jurassic	Lias	Waterloo Mudstone	
			'Pre-planorbis beds'
Triassic	Penarth	Lilstock	Langport
			Cotham
		Westbury	

Table 10.1
Detailed lithostratigraphy of the Late Triassic (Rhaetian) and Jurassic rocks.

fossiliferous brown and grey mudstones with a distinctive striped appearance caused by siltstone laminae. Above the Cotham Member, and below the base of the succeeding *Pre-planorbis* beds, the **Langport Member** comprises about 7m of dark grey calcareous micaceous mudstone with bivalves, laminae of siltstone with desiccation cracks and cross laminations and thin beds of micritic limestone.

The top of the Mercia Mudstone Group and most of the Penarth Group were exposed in the gorge of The Lynn [C709 278], near Limavady (11). The section at Cloghfin exposes rocks, with the exception of Jurassic strata, between the top of the Mercia Mudstone Group and the Glenarm Chalk Member of the Late Cretaceous Ulster White Limestone Formation.

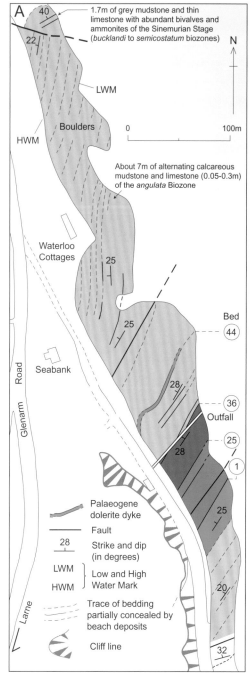

A — 40

1.7m of grey mudstone and thin limestone with abundant bivalves and ammonites of the Sinemurian Stage (*bucklandi* to *semicostatum* biozones)

N

LWM

Boulders

0   100m

HWM

About 7m of alternating calcareous mudstone and limestone (0.05-0.3m) of the *angulata* Biozone

Waterloo Cottages

25

Road

Glenarm

Seabank

28

25

25

Bed

28

44

36

Outfall

25

1

28

25

Larne

20

Palaeogene dolerite dyke

Fault

28   Strike and dip (in degrees)

LWM
HWM   } Low and High Water Mark

Trace of bedding partially concealed by beach deposits

Cliff line

32

Figure 10.3 A
Detailed geological map of the Waterloo section near Larne.

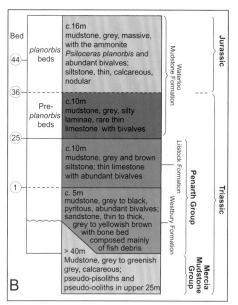

Bed	*planorbis* beds	*c.*16m mudstone, grey, massive, with the ammonite *Psiloceras planorbis* and abundant bivalves; siltstone, thin, calcareous, nodular	Waterloo Mudstone Formation / Jurassic
44			
36	Pre-*planorbis* beds	*c.*10m mudstone, grey, silty laminae, rare thin limestone with bivalves	
25			Lilstock Formation / Penarth Group / Triassic
1		*c.*10m mudstone, grey and brown siltstone; thin limestone with abundant bivalves	
		c. 5m mudstone, grey to black, pyritous, abundant bivalves; sandstone, thin to thick, grey to yellowish brown with bone bed composed mainly of fish debris	Westbury Formation
		> 40m Mudstone, grey to greenish grey, calcareous; pseudo-pisoliths and pseudo-ooliths in upper 25m	Mercia Mudstone Group
B			

Figure 10.3 B
Description of the main lithological divisions

1cm

Fossil 12
Late Triassic (Rhaetian) bivalve
(12) *Rhaetavicula contorta* from the Penarth Group at Waterloo, Co. Antrim.

Waterloo Mudstone Formation

The succession of conformable strata at the Triassic-Jurassic boundary (Rhaetian-Hettangian stages) is exposed at Waterloo, near Larne (Figure 10.3) (13). Between the top of the Penarth Group (Rhaetian) and the lowest bed in the Waterloo Mudstone Formation with the ammonite *Psiloceras planorbis* (Chapter 11, Fossil 3), which defines the base of the Jurassic System (Hettangian Stage), are strata with no ammonites that are termed the 'Pre-*planorbis* beds' (Table 10.1). At Waterloo the 'Pre-*planorbis* beds' of the **Waterloo Mudstone Formation** are up to 10m thick.

At the base of the Waterloo Mudstone Formation the Triassic (Rhaetian) age of the **'Pre-*planorbis* beds'** is defined by the composition of miospore assemblages recovered from the Larne No. 1 and Langford Lodge boreholes (14, 15). Between the base and top of these strata the effects of marine transgression cause an overall increase in the numbers of organic-walled marine microplankton relative to land-derived miospores. The presence of the dinoflagellate cyst *Rhaetogonyaulax rhaetica*, the index fossil of the latest Triassic Rr Biozone, in the Westbury and Lilstock formations and in the 'Pre-*planorbis* beds' confirms their Rhaetian age (Table 10.1). The Pre-*planorbis* beds in Northern Ireland predate the *Psiloceras planorbis* Subzone of the Hettangian Stage (Early Jurassic), and are therefore Late Triassic (Rhaetian).

Depositional environment

Arid and semi-arid conditions prevailed in Northern Ireland in Mid-Triassic and early Late Triassic times during deposition of the Mercia Mudstone Group, although the development of thick halite beds requires a marine connection. It is now believed that two different environments existed at this time (16). A lower, halitic, succession, restricted to southeast Co. Antrim, was deposited in a marine environment subjected to periodic desiccation and was succeeded by anhydritic sediments that were deposited on an arid plain, prone to desiccation, in a lacustrine environment or on a sabkha (Figure 10.4).

In the latest Triassic the shallow, hypersaline lagoons in which the sediments of the Collin Glen Formation (Mercia Mudstone Group) were deposited heralded the approach of a marine transgression. At the outset, the succeeding Penarth Group was deposited during a period of fluctuating sea-levels in a shallow epeiric sea in which salinity changes may have caused mass mortality of bivalves and fish faunas. Desiccation cracks in the Langport Member of the Lilstock Formation (Table 10.1) resulted from periodic exposure of the sea bed. With the continued advance of the marine transgression the rocks of the Pre-*planorbis* beds and the remainder of the Waterloo Mudstone Formation were deposited in deeper water, open marine conditions that were established by the end of Rhaetian times and persisted into the Jurassic.

Tectono-depositional model for the Triassic in Northern Ireland

Traditional models of Triassic sedimentation assumed that the transition from coarse- to fine-grained sediments accompanied a decline in the rate of movement on basin bounding syn-sedimentary faults. Thus the largely fluvial Sherwood Sandstone Group possibly consisted of sediment eroded from the remnants of the Variscan Mountains during a phase of syn-rift crustal extension. Sediment was transported by a periodic influx of floodwater from higher ground and deposited in braided river systems and on alluvial fans. The Mercia Mudstone Group was presumed to have been deposited in an evaporitic seaway during a post-rift phase of thermal subsidence (Figure 10.5).

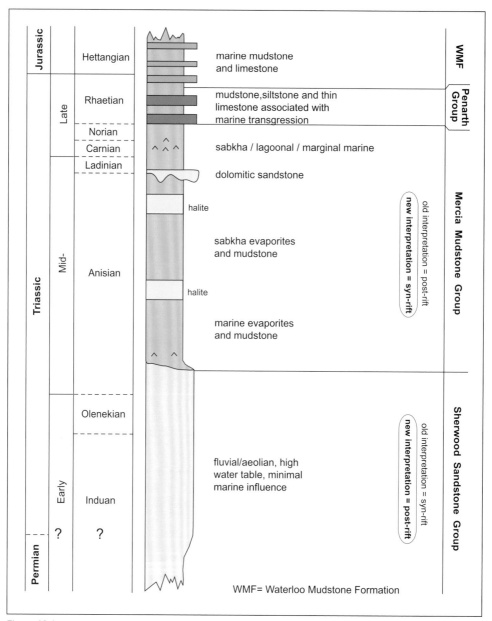

Figure 10.4
Chronostratigraphy, lithostratigraphy and interpretation of the Triassic - Early Jurassic succession in Northern Ireland (17).

However, palynological investigations of deep boreholes in the Larne-Lough Neagh basin revealed thickness variations primarily in the Mercia Mudstone Group (7). Based on the first downhole occurrence of the miospore *Tsugaepollenites oriens* (Fossil 9) the evidence restricts the period of maximum subsidence and sediment accumulation to the early Mid-Triassic (Anisian) Craiganee and Glenstaghey formations. By way of comparison, the post-Sherwood Sandstone Group Triassic rocks at Larne are about 1000m thick of which the Anisian section, including halite units, accounts for 722m and accumulated over a period of about 7Ma. Succeeding Ladinian-Norian rocks are only 285m thick but represent a time span

142

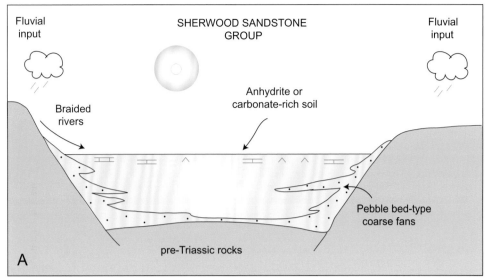

Figure 10.5A
Depositional model for the Sherwood Sandstone Group (17).

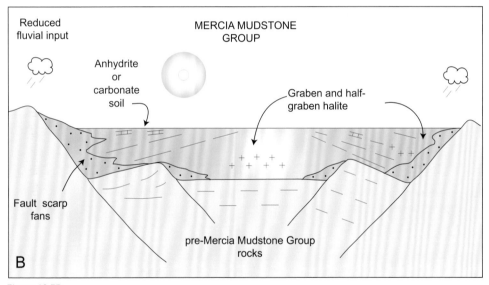

Figure 10.5B
Depositional model for the Mercia Mudstone Group (17).

of up to 25Ma. Further evidence, based on an interpretation of seismic images, demonstrates that the Mercia Mudstone Group, rather than the Sherwood Sandstone Group, thickens markedly into faults (17) (Figure 10.5). In the Mercia Mudstone Group, marine incursions resulted in the formation of localised halites and were accompanied by sediment thickening in the hanging wall of active faults. Syn-depositional faulting in the Sherwood Sandstone Group is now believed to represent residual movement superimposed on thermal subsidence, that post-dates earlier Permian regional extension.

References

1) Osborne, R. and Tarling, D. H. 1995. *The Historical Atlas of the Earth (A Visual Exploration of the Earth's Physical Past)*. Viking. Penguin Books Ltd., London.

2) Parnell, J., Monson, B. and Buckman, J. O. 1992. Excursion Guide: Basins and petroleum geology in the north of Ireland. *In*: Parnell, J. (ed.). *Basins on the Atlantic Seaboard: Petroleum Geology, Sedimentology and Basin Evolution*. Geological Society Special Publication No 62, 449-64.

3) Wilson, H. E. and Manning, P. I. 1978. Geology of the Causeway Coast. *Memoir of the Geological Survey of Northern Ireland*, Sheet 7 (Northern Ireland).

4) Buckman, J. O., Doughty, P. S., Benton, M. J. and Jeram, A. J. 1997/8. Palaeoenvironmental interpretation of the Triassic sandstones of Scrabo, County Down, Northern Ireland: Ichnological and sedimentological studies indicating mixed fluviatile-aeolian succession. *Irish Journal of Earth Sciences*, 16, 85-102.

5) Smith, R. A., Johnston, T. P. and Legg, I. C. 1991. Geology of the country around Newtownards. *Memoir of the Geological Survey of Northern Ireland*, Sheet 37 and part of sheet 38 (Northern Ireland).

6) Fowler, A. and Robbie, J. A. 1961. Geology of the country around Dungannon. *Memoir of the Geological Survey of Northern Ireland*, Sheet 35 (Northern Ireland).

7) Warrington, G. 1995. The Permian, Triassic and Jurassic in Northern Ireland: A palynological study with special reference to the hydrocarbon prospectivity of the Larne-Lough Neagh Basin. *Geological Survey of Northern Ireland Technical Report GSNI/95/7*.

8) Penn, I. E., Holliday, D. W., Kirby, G. A., Kubala, M., Sobey, R. A., Mitchell, W. I., Harrison, R. K. and Beckinsale, R. D. 1983. The Larne No. 2 Borehole: discovery of a new Permian volcanic centre. *Scottish Journal of Geology*, 19, 333-46.

9) Warrington, G., Audley-Charles, M. G., Elliot, R. E., Evans, W. B., Ivimey-Cook, H. C., Kent, P. E., Robinson, P. L., Shotton, F. W. and Taylor, F. M. 1980. *A correlation of Triassic rocks in the British Isles*. Special Reports of the Geological Society of London, 13.

10) Geological Survey of Northern Ireland 1997. Northern Ireland. Solid Geology (second edition). 1:250 000. (Keyworth, Nottingham: British Geological Survey).

11) Bazley, R. A. B., Brandon, A. and Arthurs, J. W. 1997. Geology of the country around Limavady and Londonderry. *Geological Survey of Northern Ireland Technical Report GSNI/97/1*.

12) Manning, P. I. and Wilson, H. E. 1975. The stratigraphy of the Larne Borehole, County Antrim. *Bulletin of the Geological Survey of Great Britain*, 50, 1-50.

13) Ivimey-Cook, H. C. 1975. The stratigraphy of the Rhaetic and Lower Jurassic in East Antrim. *Bulletin of the Geological Survey of Great Britain*, 50, 51-69.

14) Warrington, G. and Harland, R. 1975. Palynology of the Trias and Lower Lias of the Larne Borehole. *Bulletin of the Geological Survey of Great Britain*, 50, 37-50.

15) Manning, P. I., Robbie, J. A. and Wilson, H. E. 1970. Geology of Belfast and the Lagan Valley. *Memoir of the Geological Survey of Northern Ireland*, Sheet 36 (Northern Ireland).

16) Warrington, G. 1981. The indigenous micropalaeontology of the British Triassic shelf sea deposits. *In*: Neale, J W. and Brasier, M. D. (eds.). *Microfossils from recent and fossil shelf seas*. Ellis Horwood, Chichester for British Micropalaeontological Society, 61-70.

17) Ruffell, A. and Shelton, R. 1999. The control of sedimentary facies by climate during phases of crustal extension: examples from the Triassic of onshore and offshore England and Northern Ireland. *Journal of the Geological Society, London*, 156, 779-89.

Chapter 11

Jurassic

W. I. MITCHELL

Introduction

The break up of Pangea in the Late Triassic brought an end to the protracted period of predominantly continental conditions that had influenced the climate of Ireland since the end of the Carboniferous (1). The gradual spread of the Late Triassic marine transgression resulted from a global rise in sea level and by the Early Jurassic much of Ireland and Britain was covered by the sea (Figure 11.1).

Early Jurassic rocks in Northern Ireland, consisting mostly of grey calcareous mudstone and thin nodular limestone, only crop out around the margins of the Antrim Plateau (Figure 9.2). The incompetent mudstone below precipitous cliffs of chalk and basalt has caused landslips, so exposures of Jurassic rocks are rare, of limited extent and commonly occur within slumped blocks.

The maximum thickness of Jurassic rocks recorded is 248m in the Port More borehole and about 125m in the Mire House borehole (Figure 9.2). The strata range in age from

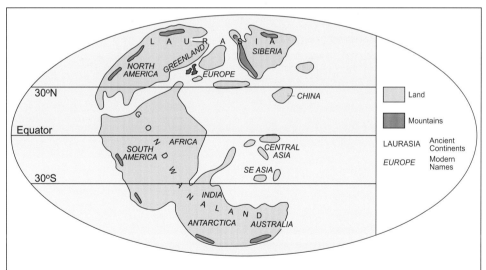

The splitting of Pangea accelerated as anticlockwise rotation took Africa and South America away from North America and commenced the closure of the Tethys Ocean. In eastern Gondwanaland although rifting began to isolate Australia, Antarctica and India, that landmass still remained joined to Asia. Rifts started to develop between North America and Africa and at a slightly later date between North America and Europe and heralded the formation of the South and North Atlantic oceans respectively. In the Early Jurassic Ireland and Britain were submerged by a shallow sea that transgressed across the end-Triassic desert landscape.

Figure 11.1
Position of the continents in the Early Jurassic (c. 195Ma (1))

Hettangian to Pliensbachian and contain ammonites representing most of the zones between the *planorbis* and *ibex* biozones (Table 11.1). In the former borehole the absence of Hettangian and mid-Sinemurian strata in an otherwise almost complete sequence is caused by intrusion of Palaeogene dolerite sills. Although younger Jurassic deposits (post-*ibex* Zone) are not known, the occurrence of derived ammonites of the *spinatum* Biozone in the basal Cretaceous conglomerate and as erratics in the glacial till of north Co. Antrim suggests their presence offshore beneath the North Channel and around Rathlin Island. It is likely that younger Jurassic rocks were once present in Northern Ireland but were removed by erosion in pre-Cretaceous times.

A single formation, the **Waterloo Mudstone Formation**, based on the Waterloo section at Larne (Figure 10.3), is recognised consisting mostly of fossiliferous medium to dark grey calcareous mudstone with laminae of silty mudstone and pale grey siltstone and thin beds of nodular limestone. In the Port More borehole the formation is again represented by grey calcareous mudstone with thin limestone beds becoming common in the *raricostatum* and lower part of the *jamesoni* biozones (Table 11.1). In the upper part of the *jamesoni* Biozone in the borehole, siltstone beds and ironstone nodules are common. Strata of the succeeding *ibex* Biozone consist of dark grey micaceous mudstone. Jurassic strata in the Tircrevan Burn section [C703 320] north of Limavady are about 52m thick and include the 13m thick **Tircrevan Sandstone Member** (2). The lower contact of the sandstone is a non-sequence with invertebrate burrows excavated into the underlying grey mudstone (3) but elsewhere, as at the Larne stratotype it appears conformable. The succeeding 6m of strata consist of grey and brown, fine-grained, micaceous and bioturbated silty sandstone that contains plant fragments and grades up through calcareous sandstone to sandy limestone with bivalves, gastropods and crinoid ossicles in the upper 7m. The upper contact is concealed. Because mudstones of the Waterloo Mudstone Formation readily absorb water, internal cohesion is lowered and at some localities they appear at surface as superficial mudflows, for example at Minnis North [D338 135] in east Co. Antrim

Stage		Zone	Subzone
Jurassic (Early)	Pliensbachian	* Pleuroceras spinatum	P. hawskerense
			P. apyrenum
		Amaltheus margaritatus	A. gibbosus
			A. subnodosus
			A. stokesi
		Prodactylioceras davoei	Oistoceras figulinum
			Aegoceras capricornus
			A. maculatum
		Tragophylloceras ibex	Beaniceras luridum
			Acanthopleuroceras valdani
			Tropidoceras masseanum
		Uptonia jamesoni	U. jamesoni
			Platypleuroceras brevispina
			Polymorphites polymorphus
			Phricodoceras taylori
	Sinemurian	Echioceras raricostatum	Paltechioceras aplanatum
			Leptechioceras macdonnelli
			E. raricostatoides
			Crucilobiceras densinodulum
		Oxynoticeras oxynotum	O. oxynotum
			O. simpsoni
		Asteroceras obtusum	Eparietites denotatus
			A. stellare
			A. obtusum
		Caenisites turneri	Microderoceras birchi
			C. brooki
		Arnioceras semicostatum	Euagassiceras sauzeanum
			Agassiceras scipionianum
			Coroniceras reynesi
		Arietites bucklandi	A. bucklandi
			Coroniceras rotiforme
			Vermiceras conybeari
	Hettangian	Schlotheimia angulata	S. complanata
			S. extranodosa
		Alsatites liasicus	A. laqueus
			Waehneroceras portlocki
		Psiloceras planorbis	Caloceras johnstoni
			P. planorbis

Table 11.1
Ammonite subzones recognised (brown) in the Jurassic rocks in Northern Ireland (ammonite subzones uncoloured are not proven).

Fossils 1-7
Early Jurassic (Hettangian-Sinemurian) fossils from the Waterloo Mudstone Formation:
Bivalves: **1** *Gryphaea arcuata* (x 0.4), **2** *Plagiostoma giganteum* (x 0.4)
Ammonites: **3** *Psiloceras planorbis* (x 0.75), **4** *Alsatites liasicus* (x 0.25),
5 *Schlotheimia angulata* (x 0.5), **6** *Arnioceras semicostatum* (x 0.4), **7** *Paltechioceras* sp. (x 0.4)

where the coast road is frequently inundated (Figure 9.2; Chapter 23, Photograph 6).

The Waterloo Mudstone Formation contains a rich macrofauna, with ammonites proving the standard zonal sequence. The formation outcrop is divided into two geographically separate areas that are composed of rocks of different ages (Table 11.1). The earliest Jurassic rocks, of Hettangian and early Sinemurian age, crop out in southeast Co. Antrim, particularly at Waterloo [D409 037] near Larne (Figure 10.3) and are recorded in boreholes in east Co. Tyrone. At Waterloo, above the exposed conformable Triassic-Jurassic boundary the lowest 25m of the Waterloo Mudstone Formation contains abundant bivalves such as *Gryphaea* and *Plagiostoma* (Fossils 1 and 2) and rare ammonites, including the zonal taxon *Psiloceras planorbis* (Fossil 3). In higher strata, specimens of the index taxa of the *liasicus, angulata*

Photograph 1
White Park Bay on the north coast of Co. Antrim, 7km east of the Giant's Causeway with Rathlin Island in the distance.

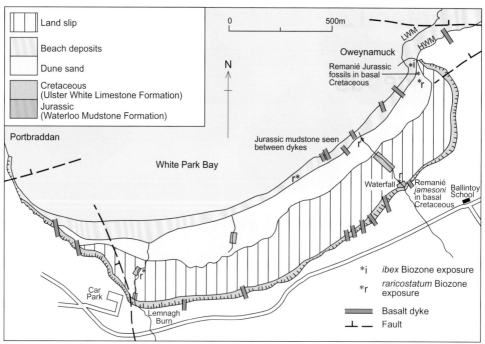

Figure 11.2
Distribution of Jurassic rocks at White Park Bay in north Co. Antrim (5).

(Fossils 4 and 5) and *bucklandi* biozones (4) are rare. North of Larne, some 10m of vertically bedded grey mudstone and thin limestone of the early Sinemurian *bucklandi* Biozone are exposed 300m north of Garron Point (Figure 9.2) [D301 245].

The sequence of Jurassic rocks in the Port More borehole ranges in age from the late Sinemurian to Pliensbachian (5). Fossiliferous mudstone exposed at White Park Bay [D015 440] is often concealed by landslip and sand dunes (Photograph 1 and Figure 11.2).
At Oweynamuck the fauna includes bivalves, brachiopods and ammonites of the *valdani* Subzone of the *ibex* Biozone. The remaining exposures belong to the *raricostatum* Biozone and in particular the *macdonnelli* Subzone (Table 11.1). In north Co. Londonderry, mudstones below the Tircrevan Sandstone Member yields *Schlotheimia* of the late Hettangian *angulata* Biozone while those above the sandstone contain *Arnioceras semicostatum* (Fossil 6) and *Euagassiceras* indicating the *sauzeanum* Subzone of the *semicostatum* Biozone (3).

One of the classic geological localities in the British Isles is at Portrush in north Co. Antrim (Figure 9.2). Here, fossiliferous Jurassic mudstone ('Portrush Rock') containing the ammonite *Paltechioceras* (Fossil 7) exposed on the east side of the main promontory has been hornfelsed by a Palaeogene dolerite intrusion, the Portrush Sill.

References
1) Osborne, R. and Tarling, D. H. 1995. *The Historical Atlas of the Earth (A Visual Exploration of the Earth's Physical Past)*. Viking. Penguin Books Ltd., London.

2) Geological Survey of Northern Ireland 1981. Limavady, Northern Ireland Sheet 12 and part of sheet 6. Solid Geology. 1:50,000. (Southampton: Ordnance Survey for the Geological Survey of Northern Ireland).

3) Bazley, R. A. B., Brandon, A. and Arthurs, J. W. 1997. Geology of the country around Limavady and Londonderry. *Geological Survey of Northern Ireland. Technical Report GSNI/97/1.*

4) Ivimey-Cook, H. C. 1975. The stratigraphy of the Rhaetic and Lower Jurassic in East Antrim. *Bulletin of the Geological Survey of Great Britain*, **50**, 51-69.

5) Wilson, H. E. and Manning, P. I. 1978. Geology of the Causeway Coast. *Memoir of the Geological Survey of Northern Ireland*, Sheet 7 (Northern Ireland).

Chapter 12

Cretaceous

W. I. MITCHELL

Introduction

Throughout the upper Jurassic and Early Cretaceous, the break up of the supercontinent Pangea continued. In the Southern Hemisphere, South America drifted westwards away from Africa while north of the equator the proto-North Atlantic Ocean continued to widen (1). During the Early Cretaceous, Ireland was represented by a landmass of uncertain extent and the absence of Cretaceous strata may indicate a period of non-deposition that possibly started in the late Early Jurassic (Chapter 11), and extended for 90Ma to the early Cenomanian. However, in the early Late Cretaceous a widespread rise in sea level, the Cenomanian transgression, advanced across the margins of the former land areas and was followed by warm, clear seas that ultimately may have covered much of Ireland (Figure 12.1).

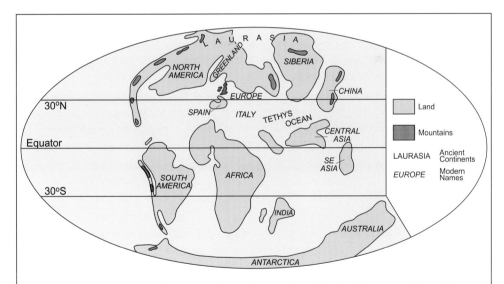

Throughout the Cretaceous period, the breakup of the continents continued. As South America and Africa drifted apart, the south and central parts of the Atlantic Ocean were formed. The southwards motion of eastern parts of the Laurasian landmass, in particular Europe and Siberia, towards Africa and Central Asia which were moving northwards at that time, resulted in the partial closure of the Tethys Ocean. In the early Late Cretaceous the Cenomanian transgression raised sea-levels world-wide by as much as 200m above present levels. In Ireland this resulted in the drowning of the remaining land areas by the warm, shallow sea in which the chalk was deposited. At the end of the Cretaceous the mass extinction of many animals in the sea, in particular of the ammonites, was matched on land by the extinction of the dinosaurs.

Figure 12.1
Position of the continents in the Late Cretaceous (*c.* 80Ma (1))

In Northern Ireland, the outcrop of Late Cretaceous rocks is located at the margins of the Antrim Plateau, primarily in Counties Antrim and Londonderry (Figure 12.2). During this period the impact of tectonic activity was varied across Northern Ireland. In the east and south the sub-Cretaceous unconformity rests on Late Triassic or Jurassic rocks whereas in the west the unconformity

Stage		Formation	Lithology
Maastrichtian	late		
	early		
Campanian		Ulster White Limestone	Limestone, white chalk, hard, with flints and basal glauconite-rich beds
Santonian			
Coniacian		Hibernian Greensands	Sandstone, siltstone, mudstone, green to yellowish brown, variably glauconitic
Turonian			
Cenomanian			

Table 12.1
Lithostratigraphical divisions of the Late Cretaceous in Northern Ireland.

progressively oversteps the entire Triassic and Carboniferous succession to overlie the Ordovician rocks on Slieve Gallion [H813 896]. The Late Cretaceous depositional basin covered the Dalradian outcrop in northeast Co. Antrim and may also have extended over much of the eastern Sperrin Mountains (2).

The Cretaceous rocks are divided (Table 12.1) into the **Hibernian Greensands Formation** (3) and the **Ulster White Limestone Formation** (4). The restriction of the Hibernian Greensands Formation to the south and eastern fringes of the Antrim Plateau between Lisburn and Glenarm, with a small area east of Limavady, is the result of episodes of regional uplift and erosion during and after its deposition. In contrast, the Ulster White Limestone Formation occurs throughout the Cretaceous outcrop and is exposed in spectacular coastal sections and in several quarries (Photograph 1).

Four members are recognised in the Hibernian Greensands Formation (3, 5) and fourteen members in the Ulster White Limestone Formation (4). The use of the lithological term limestone in the Ulster White Limestone Formation is replaced in all but one of those members by the term chalk, which has an age connotation and by implication is Late Cretaceous.

Photograph 1
Aerial view of part of The White Rocks [C893 409] showing the contrast between the white chalk of the Ulster White Limestone Formation and black basalt lavas of the Antrim Lava Group, 3.5km ENE of Portrush, Co. Antrim.

150

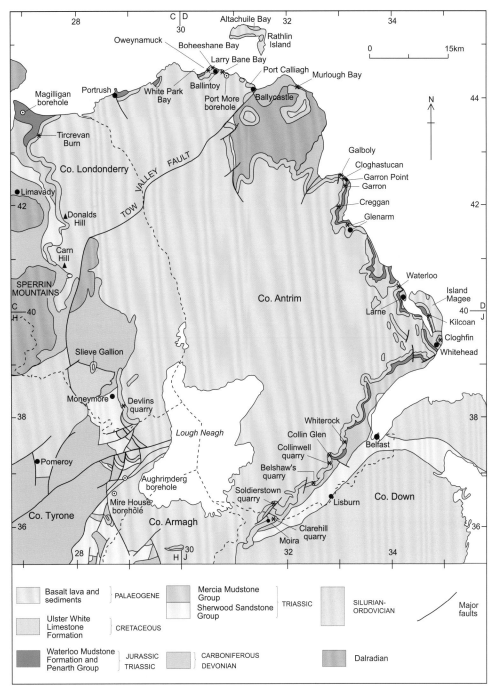

Figure 12.2
Simplified geological map of northeast Northern Ireland highlighting the distribution of Cretaceous rocks and in particular of the Ulster White Limestone Formation.

The Late Cretaceous rocks in Northern Ireland are equivalent in age to the Chalk Group in England and make up one of the most complete and best-exposed post-Santonian sequences in Northern Europe (2). Although a complete succession is not exposed at any one locality, lateral thickness variations in individual members are determined by the presence of marker horizons, particularly in the Ulster White Limestone Formation (4).

On this basis, it is possible to define the distribution of depositional basins and structural highs and to identify syndepositional basement controls.

The limestone of the Ulster White Limestone Formation is extremely hard compared to much of the rock of the English Chalk Group. This is due to secondary calcite cementation in pore spaces with the calcite being derived from pressure solution during compaction (6). The Irish chalk has a much higher density (2.60 compared to 1.95) and lower porosity (5% compared to up to 50%) than the English Chalk Group.

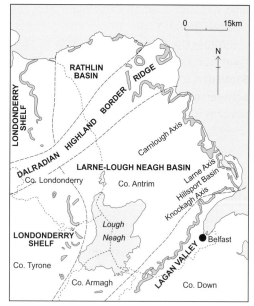

Figure 12.3
Distribution of the main depositional areas of the Ulster White Limestone Formation.

Structural setting and depositional history

Deposition of the Late Cretaceous sediments was strongly influenced by contemporaneous tectonism and the control of Caledonoid basement structures on the location and extent of depositional basins (Figure 12.3). Although the main depositional basins occur on opposite sides of the Dalradian Highland Border Ridge, areas of minor subsidence and uplift within them created localised basins and attenuated successions. However, by late Campanian times (Table 12.1)

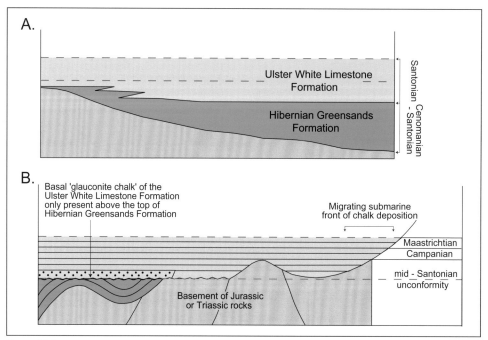

Figure 12.4
Two depositional models for the Hibernian Greensands and Ulster White Limestone formations.
A) diachronous relationships, B) unconformable relationship (preferred).

land areas in the west were submerged by the transgression and in the process created the Londonderry shelf.

Within the Hibernian Greensands Formation, a major unconformity separates the lowermost three members (Cenomanian-Turonian) from the upper member of Coniacian-Santonian age (Table 12.2). More controversial however, is the nature of the junction between the greensands and chalk. One model envisages a diachronous relationship at the margins of a subsiding chalk basin (Figure 12.4A) but a more likely scenario is an unconformity. Glauconite and detrital sand in the basal unit of the chalk was thus derived by erosion of the Hibernian Greensands Formation (Figure 12.4B).

Hibernian Greensands Formation

The main outcrop of this formation is in southeast Co. Antrim and all the sediments were deposited prior to the *Uintacrinus socialis* Biozone (late Santonian) when chalk deposition commenced (3). The four members (Table 12.2) are about 30m thick with a maximum of 14m recorded for the lowest three members at the section in Collin Glen [J269 722], 350-412m upstream from Glen Bridge (Figure 12.2).

The transgressive base of the fossiliferous **Belfast Marls Member**, formerly known as the Glauconitic Sands (7), rests on the Waterloo Mudstone Formation, Penarth Group and the Mercia Mudstone Group. The fauna is dominated by bivalves, especially large specimens of the oyster *Amphidonte obliquata* (Fossil 1), but also contains brachiopods, cephalopods, gastropods and serpulids. The earliest Cenomanian (*Mantelliceras mantelli* Biozone) age of the lower part of the member is based on the presence of the ammonites *Schloenbachia* and *Mantelliceras* (Fossil 2). At Cloghfin [J484 942] (Figure 12.2), the belemnite *Actinocamax primus* (Fossil 3) confirms a mid-Cenomanian age for the upper part of this unit.

Stage	Zone	Member	Lithology
Santonian (pars)	*Micraster coranguinum*	Kilcoan Sands (0.6-7.5m)	Unconformity
Coniacian			Sand, pale to dark green, glauconitic, coarse-grained, poorly cemented, quartz-rich, fossiliferous with abundant *Inoceramus* fragments; basal conglomerate, variably gritty, coarse-grained, phosphatised nodules
	Micraster cortestudinarium		
Turonian	*Holaster planus*	Collinwell Sands (8.7m)	Unconformity
	Terebratulina lata		Upper unit (5m) of unconsolidated quartz sand, white, fine- to medium-grained, unfossiliferous
	Inoceramus labiatus		
	Sciponoceras gracile		Lower unit (3.7m) of unconsolidated sand, pale green, coarse-grained glauconitic, fossiliferous; beds of hard siliceous sandstone at top
	Calycoceras naviculare		Unconformity
Cenomanian	*Acanthoceras rhotomagense*	Island Magee Siltstones (0.67-10.7m)	Siltstone, hard and marl, soft, bluish grey, weathering pale yellow, calcareous; fossiliferous
		Belfast Marls (1.6-3.0m)	Marl, pale grey, silty, dark green glauconite grains, fossiliferous; basal pebble bed; phosphatic nodules, bioturbated
	Mantelliceras mantelli		Unconformity

Table 12.2
Bio- and lithostratigraphy of the Hibernian Greensands Formation.

At the base of the **Island Magee Siltstones Member** is a transitional zone lithologically resembling the top of the Belfast Marls Member but consisting of 0.23m of glauconite-depleted, grey silty marl with a fauna of smooth-shelled bivalves lacking *Amphidonte*. The previous name of this member, 'Yellow Sandstones and Grey Marls' emphasised the pale bluish grey colour of the rocks when fresh and calcareous, and their pale yellow hue when weathered and decalcified. The mid-Cenomanian age is indicated by the ammonite *Cunningtoniceras cunningtoni* (Fossil 4) which is typical of the *Acanthoceras rhotomagense* Biozone, and the bivalve *'Inoceramus' hamiltoni*, which is characteristic of the late mid-Cenomanian in southern England. In Collin Glen, the member is at least 9m thick, but the fauna is restricted to rare brachiopods and serpulids. At Cloghfin Port (J484 942), the member forms foreshore reefs with fossils including the corals *Micrabacia* cf. *coronula* and *'Stephanophyllia'* cf. *bowerbankii*, serpulids, inoceramid bivalves and *Gryphaeostrea canaliculata*. The echinoid *'Epiaster'* is typical of warm water southern Tethyan faunas. The member is overlain unconformably by the Collinwell Sands Member.

The upper surface of the Island Magee Siltstones Member is commonly bored, with pipes of younger sediment from the **Collinwell Sands Member** extending down for up to 0.6m. The outcrop of the two informal units of this member is located southwest of Belfast with exposures of the upper unit restricted to small pits west of Collin Glen (8). Although abundant fossils occur in the lower unit (Table 12.2), the absence of zonal index taxa makes dating problematical and the attributed late Cenomanian to mid-Turonian age is based on the occurrence of large specimens of the oyster *Rhynchostreon suborbiculatum*.

The basal conglomerate of the **Kilcoan Sands Member** rests unconformably on the three older members (Table 12.2) and its sand component was largely derived by erosion of the Collinwell Sands Member. The thickest section of the member (7.3m) is at Kilcoan [J461 986] on Island Magee (Figure 12.2), but elsewhere the succession thins beneath the unconformity at the base of the Ulster White Limestone Formation. The succession is

Fossils 1-5
Late Cretaceous (early Cenomanian-Coniacian) fossils from the Hibernian Greensands Formation:
Bivalves: **1** *Amphidonte obliquata* (x 0.6), **5** *Volviceramus involutus* (x 0.3)
Ammonites: **2** *Mantelliceras mantelli* (x 0.6), **4** *Cunningtoniceras cunningtoni* (x 0.3)
Belemnite: **3** *Actinocamax primus* (x 0.6)

154

divided into three parts based on the presence of three, closely spaced, shell bands packed with *Inoceramus* fragments (3). The pre-*Inoceramus* bands strata are early Coniacian based on the association of the echinoid *Conulus raulini* and rhynchonellid brachiopods including 'Cretirhynchia' robusta. The *Inoceramus* bands contain the Coniacian zonal index fossil *Volviceramus involutus* (Fossil 5) that occurs near the base of the *Micraster coranguinum* Biozone. They also have numerous oysters including *Gryphaeostrea canaliculata* and *Hyotissa semiplana* and terebratulid brachiopods such as *Concinnithyris* and *Gibbithyris*. Brachiopods, including large specimens of the flat terebratulid *Gibbithyris hibernica*, are also common in the post-*Inoceramus* bands succession, but the Santonian age is based on the presence of the small and medium-sized echinoids *Conulus*, common *Echinocorys* and rare *Micraster*.

At Tircrevan Burn [C701 326], the Kilcoan Sands Member consists of 3m of chert-free and cherty greensand and is divided into two parts by an unconformity (9). In the lower part, the sandstones only contain long-ranging fossils indicative of the Cenomanian to early Coniacian. However, the basal sandstones of the upper part contain the belemnite *Actinocamax verus* and the spinose oyster *Costagyra laciniata*, which typify the upper part of the *Micraster coranguinum* Biozone and are Santonian (Table 12.2). Poorly fossiliferous strata at the top of the upper sandstones are bioturbated by chert-filled *Thalassinoides* burrows and contain large specimens of the flat echinoid *Micraster rogalae*, indicating the upper *Micraster coranguinum* Biozone and a Santonian age. In southeast Co. Antrim this is coeval with either the top of the Kilcoan Sands Member or the Cloghfin Sponge Beds Member of the Ulster White Limestone Formation.

Ulster White Limestone Formation

The Ulster White Limestone Formation (Table 12.1) is a coccolith-foraminiferal micrite with flints and is divided into fourteen members (Table 12.3). It ranges in age from the late Santonian *Uintacrinus socialis* Biozone (Fossil 6) to the early Maastrichtian *Belemnella occidentalis* Biozone. Although the full succession is never exposed at one locality, individual members are recognisable across the outcrop based on flint type, the presence and spacing of distinctive flint bands and the characteristics of individual beds or groups of beds (4). Wind-weathered sections on the east and north coast of Co. Antrim are key reference sections and exhibit the characteristic sedimentary structures and faunas.

The composite thickness of all the members at their type sections is approximately 133m with a maximum of 120m of chalk exposed between Ballycastle and Portrush (Figure 12.2). This section, which is typical of the succession in the Rathlin basin, is similar to that in the Larne-Lough Neagh basin (Figure 12.3), demonstrating that the thickness and lateral continuity of individual beds is consistent over the entire chalk outcrop. The same succession in north Co. Down is 30m thick and only 25m on the Londonderry shelf. Sedimentation on shelf areas commenced in mid- to late Campanian times. The older biostratigraphical subdivisions of the chalk were based on the definition of strata that were either, "earlier than the zone of *Belemnitella mucronata*" (Fossil 7) or, "in the zone of *Belemnitella mucronata*" (10). The base of the *Belemnitella mucronata* Biozone coincides with the upper limit of *Gonioteuthis* (Fossil 8) and occurs at the level of the prominent Whitehead Flint Band. In north Co. Antrim, this occurs in one bed of the Boheeshane Chalk Member (Table 12.3), 3.66m below the prominent erosion surface at the base of the **Larry Bane Chalk Member**. All sections are divided thus into pre-Larry Bane Chalk, Larry Bane Chalk Member and post-Larry Bane Chalk (4).

Stage	Zone	Member	Lithology
Early Maastrichtian	Belemnella occidentalis	Unconformity	
Early Maastrichtian	Belemnella occidentalis	Ballycastle Chalk (13.72m)	White limestone in 7 beds; dissolution weathering of flints in upper three beds
Early Maastrichtian	Belemnella lanceolata	Port Calliagh Chalk (12.40m)	White limestone in 6 beds; flint-rich; occasional green-coated chalk pebbles
Early Maastrichtian	Belemnella lanceolata	Tanderagee Chalk (7.36m)	White limestone in 5 beds; base marked by the Long Gilbert Flint Band
Campanian	Belemnitella mucronata	Ballymagarry Chalk (10.95m)	White limestone in 3 beds; largest flints (paramoudra) in Irish chalk, continuous flint bands
Campanian	Belemnitella mucronata	Portrush Chalk (14.28m)	White limestone in 4 beds; abundant Inoceramus debris; South Antrim Hardgrounds
Campanian	Belemnitella mucronata	Garron Chalk (9.65m)	White limestone in 3 beds; giant flints often in circles; wavy-bedded at top
Campanian	Belemnitella mucronata	Glenarm Chalk (8.0m)	White limestone in 4 beds; small and large flints; North Antrim Hardgrounds
Campanian	Belemnitella mucronata	Ballintoy Chalk (12.65m)	White limestone in 2 beds; at top is the Altachuile Breccia
Campanian	Belemnitella mucronata	Larry Bane Chalk (7.29m)	White limestone in 2 beds; demarcated by three marked erosion surfaces
Campanian	Gonioteuthis quadrata (pars)	Boheeshane Chalk (24.19m)	White limestone in 3 beds; very fine-grained chalk lacking Inoceramus fragments; small to massive flint bands; Whitehead Flint Band
Campanian	Offaster pilula (pars)	Creggan Chalk (3.45m)	White limestone in 1 bed; abundant Inoceramus fragments; stromatolite biostrome; Bendoo Pebble Bed at top
Santonian (pars)	Marsupites testudinarius	Cloghastucan Chalk (2.23m)	White limestone in 1 bed; small scattered flint nodules are burrow fills; Oweynamuck Flint Band just below top
Santonian (pars)	Uintacrinus socialis (pars)	Galboly Chalk (5.85m)	White limestone in 1 bed; abundant Inoceramus fragments; wavy bedding; white and black flints
Santonian (pars)	Uintacrinus socialis (pars)	Cloghfin Sponge Beds (1.47m)	Glauconitic limestone in 3 beds; flint-free; cobbly base and wavy-bedded top
Santonian (pars)	Uintacrinus socialis (pars)	Unconformity	

Table 12.3
Bio- and lithostratigraphy of the Ulster White Limestone Formation.

Pre-Larry Bane Chalk White Limestone

The distribution of these five members (Table 12.3) mirrors the configuration of the late Santonian to early Campanian depositional basin. They attain a maximum thickness of 26m at Glenarm, but thin rapidly elsewhere due to variations in base levels and are absent on the Dalradian Highland Border Ridge and in north Co. Down, south of the Lagan Valley (Figure 12.3). In the Larne-Lough Neagh basin, minor axes of uplift influenced the amount of pre-Cretaceous erosion, Cretaceous sedimentation and the depth of erosion in the early Palaeogene prior to the extrusion of the basalt lavas. The location of the Carnlough, Larne and Knockagh axes (Figure 12.3) is defined by thickness variations in the Galboly, Cloghastucan and Creggan Chalk members (Figure 12.5). All five members are exposed at Whitepark Bay (Figure 11.2).

Sedimentation commenced simultaneously in both the Larne-Lough Neagh and Rathlin basins. In the former basin, in east Co. Antrim, the **Cloghfin Sponge Beds Member** (Table 12.3), which rests on the Hibernian Greensands Formation, includes reworked glauconite grains and is characterised by abundant hexactinellid sponge pseudomorphs. By comparison, in the Rathlin basin, the Hibernian Greensands Formation is absent and the member is glauconite-free. The four succeeding members contain comminuted Inoceramus

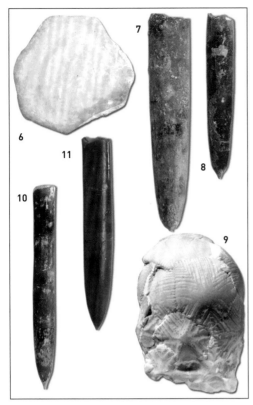

Fossils 6-10
Late Cretaceous (late Santonian-early
Maastrichtian) fossils from the Ulster White
Limestone Formation:
Crinoids: **6** *Uintacrinus socialis* (x 4),
9 *Marsupites testudinarius* (x 0.2)
Belemnites: **7** *Belemnitella mucronata* (x 0.6),
8 *Gonioteuthis* sp. (x 0.6),
10 *Belemnella lanceolata* (x 0.6),
11 *Belemnella occidentalis* (x 0.6)

shell debris. Flint occurs in three forms. In the **Galboly Chalk Member** flint forms bands, which are reliable lithostratigraphical markers, it occurs as secondary silicification of burrow fills in the **Cloghastucan Chalk Member** and as randomly distributed nodules in the **Creggan Chalk Member**. The Cloghastucan Chalk Member contains the brachials and calyx plates of the zonal index crinoid *Marsupites testudinarius* (Fossil 9).

In the pre-Larry Bane Chalk, the prominent Oweynamuck Flint Band (Photograph 2) and Whitehead Flint Band occur immediately below the top of the Cloghastucan Chalk Member and **Boheeshane Chalk Member** respectively. Transitory breaks in chalk sedimentation are recognised by the development of hardgrounds, which are deeply burrowed, disconformable, glauconitised erosion surfaces with green-coated chalk pebbles and rolled and phosphatised fossils (4). In shallower water, depositional breaks are associated with stromatolitic biostromal surfaces (top Creggan Chalk Member). The contact between the Creggan Chalk and Boheeshane Chalk members is a disconformity representing the late *Offaster pilula*-earliest *Gonioteuthis quadrata* biozones.

Larry Bane Chalk Member
Ubiquitous and prominent minor disconformities bracket the two beds of the **Larry Bane Chalk Member** (Table 12.3), in which the upper bed is twice the thickness of the lower bed. Large specimens of *Belemnitella* sp. are common.

Post-Larry Bane Chalk White Limestone
The maximum thickness of these eight members (Table 12.3) is over 85m in north Co. Antrim although nowhere is the succession continuously exposed. The **Ballintoy Chalk Member** consists of two beds, the lower one being twice the thickness of the upper bed of the preceding Larry Bane Chalk Member. The upper bed, which forms the rock platform at Ballintoy Harbour (Figure 12.2) [D039 455] and crops out on the foreshore at Waterloo [D410 033] near Larne, contains specimens up to 1m across of the ammonite *Pachydiscus*. At its top, the **Altachuile Breccia** (bed) consists of 0.35m of wavy-bedded and slumped chalk containing pellet-like lumps of indurated chalk and angular chips of fragmented flint (4). This breccia is recognised on Rathlin Island and in the Belfast area and probably formed by the churning of semi-consolidated sediment during violent weather conditions.

157

Photograph 2
Tilted (rotational landslip) blocks of the Ulster White Limestone Formation. The nearest block shows the contact between the Galboly Chalk Member at the base and the *Marsupites testudinarius*-bearing Cloghastucan Chalk Member with the Oweynamuck Flint Band (OFB). The *Inoceramus*-rich Creggan Chalk Member occurs at the top of the block. West side of White Park Bay, 7km east of the Giant's Causeway, Co. Antrim.

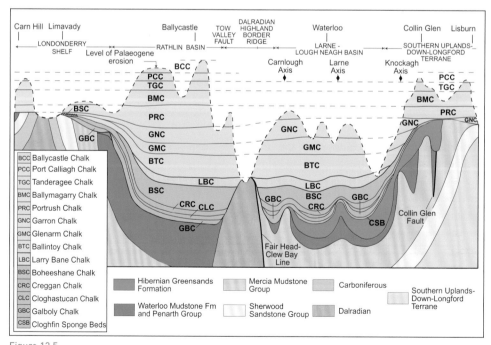

Figure 12.5
Schematic reconstruction of the spatial relations of the members of the Ulster White Limestone Formation (4).

Photograph 3
Paramoudra in the Ballymagarry Chalk Member of the Ulster White Limestone Formation.
Clarehill quarry [J154 603], 500m southeast of Moira, Co. Down.

The four remaining chalk members referred to the *Belemnitella mucronata* Biozone are distinguished by the development of hardgrounds and pebble beds and especially by flint morphology. In the **Garron Chalk Member** the flints are particularly large and define flint circles. The **Ballymagarry Chalk Member** contains the largest flints in the Irish Cretaceous termed paramoudra, which are barrel-shaped, and lie vertically across bedding planes (Photograph 3). These are best developed where the Ballymagarry Chalk Member overlies the Southern Uplands-Down-Longford Terrane and are exposed in Clarehill quarry [J154 603] near Moira (Figure 12.2). Both the **Glenarm Chalk** and **Portrush Chalk members** contain prominent hardgrounds with a concentration of green, glauconitised chalk pebbles. In the former, the **North Antrim Hardgrounds** are only developed in the Rathlin basin and consist of two horizons approximately 0.5m apart. The eponymous **South Antrim Hardgrounds** in the Portrush Chalk Member (Table 12.3) consist of several levels of glauconitised chalk pebbles.

Maastrichtian chalk (Table 12.3) is confined to the Rathlin basin, the Londonderry shelf and the Lagan Valley and north Co. Down (Figure 12.3). In north Co. Antrim the **Long Gilbert Flint Band** marks the base of the **Tanderagee Chalk Member** and of the Maastrichtian Stage (Photograph 4). However, this flint band is a local development and is replaced elsewhere by a prominent bedding plane with no flint. Although the Tanderagee Chalk Member contains brachiopods and echinoids of Maastrichtian aspect, it has not yielded the zonal taxon

Photograph 4
Post-Larry Bane Chalk members of the Ulster White Limestone Formation. At the base of the face large flints characterise the Ballymagarry Chalk Member. The Long Gilbert Flint Band (LGFB) marks the contact with the succeeding Tanderagee Chalk Member. The slight overhang near the top of the face is the contact with the Port Calliagh Chalk Member. Long Gilbert quarry [C888 407], south face of west quarry, 3km east of Portrush, Co. Antrim.

Belemnella. The **Port Calliagh Chalk** and **Ballycastle Chalk members** contain the Maastrichtian zonal belemnites *Belemnella lanceolata* (Fossil 10) and *Belemnella occidentalis* (Fossil 11) respectively and are exposed on rock platforms and low cliffs at Port Calliagh (Figure 12.2) [D112 420].

References
1)   Osborne, R. and Tarling, D. H. 1995. *The Historical Atlas of the Earth (A Visual Exploration of the Earth's Physical Past).* Viking. Penguin Books Ltd., London.

2)   Reid, R. E. H. 1971. The Cretaceous rocks of north-eastern Ireland. *Irish Naturalist's Journal,* 17, 105-29.

3)   Griffith, A. E. and Wilson, H. E. 1982. Geology of the country around Carrickfergus and Bangor. *Memoir of the Geological Survey of Northern Ireland,* Sheet 29 (Northern Ireland).

4)   Fletcher, T. P. 1977. Lithostratigraphy of the Chalk (Ulster White Limestone Formation) in Northern Ireland. *Report of the Institute of Geological Sciences,* 77/24.

5)   Portlock, J. E. 1843. *Report on the geology of the County of Londonderry and parts of Tyrone and Fermanagh.* 784pp. (Dublin: HMSO).

6)   Wolfe, M. J. 1968. Lithification of a carbonate mud: Senonian Chalk in Northern Ireland. *Sedimentary Geology,* 2, 263-90.

7)   Tate, R. 1865. On the correlation of the Cretaceous formations of the north-east of Ireland. *Quarterly Journal of the Geological Society of London,* 21, 15-44.

8)   Manning, P. I., Robbie, J. A. and Wilson, H. E. 1970. Geology of Belfast and the Lagan Valley. *Memoir of the Geological Survey of Northern Ireland,* Sheet 36 (Northern Ireland).

9)   Bazley, R. A. B., Brandon, A. and Arthurs, J. W. 1997. Geology of the country around Limavady and Londonderry. *Geological Survey of Northern Ireland. Technical Report GSNI/97/1.*

10) Hancock, J. M. 1961. The Cretaceous System in Northern Ireland. *Quarterly Journal of the Geological Society, London,* 117, 11-36.

Chapter 13

The Cretaceous-Palaeogene (K-T) Boundary

W. I. MITCHELL

Introduction

The **Clay-with-Flints** is the only deposit in Northern Ireland that represents part of the 10Ma gap between the Late Cretaceous chalk (late-early Maastrichtian) and earliest Palaeogene basalt lavas (*c.* 59Ma). It is exposed at the margins of the Antrim Plateau and consists of multicoloured clay with clasts of flint derived from the Cretaceous chalk. The deposit was traditionally believed to have formed as a palaeosol (Photograph 1), combining the weathering products of chalk and flint, an aeolian component and illuvium from the overlying basalt lavas (1). It is now recognised that contemporaneous volcanism contributed much of the clay fraction (2).

Photograph 1
The Clay-with-Flints deposit sandwiched between white chalk of the Late Cretaceous Ulster White Limestone Formation and basalt lava of the Early Palaeogene Antrim Lava Group. Devlin's quarry [H872 816], 2.5km SSE of Moneymore, Co. Tyrone.

Photograph 2A
The Donald's Hill Ignimbrite Formation (DHIF) at its stratotype. West flank of Donald's Hill [C738 180], 8.5km southeast of Limavady, Co. Londonderry.

The present thickness of Cretaceous chalk is a reflection of tectonism and the severity of weathering prior to the accumulation of the Clay-with-Flints. Some indication of the thickness of eroded chalk is provided by the occurrence of paramoudra (Chapter 12, Photograph 3) in the Clay-with-Flints at Cloghfin [J484 942]. There, the deposit rests on the Glenarm Chalk Member, but since paramoudra are restricted to the uppermost Ballymagarry Chalk Member (Table 12.3) at least 38m of post-Glenarm Chalk Member, and probably much more, has been removed to release them for incorporation into the Clay-with-Flints. Despite the erosion of the chalk, the Clay-with-Flints probably accumulated on a gently undulose land surface. At many exposures, the presence of grikes up to 5m deep illustrate the effects of solution on the chalk and while usually infilled by the Clay-with-Flints, the intervening clints may also be buried by 1-2m of the deposit.

Photograph 2B
The DHIF between white chalk of the Late Cretaceous Ulster White Limestone Formation and basalt lava of the Early Palaeogene Antrim Lava Group.

In detail the Clay-with-Flints comprises a soft, highly weathered, clay matrix consisting of an intergrowth of fine-grained quartz, clay minerals, disseminated opaque oxides and haematite. While many of the flint clasts are broken into sharp fragments, some still retain their original shape. This is evident at a shoreface exposure [D119 416] 250m northwest of Ballycastle harbour, where there is no clay matrix and the 0.4m thick deposit consists of self-supporting, whole and fragmented, flints and a matrix of coarse flint chips. The typical Clay-

Photograph 2C
Close up of the DHIF showing whole and broken discoloured flints. (Hammer head 16cm long).

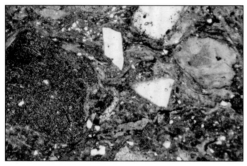

Photomicrograph 1
Photomicrograph of the Donald's Hill Ignimbrite Formation showing three white flint fragments (centre upper half of the field of view), a large equant crystalline lithic fragment (left hand side) and large glassy fragments wrapped by deformed glass shards defining a eutaxitic texture. (Field of view 9.2 x 6.1mm).

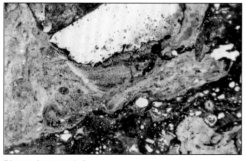

Photomicrograph 2
Photomicrograph showing a large white flint clast (top, centre) with a slightly embayed margin due to reaction with the hot ash flow entraining it wrapped by deformed (probably originally pumiceous) fiammé. (Field of view 4.5 x 3mm).

with-Flints deposit is exposed in the cliff face, 100m to the northwest. The colour of the Clay-with-Flints reflects those of the component clay minerals and ranges from grey and dark bluish grey to white, pale fawn, purplish to deep reddish brown. Flints usually retain the dull grey and greyish brown hues, with a white weathering crust, which predominate in the chalk. At some localities the flints have a superficial red colour which is merely surface staining. However, at others, such as Donald's Hill, the flints show a pervasive concentric banding in shades of brown, pink, purple and red probably due to baking. The flint is reddest where it cooled most slowly and in the centre of the clasts is intensely coloured jasper due to haematite production.

It is now recognised that the main source of the clay component was a volcanic episode or episodes, which occurred before the eruption of basalt lava of the Antrim Lava Group. This is particularly evident at Donald's Hill (Figure 12.2) (Photograph 2A) [C738 180], where the Clay-with-Flints is represented by the **Donald's Hill Ignimbrite Formation** (2). This silicic welded ash-flow tuff, although not more than 1m thick (Photographs 2B and 2C), has a 30km long outcrop and formed as a rhyolitic ignimbrite (pyroclastic flow) that resulted from a cataclysmic volcanic explosion. Silicification of the original sediment by fluids percolating downwards from the basalt lavas has produced a bed of extremely hard ash composed of 98% cryptocrystalline silica. The degree of silicification decreases towards the base of the deposit which consists of hard, unsilicified, pink-stained, flint-rich clay. Preservation of flow banding is characteristic of the creamy white to pale brown, pink or pinkish grey fine-grained matrix. Its eutaxitic texture is defined by deformed glass shards, compacted pumice (fiammé) and volcanogenic lithic clasts of more basic lava and large glassy fragments that are surrounded by the fiammé (Photomicrograph 1). Flint clasts in the upper part of the deposit are coloured reddish brown, purple or pink but towards the base, retain their original pale grey-brown colour. Small pieces of flint show evidence of melting and lobate margins indicating some reaction with the hot ash that probably had a minimum temperature of about 750°C (Photomicrograph 2).

Textures and sedimentary structures that are typical of air-fall ash deposits and lahars are also evident in the Clay-with-Flints. At Devlin's quarry [H872 816] (Figure 12.2), the typical soft clay deposit (Photograph 1) is an unsilicified extension of the Donald's Hill Ignimbrite Formation. In Gibson's quarry [H980 546], west of Portadown, the upper layer of the deposit is an air-fall accretionary lapilli-rich ash almost devoid of flint clasts (Photographs 3A, 3B and Photomicrograph 3).

At Soldierstown quarry [J157 634] north of Moira, in addition to the Clay-with-Flints deposit located between the chalk and basalt lava, there is a higher occurrence of lithologies typical of the Clay-with-Flints that are confined to a channel excavated into the top of the lowest lava flow (Photograph 4A). This feature, which occurs on both sides of the quarry, is between 2m and 10m deep and over 100m wide at its north end. The channel fill consists of several layers of bluish grey clay with whole or fragmented flints (Photograph 4B). Successive pulses of sediment originated from the south in the form of lahars that flowed over a chalk surface gathering residual flints and mixing them with contemporaneous volcanic ash (Photograph 4C).

The Palaeogene age of the Clay-with-Flints is determined from low diversity assemblages of pteridophyte spores and bisaccate plant pollen such as

Photograph 3A
The Clay-with-Flints deposit comprising a lower section of greyish brown clay with numerous, self-supporting whole, uncoloured flints and an upper section of brown, lapilli-rich clay almost devoid of flints. Gibson's quarry [H980 546], 3km WNW of Portadown, Co. Armagh. (Pen length 14cm).

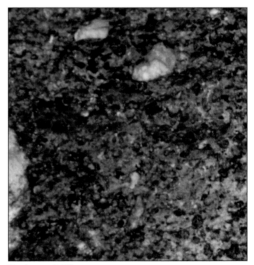

Photograph 3B
Detail of the upper section of lapilli-rich clay with small scattered flints.

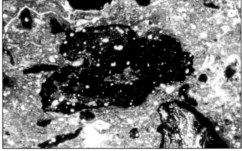

Photomicrograph 3
Photomicrograph of the lapilli-rich clay showing one deformed lapilli which suggests that it was maleable when incorporated into the deposit and that the deposit has been subject to flow.
Width of field of view 9mm.

164

Photograph 4A
Intra-basalt lava flow channel feature in the south face of quarry excavated into the top of the lowest lava flow of the Antrim Lava Group overlying the Late Cretaceous Ulster White Limestone Formation. Note the crude columnar jointing of both lava flows suggesting the presence of surface water when the lava was cooling. Soldierstown quarry [J157 634], 3km NNE of Moira, Co. Antrim.

Location of Photograph 4C

Photograph 4B
Channel feature in north face of quarry showing layering produced by multiple lahar flows.

Photograph 4C
Detail of the base of the clay-with-flints deposit filling the channel on the north face of the quarry. Note the abundance of hematised (reddened) flints which are internally heavily fractured, but still retain their original outline, suggesting that they have been subject to stress. The pinkish brown clay contains scattered lapilli indicating an air-fall ash component. The clast of weathered vesicular basalt (base, centre) is the only example found in the channel fill. (Trowel head 15cm long).

Liquidambar and *Milfordia* which have a Palaeogene range base. At Belshaw's quarry [J229 671] (Figure 12.2) the basal clay of the deposit yields abundant reworked Late Cretaceous dinoflagellate cysts. Key taxa such as *Cannosphaeropsis utinensis* (Fossil 1) *Neoeurysphaeridium glabrum* (Fossil 2) and *Odontochitina operculata* (Fossil 3), of late Campanian-early Maastrichtian age (*Belemnella lanceolata* Biozone) are associated with the long ranging form *Palaeoperidinium pyrophorum* (Fossil 4). The black colour of the dinoflagellate cysts is caused by secondary heating, in excess of *c.* 200°C, by a nearby basalt dyke. The organic residues also contain wood and plant tissue, rare insect debris (largely wing material) and other biogenic material from the chalk such as phosphatic nodules, fish scales and teeth.

At Tircrevan Burn [C703 322] the Clay-with-Flints is succeeded by at least 0.4m of soft, greyish blue, carbonaceous clays and dark grey to black lignitic clay and lignite which are overlain by basalt lava. Organic residues contain plant tissue, wood fragments, long-ranging Cretaceous and Palaeogene spores and pollen including *Caryapollenites simplex*, *Triatriopollenites*, *Tricolporopollenites* and *Trivestibulopollenites betuloides* (Fossil 5) of Palaeogene aspect. The range base of *Carya* pollen is in the Palaeocene. Based on an age of 59Ma (early Thanetian) for the first basalt lava, the lignitic beds are either late Danian or Selandian in age and were deposited in low-lying, swamp conditions with a cool temperate climate.

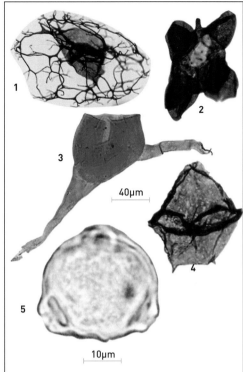

Fossils 1-5
Microfossils from the Clay-with-Flints.
Dinoflagellate cysts: **1** *Cannosphaeropsis utinensis*,
2 *Neoeurysphaeridium glabrum*,
3 *Odontochitina operculata*
(artificially stained pink with Saffranine),
4 *Palaeoperidinium pyrophorum*.
Pollen: **5** *Trivestibulopollenites betuloides*.

References
1) Smith, B. J. and McAllister, J. J. 1995. Mineralogy, chemistry and palaeoenvironmental significance of an Early Tertiary Terra Rossa from Northern Ireland: A preliminary review. *Geomorphology*, **12**, 63-73.

2) Mitchell, W. I., Cooper, M. R., Hards, V. L. and Meighan, I. G. 1999. An occurrence of silicic volcanic rocks in the early Palaeogene Antrim Lava Group of Northern Ireland. *Scottish Journal of Geology*, **35**, 179-85.

Chapter 14

Palaeogene Extrusive Igneous Rocks

M. R. COOPER

Mantle plumes, ocean spreading and the North Atlantic Igneous Province

In the Late Cretaceous and Palaeocene (1) the **Iceland Plume** or 'hot spot' impinged on the base of the lithosphere and produced huge volumes of magma. Called the Thulean Volcanic Province, it was in the present area of the North Atlantic Ocean between Greenland and Europe (Figure 14.1). Although the plume centre was probably located in Greenland (Figure 14.2), associated magmatism extended over an area with a diameter in excess of 2000km (2). Thus, igneous provinces occurring as far apart as west Greenland, northwest Scotland and Northern Ireland were all produced by this plume (3). However, magmatic activity was not constant in the volcanic province as there is evidence of two major pulses

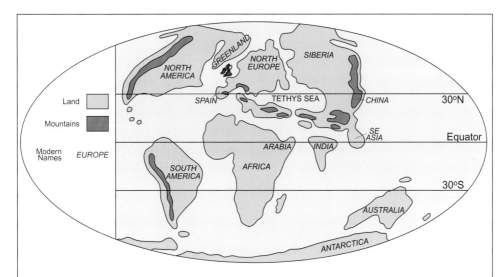

Continuing movement of the continents saw their distribution more closely resemble the geographical position that is recognisable to us today. In particular both the South Atlantic and North Atlantic Ocean continued to expand pushing Europe away from North America and Africa away from South America. Although still moving northwards India did not collide with the southern margin of Asia, and thereby create the Himalayas, until about 25Ma ago. The northward movement of Africa towards southern Europe lead to the onset of the Alpine Orogeny, but also created a water-filled depression between the two landmasses that later became the Mediterranean Sea. In the North Atlantic area the movement apart of North America and Europe stretched, thinned and ruptured the crust and allowed the migration to the surface of magma (the Iceland Plume) derived from the mantle. In Northern Ireland, basalt lavas of the Antrim Plateau represent a portion of a once more extensive lava plateau.

Figure 14.1
Position of the continents in Palaeocene times (c. 60Ma (1)).

with peaks at about 59 and 55Ma (4). Indications of an older phase of magmatic activity at about 62Ma are based on the dating of centres outside Northern Ireland.

At present in the North Atlantic region, volcanic activity is still related to the Iceland Plume. It is located beneath the mid-Atlantic Ridge, where oceanic crust is still forming, and is evident in the active surface volcanism on Iceland. The stark volcanic landscape of that island offers insights into the origin of rock types found in the Antrim Lava Group in Northern Ireland and examples of the volcanic processes that formed them such as the fissure eruptions and lava flows of Krafla.

During the Palaeocene, the continental crust of Ireland was influenced by a syn-magmatic extensional tectonic regime related to an early attempt to open the **North Atlantic Ocean** between Greenland and Europe (5). Extension, dilation and uplift of the crust were linked to doming caused by the rise of hot magma fed by the Iceland Plume. This was ultimately responsible for the initial opening of the North Atlantic Ocean by seafloor spreading at the mid-Atlantic Ridge in the latest Palaeocene-early Eocene, about 55Ma ago (Table 14.1).

Between c. 62 and 55Ma the Northern Ireland sector of the **North Atlantic Igneous Province** experienced plume-related igneous activity which led to the development of lava fields and intrusive or central complexes (6). The largest remnant of that igneous province in Britain and Ireland forms the Antrim Plateau although lava fields and central complexes occur in western Scotland (Figure 14.3). Offshore Palaeogene volcanic centres occur in the Blackstones Bank, and extend the igneous province northwest to the Rockall Trough and south to Lundy Island in the Bristol Channel.

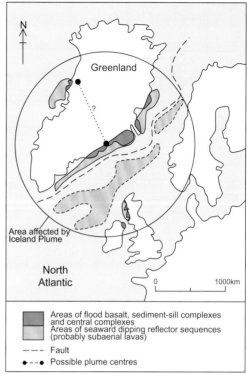

Figure 14.2
North Atlantic reconstruction during the Early Eocene (c. 50Ma (3)).

Stratigraphy and Chronology

In the c. 10Ma time gap between the end of deposition of the Cretaceous chalk (Chapter 12) and the first extrusion of basalt lava of the Palaeocene Antrim Lava Group, regional uplift and erosion produced an unconformity that is exposed at the margins of the Antrim Plateau. The earliest deposit above the chalk is the Clay-with-Flints (Chapter 13) which had masked the river valleys and karstic scenery of the gently rolling landscape. The Clay-with-Flints deposit is overlain (Table 14.1) by volcanic rocks, mainly basalt lava flows, of the **Antrim Lava Group** (7, 8). In Northern Ireland the eruption of the Lower Basalt and Upper Basalt formations of the Antrim Lava Group (Table 14.1) occurred in two cycles (9) which coincided with the two province-wide phases of magmatism recorded at about 59 and 55Ma respectively.

168

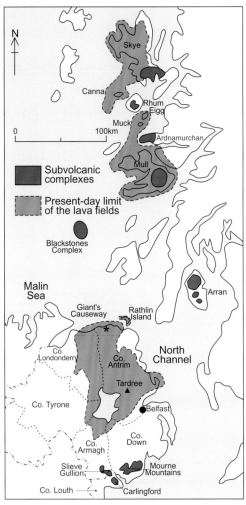

Figure 14.3
Location of the present day limits of lava fields and sub-volcanic complexes in the North Atlantic Igneous Province (6).

In Co. Antrim, the first evidence of volcanic activity is in the form of ash-fall deposits and small volcanic cones that resulted from localised, explosive activity and were followed by fissure eruptions of olivine tholeiite lavas of the **Lower Basalt Formation** (Figure 14.4 and Table 14.1). Fractionation of the parental magma gave rise to intermediate lavas near the top of the Lower Basalt Formation. The associated decrease in volcanic activity ultimately led to the formation of the **Interbasaltic Formation**, which consists mainly of lateritised basalt of the Lower Basalt Formation. Deep weathering and lateritisation of basalt lava occurred during a relatively short period of sub-tropical weathering. Although frequently categorised as a time of volcanic quiescence, contemporaneous volcanism during the interbasaltic period produced the columnar basalts of the Giant's Causeway and the silicic volcanic complex at Tardree (Figure 14.4). The second cycle is characterised by a return to the eruption of the olivine tholeiite lavas of the **Upper Basalt Formation**.

Volcanic activity related to the Iceland Plume continued after the extrusion of the Upper Basalt Formation (Table 14.1). This is supported by the dating of the Portrush Sill at 57.1 ± 0.2Ma (pers. comm. Bergman, Phillips and Allen, 2003) and the presence of lava of the Upper Basalt Formation in the central volcanic complex at Slieve Gullion that is dated to 58-56Ma. Emplacement of granites of the Mourne Mountains Complex, between 56 and 55Ma (Dr I. G. Meighan pers. comm. 2003), was characterised by an increase in the proportion of felsic magma as a result of differentiation of crustally contaminated basic magma derived from the upper mantle (10).

Finally, in the north of Ireland there are numerous examples of **dykes, dyke swarms, sills, cone sheets** and **ring dykes**, that formed by the movement of magma along faults and bedding planes. All ages of older rocks are affected by these intrusions including the Upper Basalt Formation and the youngest granite of the Mourne Mountains Complex demonstrating that plume-related volcanism continued after 55Ma.

Antrim Lava Group

The Antrim Lava Group consists mainly of basaltic rocks that cover much of Co. Antrim and parts of Co. Londonderry and north Co. Armagh (Figure 14.3). Its outcrop extends only a short distance offshore beyond the east coast of Co. Antrim into the North Channel and into the Malin Sea north of the outcrop on Rathlin Island. The former extent of the Antrim Lava Group onshore is not known. However, based on comparisons with the island of Mull, where it is estimated that 1000m of basalt lava was eroded (11), if a similar thickness had been removed in Northern Ireland, then it is probable that the lavas extended far beyond their present outcrop. Supporting evidence for an erosive event of similar magnitude is found in the presence of basalt outliers on Slieve Gallion [H813 896] and Knocklayd [D115 364]. The outliers in Co. Armagh, between the southern margin of the Antrim Plateau and Slieve Gullion are an indication of the minimum southerly extent of the basalt lava field (Figures 14.3 and 14.4).

The earliest evidence of explosive volcanism at the base of the Antrim Lava Group is vent agglomerates, ash cones and layers of pyroclastic tuff in north Co. Antrim. Chalky and basaltic tuff, some 60m thick, occur at the base and in lower levels of the Lower Basalt Formation, and extend for at least 7km from the source between Ballintoy and Ballycastle (Figure 14.4) (12). At Kinbane [Do88 439],

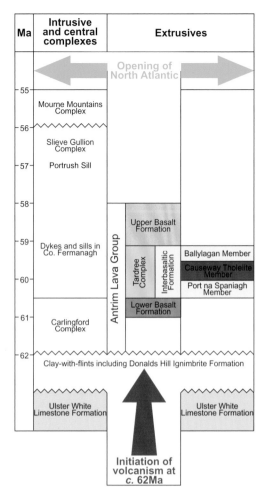

Table 14.1
Stratigraphy and chronology of Palaeocene extrusive and intrusive igneous rocks in Northern Ireland.

chalky tuff overlain by basaltic tuff is exposed in the cliffs southwest of the headland (Figure 14.5). Although the volcanic vent that produced these pyroclastic deposits is now concealed, the chalk outcrop at Kinbane is riddled with subsidiary vents filled by shattered chalk, basaltic agglomerate and doleritic intrusions (12, 13). At Carrickarade [Do62 448], the footpath and rope bridge provide excellent views of an agglomerate-filled vent (Photograph 1). At White Rocks [C886 407] east of Portrush, vents exposed on the foreshore are also filled with chalk boulders and basalt agglomerate.

Within the Antrim Lava Group there are very few examples of sedimentary deposits intervening between the basalt lava flows. However, in the area east of Cookstown, the **Coagh Conglomerate Member** (14) represents a fluvial deposit that is located near the base of the Lower Basalt Formation (Figure 14.4). The conglomerate crops out in a stream [H898 789] 800m ENE of Coagh Bridge and is underlain by about 5m of basalt lava. It comprises about 6m of clast-supported conglomerate composed of well-rounded pebbles and cobbles of basalt in a dark greyish green clay matrix with multicoloured chips and rounded granules of red clay. Very rare clasts of flow-banded porphyritic rhyolite are recorded in the conglomerate (15).

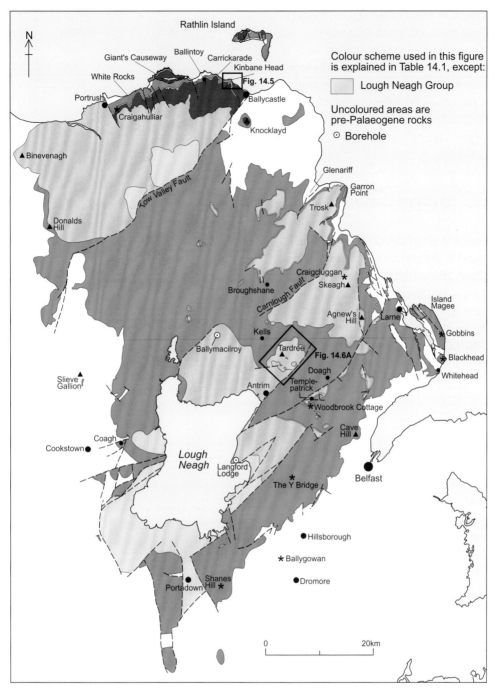

Figure 14.4
Distribution of the Antrim Lava Group in Northern Ireland.

The early phase of localised explosive volcanism was followed by the widespread eruption of basalt lava flows of the **Lower Basalt Formation**. Lava reached the surface from vents and along NNW-aligned fissures and has a maximum thickness of 531m (16) in the Langford Lodge borehole (Figure 14.4). Flows are exposed in numerous cliff sections both at the coast and inland, particularly in quarries. In Co. Antrim they are exposed at Cave Hill

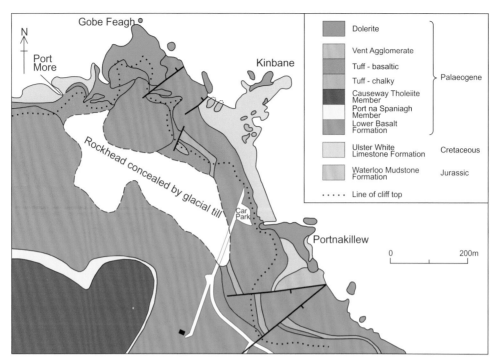

Figure 14.5
Geological map of the Kinbane Head area of north Co. Antrim (13).

Dolerite

Vent Agglomerate

Tuff - basaltic

Tuff - chalky

Causeway Tholeiite Member

Port na Spaniagh Member

Lower Basalt Formation

} Palaeogene

Ulster White Limestone Formation — Cretaceous

Waterloo Mudstone Formation — Jurassic

. . . . . Line of cliff top

[J325 799], Black Head [J488 934] north of Whitehead (Photograph 2), the Gobbins [J485 976] on Island Magee and in Glenariff Forest Park [D217 206].

Lava flows of the Lower Basalt and Upper Basalt formations are usually not more than 10m thick and can be divided into three parts. Flow bases commonly exhibit concentrations of vesicles (Photograph 3) that were originally gas bubbles which develop into vesicle cylinders with a pipe-like form that extends upwards through a flow (Photograph 4). Central portions of flows are often massive with irregular columnar jointing. Flow tops are frequently vesicular but are most commonly weathered to purplish red lithomarge (palaeosol) and may be capped by a layer of bright red, weathered volcanic dust. Vesicles are referred to as amygdales when they are filled with zeolite minerals precipitated from hot groundwater.

Photograph 1
Carrickarade rope bridge and cliffs of volcanic agglomerate. Carrickarade [D062 449], 7km northwest of Ballycastle, Co. Antrim.

172

Thin lava flows of the Lower Basalt Formation (Antrim Lava Group). Black Head [J488 935], 2km northeast of Whitehead, Co. Antrim.

The Lower Basalt Formation showing the top of a lower flow (reddened) and base of the succeeding flow with numerous pipe vesicles. Black Head [J488 935], 2km northeast of Whitehead, Co. Antrim. (Hammer 36cm long).

Petrographical and geochemical studies demonstrate that basalt lava from both the lower and upper formations consists of fine-grained, olivine basalt (olivine tholeiites) composed of plagioclase feldspar, olivine, augite and opaque minerals (9, 17). Plagioclase, as the dominant phase, is either randomly orientated or more rarely will show a flow alignment and fluxion around olivine phenocrysts (Photomicrograph 1).

Tholeiitic andesite lava flows (formerly referred to as mugearite) with an outcrop length of up to 8km occur towards the centre and top of the Lower Basalt Formation near Antrim and Templepatrick (18, 19, 20) and at Larne (21) in south and southeast Co. Antrim. They are fine-grained and flow banded with a flaggy to massive aspect in exposures in the Stoneyford River at The Y Bridge [J201 723] and in streams at Woodbrook Cottage [J229 850] near Templepatrick (Figure 14.4).

Photograph 4
Lava flow of the Lower Basalt Formation with vesicle cylinders. Black Head [J488 935], 2km northeast of Whitehead, Co. Antrim. (Umbrella 40cm long).

The **Interbasaltic Formation** normally consists of 10-15m of orange-red lateritic palaeosol, but also in parts may still retain relict igneous and mineral textures in the purplish red, deeply weathered basalt and is referred to as lithomarge. Alteration has resulted in an iron-rich laterite composed mainly of the secondary clay mineral kaolinite and containing at least 30% iron as Fe_2O_3 and 5% titanium as TiO_2. Bauxite or aluminous laterite is more restricted in distribution than the ferruginous laterite and was produced by the weathering of silicic volcanic rocks and ash. The dominant clay mineral is gibbsite and the aluminium content as Al_2O_3 is at least 50%.

Photomicrograph 1
Olivine basalt containing phenocrysts of plagioclase feldspar and olivine in a very fine-grained matrix of olivine, augite, opaque ore minerals and flow aligned microlites of plagioclase. Lower Basalt Formation at the Giant's Causeway, Co. Antrim.

In north Co. Antrim, the period of time in which the Interbasaltic Formation was formed was associated with the eruption of the mainly quartz-tholeiites of the **Causeway Tholeiite Member** (Table 14.1). As the first flow crossed the land surface it filled several valleys known to have existed in lavas at the top of the Lower Basalt Formation. Trapped there, the ponded lava cooled slowly forming the famous columns of the Giants Causeway (Photographs 5 and 6), now a World Heritage Site. Individual flows of this member may be divided into a lower colonnade, entablature and an upper colonnade (22), as seen at the Giant's Organ. In addition to the effects of contraction and cooling of the lava other factors may have contributed to the formation of the columnar jointing. The first prerequisite seems to have been that lava flow had virtually ceased. Curvilinear jointing at the Giant's Harp would seem to indicate however, that residual movement did occur during crystallisation. Textural homogeneity may also have been essential and is born out by the petrography of the

Photograph 5
The Giant's Harp and the Chimney Tops at the Giant's Causeway [C951 448]. Two flows of tholeiitic basalt lava (Causeway Tholeiite Member) overlie the reddish brown Interbasaltic Formation. The lower part of the cliff is formed of five flows of the Lower Basalt Formation, Co. Antrim.

Photograph 6
Part of the Grand Causeway showing the irregular polygonal form of the columns.
Giant's Causeway, Co. Antrim.

tholeiites which are all composed of very fine-grained augite, plagioclase feldspar, glass and opaques with rare phenocrysts of feldspar and olivine (23). There is also a close relationship between the occurrence of a colonnade and entablature and the presence of rocks associated with water including river and lake sediments, pillow lavas and hyaloclastite breccias. It seems likely that water displaced by lava flows of the Causeway Tholeiite Member in the valleys flooded the upper surface of the flow, modifying the cooling regime and encouraging the formation of multi-tiered columnar flows. Flooding of the top cooling surface by rain probably also aided the formation of the upper colonnade. Spectacular cliffs at Port Noffer on the Giant's Causeway expose the Lower Basalt Formation, Interbasaltic Formation and lowest two flows of the Causeway Tholeiite Member.

In north Co. Antrim, extrusion of the Causeway Tholeiite Member led to the formation of two separate interbasaltic horizons (Table 14.1). The lower horizon, the **Port na Spaniagh Member**, is represented by the red laterite at the Giant's Causeway which consists of 15m of completely weathered basalt of the Lower Basalt Formation with residual masses of relatively unweathered basalt known as Giant's Eyes. At Craigahulliar quarry [C883 389] the member includes lacustrine mudstone and siltstone with well-preserved deciduous leaf impressions, and a 6m bed of lignite that was worked for fuel. Below the sediments is a pahoehoe lava surface with small domes and collapsed blisters indicating sub-aerial cooling and subsequent flooding (24). The upper bed, the **Ballylagan Member**, which rarely exceeds 1m in thickness, is the weathered top of the Causeway Tholeiite Member and is developed only intermittently between Craigahulliar quarry (25) and Ballycastle.

In central Co. Antrim, silicic igneous activity during interbasaltic times produced the rhyolite lavas and pyroclastic rocks of the Tardree Rhyolite Complex (Figure 14.6), the volcanic vent at Sandy Braes [J206 960] and 430m of rhyolite penetrated in a borehole at Templepatrick (7). Outliers of the Upper Basalt Formation in central Co. Antrim are underlain by siliceous bauxite of the Interbasaltic Formation that formed by weathering of the acidic volcanic rocks produced by the Tardree volcano.

Small, isolated acidic intrusions, that are probably contemporaneous with the Tardree Rhyolite Complex, intrude the Lower Basalt Formation at Shane's Hill, and the Silurian greywacke at Ballygowan [J190 570] between Dromore and Hillsborough in Co. Down (Figure 14.4). The **Shane's Hill intrusion** [J065 532], east of Portadown, has a roughly rectangular outline and consists of xenolithic and xenocrystic rhyodacite and latite, most probably of volcanic origin (8). Petrographic analysis reveals a complex intrusive history that commenced with minute fractures in cooled plutonic rocks of diorite, monzonite and granite composition being invaded by magma of basaltic or intermediate composition that quenched to a brown glass. Subsequent intrusion by the later rhyodacite/latite magma entrained and partially remelted fragments of the plutonic rocks and erupted at the surface having penetrated the overlying basalt lavas. Outcrops consist mainly of pale grey to white rhyodacite. However, this dominant colour is secondary and is the result of hydrothermal alteration of the original dark grey lithology, which is now restricted to small, sharp-edged patches in exposures. Xenocrysts consist mainly of rounded quartz, orthoclase (with residual spots of plagioclase due to alteration), plagioclase and acicular pyroxene (primarily augite) or amphibole.

The maximum thickness recorded for the **Upper Basalt Formation** is 346m in the Ballymacilroy borehole [J057 976] (26) although the largest part of the outcrop occurs north of the Tow Valley Fault and on the eastern side of the Antrim Plateau (Figure 14.4). Its present distribution indicates that the new lava flows overstepped the Lower Basalt Formation onto Dalradian, Carboniferous and Mesozoic rocks beyond the western edge of the Antrim Plateau. These flows also originated from NNW-orientated fissures and vents and at first encountered a vegetated and wet land surface of lateritised basalt that gave rise to flow-ploughing into pre-existing soil deposits (27). The Upper Basalt Formation is divided into a lower aphyric group and an upper olivine-phyric, flow-banded group that are separated by a layer of grey bauxite which is 9m thick at Agnew's Hill [D327 015] (28). Although texturally and chemically distinct, it is nevertheless believed that olivine fractionation was the main differentiation process in both groups. At the top of the formation the flow-banded, olivine-phyric lava probably indicates a source in close proximity to the outcrop. North of the Tow Valley Fault, the association of thin layers of pahoehoe lava,

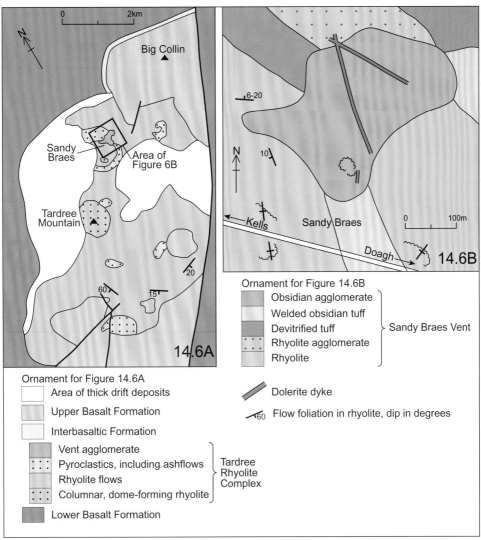

Figure 14.6
Location map of the Tardree Rhyolite Complex (A) and details of the Sandy Braes vent (B) (7,20).

spatter ramparts and of scoriaceous and oxidised vent material indicates close proximity to active fissures. In the formation outcrop south of the Carnlough Fault (Figure 14.4) there is an association between the upper, flow-banded, lavas and flow-banded dolerite plugs at Craigcluggan [D293 080] and Skeagh [D303 060]. The outcrop between Garron Point and Broughshane is related to the dolerite plug at Trosk [D263 196].

Geochemical trends for major and minor elements in the Lower Basalt and Upper Basalt formations show that there is a progression towards mantle depletion in the latter formation, particularly in east and south Co. Antrim where there is a thick Lower Basalt Formation (29). However, in the Antrim Plateau northwest of the Tow Valley Fault, the Lower Basalt Formation is either very thin or possibly absent in some places, such as at Binevenagh [C692 302]. Geochemical trends in the Upper Basalt Formation in that area more closely resemble those for the Lower Basalt Formation in south and east Co. Antrim. This reflects the melting of a less depleted mantle source northwest of the Tow Valley Fault with lava of the Upper Basalt Formation often being the first products derived from that new mantle source.

References

1) Osborne, R. and Tarling, D. H. 1995. *The Historical Atlas of the Earth (A Visual Exploration of the Earth's Physical Past)*. Viking. Penguin Books Ltd., London.

2) White, R. S. 1989. Initiation of the Iceland Plume and opening of the North Atlantic Margins. *In*: Tankard, A. J. and Balkwill, H. R. (eds.). *Extensional Tectonics and Stratigraphy of the North Atlantic Margins*. American Association of Petroleum Geologists Memoir, **46**, 149-54.

3) Ritchie, J. D., Gatliff, R. W. and Richards, P. C., 1999. Early Tertiary magmatism in the offshore NW UK margin and surrounds. *In*: Fleet, A. J. and Boldy, S. A. R. (eds.). *Petroleum Geology of Northwest Europe: Proceedings of the 5th Conference*, 573-84. © Petroleum Geology '86 Ltd. Published by the Geological Society, London.

4) Dickin, A. P. 1988. The North Atlantic Tertiary Province. *In*: Macdougall, J. D. (ed.). Continental Flood Basalts. Kinwer Academic Publishers, 111-49.

5) Geoffroy, L., Bergerat, F. and Angelier, J. 1996. Brittle tectonism in relation to the Palaeogene evolution of the Thulean/NE Atlantic domain: a study in Ulster. *Geological Journal*, **31**, 259-69.

6) Bell, B. R. and Jolley, D. W. 1997. Application of palynological data to the chronology of the Palaeogene lava fields of the British Province: implications for magmatic stratigraphy. *Journal of the Geological Society, London*, **154**, 701-708.

7) Old, R. A. 1975. The age and field relationships of the Tardree Tertiary Rhyolite Complex, County Antrim, Northern Ireland. *Bulletin of the Geological Survey of Great Britain*, **51**, 21-40.

8) Geological Survey of Northern Ireland 1997. Northern Ireland. Solid Geology (second edition). 1:250,000. (Keyworth, Nottingham: British Geological Survey).

9) Lyle, P. 1980. A petrological and geochemical study of the Tertiary basaltic rocks of northeast Ireland. *Journal of Earth Sciences, Royal Dublin Society*, **2**, 137-52.

10) Meighan, I. G., Fallick, A. E. and McCormick, A. G. 1992. Anorogenic granite magma genesis: new isotopic evidence for the southern sector of the British Tertiary Igneous Province. *Transactions of the Royal Society of Edinburgh:Earth Sciences*, **83**, 227-33.

11) Walker, G. P. L. 1971. The distribution of amygdale minerals in Mull and Morven (western Scotland). *In*: Murty, T. V. V. G. G. R. K. and Roa, S. S. (eds.). *Studies in Earth Sciences*, W. D. West commemorative volume, 181-94.

12) Wilson. H. E. and Manning, P. I., 1978 Geology of the Causeway Coast. *Memoir of the Geological Survey of Northern Ireland*, Sheet 7. HMSO, Belfast.

13) Emeleus, C. H. and Preston, J., 1969. Field excursion guide to the Tertiary Volcanic rocks of Ireland. Belfast.

14) Cameron, I. B. and Old, R. A. 1997. *Geology of the country around Cookstown. 1:50 000 Geological Sheet 27 (Cookstown)*. Geological Survey of Northern Ireland. Technical Report GSNI/97/7.

15) Patterson, E. M., 1955. The Tertiary lava succession in the western part of the Antrim plateau. *Proceedings of the Royal Irish Academy*, **57B**, 155-78.

16) Manning, P. I., Robbie, J. A. and Wilson, H. E. 1960. Geology of Belfast and the Lagan Valley. *Memoir of the Geological Survey of Northern Ireland*. HMSO, Belfast.

17) Lyle, P. 1985. The geochemistry and petrology of Tertiary basalts from the Binevenagh area, County Londonderry. *Irish Journal of Earth Sciences*, **7**, 59-64.

18) Lyle, P. and Thompson, S. J. 1983. The classification and chemistry of the Tertiary intermediate lavas of Northeast Ireland. *Scottish Journal of Geology*, **19**, 17-27.

19) Thompson, S. J. 1997. *Geology of the country around Antrim. 1:50 000 Geological Sheet 28 (Antrim)*. Geological Survey of Northern Ireland. Technical Report GSNI/97/6.

20) Geological Survey of Northern Ireland 1994. Antrim, Northern Ireland Sheet 28. Solid and Drift Geology. 1:50,000. (Keyworth, Nottingham: British Geological Survey).

21) Geological Survey of Northern Ireland 1994. Larne, Northern Ireland Sheet 21. Solid and Drift Geology. 1:50,000. (Keyworth, Nottingham: British Geological Survey).

22) Lyle, P. and Preston, J. 1997/8. The influence of eruptive conditions on joint development in the Causeway Tholeiite Member of the Tertiary Antrim Lava Group, Northern Ireland. *Irish Journal of Earth Sciences*, **16**, 19-32.

23) Lyle, P. and Preston, J. 1993. Geochemistry and volcanology of the Tertiary basalts of the Giant's Causeway area, Northern Ireland. *Journal of the Geological Society, London*, **150**, 109-20.

24) Lyle, P. *A geological excursion guide to the Causeway Coast*. W. & G. Baird Ltd. Second printing, 1998.

25) Geological Survey of Northern Ireland 1998. Causeway Coast, Northern Ireland Sheet 7. Solid Geology. 1:50,000. (Keyworth, Nottingham: British Geological Survey).

26) Thompson, S. J. 1979. Preliminary report on the Ballymacilroy No. 1 borehole, Ahoghill, Co. Antrim. *Open File Report No. 63, Geological Survey of Northern Ireland*. Belfast.

27) Wilson, H. E. 1965. Lava ploughing in the Tertiary Basalts of County Antrim. Geological Magazine, **10**, 538-40.

28) Lyle, P. and Patton, D. J. S. 1989. The petrography and geochemistry of the Upper Basalt Formation of the Antrim Lava Group in northeast Ireland. *Irish Journal of Earth Sciences*, **10**, 33-41.

29) Lyle, P. 1988. The geochemistry, petrology and volcanology of the Tertiary lava succession of the Binevenagh-Benbraddagh area of County Londonderry. *Irish Journal of Earth Sciences*, **9**, 141-52.

Chapter 15

Palaeogene Intrusive Igneous Rocks

M. R. COOPER and T. P. JOHNSTON

Introduction

The focus of intrusive Palaeogene igneous activity was located in Counties Down and Armagh in Northern Ireland and in Co. Louth in the Republic of Ireland (Figure 15.1). Three central complexes, the Mourne Mountains, Slieve Gullion and Carlingford intrude the deformed Silurian turbidite succession of the Southern Uplands-Down-Longford Terrane (Photograph 1).

The rocks formed at this time were predominantly silicic in composition and included large volumes of granite, felsite and granophyre. However, significant bodies of basalt,

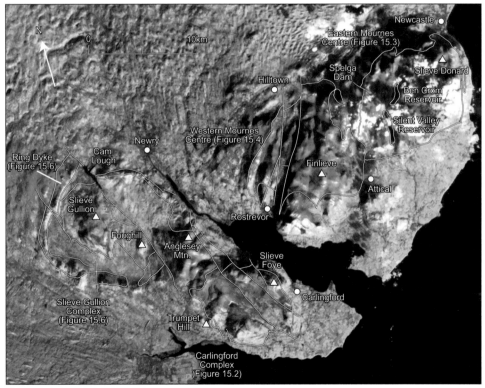

Photograph 1
Landsat TM5 winter scene of the southeastern part of Northern Ireland showing the three principal Palaeogene intrusive igneous centres of Carlingford, Slieve Gullion and the ring dyke and the Mourne Mountains.

dolerite and gabbro also formed at this time in the Sleve Gullion and Carlingford complexes. The regional gravity map of Northern Ireland shows a large positive Bouguer anomaly slightly offset to the north of Slieve Gullion and the Mourne Mountains which may represent a concealed, high density, basic or ultrabasic body (1).

Intrusive Centres
Carlingford Complex

Although the Carlingford Complex is located entirely in Co. Louth (2) it is one of three closely associated Palaeogene intrusive igneous centres (Figure 15.1) and is therefore included here (Photograph 2). The Carlingford Complex is the oldest intrusive complex dated (U-Pb zircon SHRIMP age) to 61.4 ± 0.8Ma (3).

The earliest component of the Carlingford Complex consists of 275m of **tholeiitic basalt** and **hawaiite lavas** that are exposed at the southern edge of the complex on south-facing slopes of

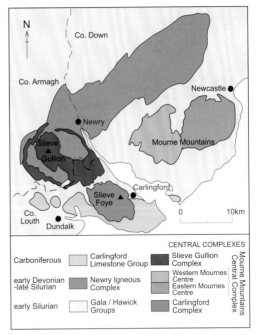

Figure 15.1
Distribution of Palaeogene intrusive centres in the north of Ireland

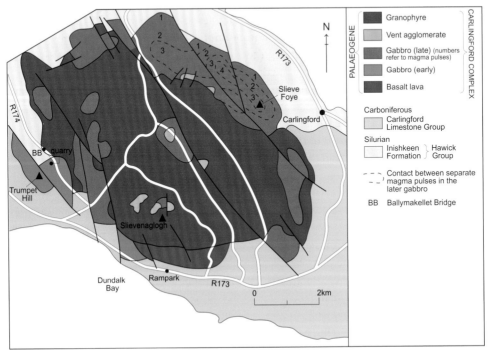

Figure 15.2
Geological map of the Carlingford Complex (2).

Photograph 2
Looking southeast along Carlingford Lough which is flanked by the southern edge of the Western Mournes Centre (left) and Slieve Foye and the Carlingford Complex on the south side of the lough.

Slievenaglogh [J145 075] near Rampark (4). The lavas were subsequently intruded by at least two separate phases of **gabbro** (5). An **early gabbro** was confined to the southwest part of the complex and is now exposed in a series of north-south elongated plugs in the Trumpet Hill area [J098 101] and in the disused quarry [J104 104] near Ballymakellet Bridge. The **later gabbro** was intruded into the roof of the intrusive complex and is now preserved as isolated patches within the complex and as hills and knolls at its periphery. On Slieve Foye [J169 120], the later gabbro consists of four layers with a total thickness of over 365m that were formed by four separate magma pulses along the unconformity between the Silurian country rocks and the earlier basalt lava. Each magma pulse produced a layer between 60-150m thick and each layer shows the effects of crystal fractionation. The resulting compositional layering in each layer is defined by a more mafic-rich base, enriched in olivine, and a less-mafic top that is more plagioclase-rich. The later gabbro contains xenoliths of Silurian country rock altered to pyroxene hornfels, and of Carboniferous limestone altered to a calcsilicate rock.

Following the emplacement of the gabbro, there was a return to predominantly silicic intrusive magmatism and the intrusion of at least two phases of granophyre (6). The **early granophyre** is not exposed in the complex but is preserved as xenoliths in vent agglomerates on Slievenaglogh [J135 090]. The **agglomerates** were associated with a brief episode of explosive volcanic activity prior to the intrusion of the later granophyre. The **later (Carlingford) granophyre** occupies the centre of the complex forming a ring dyke with a laccolithic top. The geochemical signature of certain silicic rocks in the Carlingford Complex suggests that the granitic magmas were largely generated by basaltic differentiation (7). At the southern margin of the Carlingford Complex, Carboniferous limestone recrystallised by intrusion of the granophyre now contains forsteritic olivine, garnet and spinel and calcsilicate minerals including wollastonite and diopside. During the closing stages of igneous activity at Carlingford increasing pressure from beneath, and uplift of the caldera, resulted in the dilation of surface fractures and facilitated the repeated intrusion of basic magma in the form of cone sheets and a linear dyke swarm.

Photograph 3
Panoramic view of the south side of the Mourne Mountains extending from the east flank of Finlieve to the west flank of Slieve Binnian. Looking north from Aughrim Hill [J282 180] the contact between the western and eastern centres follows the Kilkeel-Hilltown Road.

Mourne Mountains Complex

The Mourne Mountains granite complex was intruded into Silurian greywacke and slate country rock at a high level in the crust around 56Ma but did not reach the surface (8). The complex consists of five principal granite intrusions (G1–G5) which are divided between a western and an eastern centre (Photograph 3). Each of the four youngest granites (G2-G5) was emplaced as a series of smaller magmatic pulses that are distinguished by distinct textural variations (9). Geophysical evidence indicates that denser, more basic rocks underlie the granite complex (10). Rare xenoliths of gabbro and anorthosite are found in some later dykes and may have originated from that basic body (11). Geochemically, the five granites form a single subalkaline acid fractional crystallization series, in which G1, the most basic, originated by differentiation of a crustally contaminated basaltic melt in the upper continental crust (7, 8).

Photograph 4
The Ben Crom reservoir from the Brandy Pad [J333 284], 1km east of the Hare's Gap. The base of the cliffs on Ben Crom is the contact between fine- to medium-grained granites of the G2 Inner facies forming the summit area and fine-grained G3 granite.

The **Eastern Mournes Centre** consists of three intrusive members (Figure 15.3 and Table 15.1). The earliest component G1, a hornblende-biotite syenogranite (Photomicrograph 1) was followed by G2, a biotite granite (Photomicrograph 2) with abundant dark quartz and finally by G3, a fine-grained aplitic biotite syenogranite (Photograph 4). Each main granite, G1 Roof, G2 Outer Mafic Facies, G2 Outer Normal, G2 Inner and G3 (Figure 15.3), can be recognised in the field by its petrographic characteristics (Table 15.1) (12). In addition, a range of textural variations from fine- to coarse-grained has been recognised within G2 and G3 and many internal contacts are exposed between the different types (9, 12).

The **Western Mournes Centre** consists of two granites (Figure 15.4). G4 is biotite granite and G5 a biotite ± amphibole microgranite or granophyre (13). Each granite can be recognised in the field by its petrographic characteristics and a range of textural variations (Table 15.2) (13). In each centre there were sufficiently long intervals between the intrusion

182

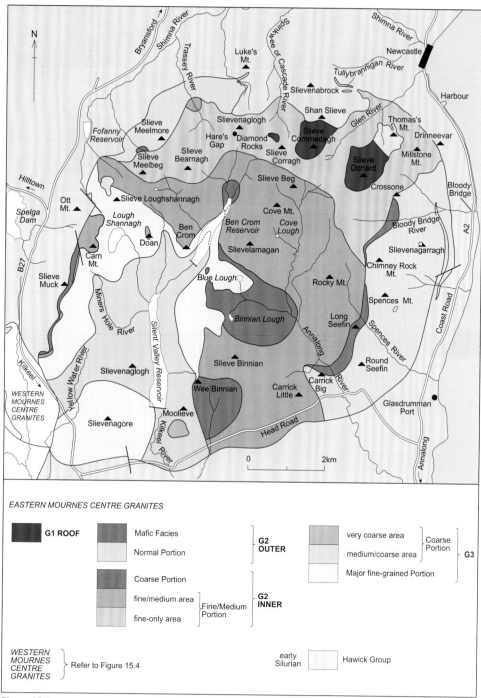

Figure 15.3
Geological map of the Eastern Mournes Centre - from Hood, D. N. 1981 (12); Cone-sheets and dykes not shown.

of successive magma pulses to allow each magma to solidify and a fine-grained margin to form on the later intrusion.

Direct field evidence of the involvement of crystal fractionation in the crystallisation of felsic magmas is rare in British Palaeogene granites. However, in the Mourne Mountains Complex a boulder, some 0.9m in length (Photograph 5), which probably originated from the

Colours as per Figure 15.3		G1	G2			G3
			G2 Outer		G2 Inner	
		G1 Roof	Mafic Facies	Normal Portion	Coarse & Fine/Medium Portions	Coarse & Major fine-grained Portions
Granite Type		hornblende (hastingsite) - biotite syenogranite	biotite hornblende syenogranite	biotite syenogranites		
Colour	weathered	dark brown	creamy/white	white to rusty brown		
	fresh	greenish/grey		creamy with pinkish tinge	pinkish in medium & coarse varieties; creamy/pinkish in fine varieties	creamy with pinkish tinge in coarse varieties; pale grey in fine varieties
Mafic Minerals		large, obvious clusters	distinct, large or clustered groundmass grains of biotite	slightly smaller clusters than G1 Roof; plus groundmass grains	less obvious groundmass grains than Normal G2 Outer	euhedral, short, stubby or acicular single grains, also in small clusters
Quartz		inconspicuous, small, rounded to sub-rounded grains	conspicuous, rounded, grey/brown grains	medium grey grains; paler than G2 Inner	dark/black, variable sizes; large gns. in coarser varieties	paler grey than G2; sparse, rounded plus groundmass grains
Plagioclase Feldspar		light grey/green when fresh, brown when weathered; anhedral to subhedral grains	creamy/white anhedral to subhedral grains			
Alkali Feldspar		greenish/grey when fresh; vitreous dusty brown/cream when weathered	creamy/white slight pinkish tinge	pinkish; paler than G2 Inner coarse-med vars. especially in NW outcrop	pink & pale pink in coarse & medium grained varieties; creamy with pinky tinge in fine vars.	creamy with slightly pinkish tinge only in coarse and medium-grained varieties; creamy in fine vars.
Texture		semiporphyritic to porphyritic; coarsest granite	porphyritic to semiporphyritic	equigranular	semiporphyritic to equigranular	typically speckled appearance; semi-porphyritic to equigranular

Table 15.1
Petrographic characteristics of the granites of the Eastern Mournes Centre (12).

Colours as per Figure 15.4	G4			G5	
	Fine-grained marginal	Finer medium to medium-grained	Coarse-grained	Mafic-poor unit	Mafic-rich unit
Granite type	extremely leucocratic granite		biotite granite	non-porphyritic microgranite to granite	amphibole-biotite granophyre or microgranite
Colour	pale, greyish-brown		deep, pinkish-brown	light brown	bluish-grey
Quartz	small, dark, equant grains				pale grey, small grains
Plagioclase Feldspar	white, small, anhedral grains	white to cream grains	white to cream with bluish tinge, subhedral grains	very fine- to medium-grained interstitial grains	white, small, subanhedral grains
Alkali Feldspar	pale pink to greyish-brown subhedral grains		distinct, euhedral, pinkish-brown	fine to medium subhedral grains	fine subhedral grains
Texture	granular with drusy cavities	granophyric intergrowths; variably drusy	coarse-grained granitic	microgranitic to granitic	microgranitic to granophyric

Table 15.2
Petrographic characteristics of the granites of the Western Mournes Centre (13).

184

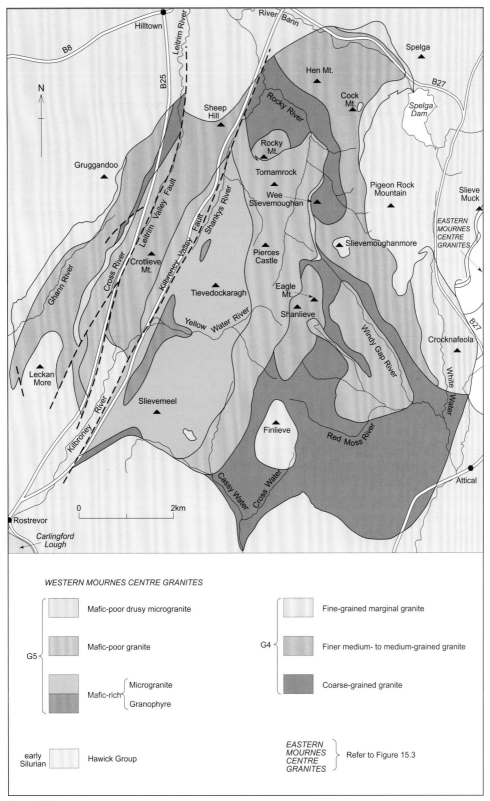

WESTERN MOURNES CENTRE GRANITES

G5
- Mafic-poor drusy microgranite
- Mafic-poor granite
- Mafic-rich { Microgranite / Granophyre }

G4
- Fine-grained marginal granite
- Finer medium- to medium-grained granite
- Coarse-grained granite

early Silurian — Hawick Group

EASTERN MOURNES CENTRE GRANITES } Refer to Figure 15.3

Figure 15.4
Geological map of the Western Mournes Centre - from Gibson, D. 1984 (13);
Cone-sheets and dykes not shown.

185

G1 Roof granite in the Eastern Mournes shows rhythmic layering (14). The layering appears to have formed by the settling of dense mineral clusters and consists of dark, 1-2cm thick mafic-rich layers enriched in fresh olivine (fayalite), amphibole, biotite, Fe-Ti oxides, zircon, apatite and allanite relative to the adjacent, paler, leucocratic cumulate (Photomicrographs 3 and 4).

One of the most notable features of the Mourne granites occurs at the Diamond Rocks (Photograph 6). Here [J328 288] the granite, which is a fine-grained facies of a pulse of G2 magma located just below a roof formed in the same granite, has developed a 'drusy' texture as a result of gas streaming in the volatile rich magma. The drusy cavities contain a concentration of euhedral crystals of smoky quartz, feldspar, mica, beryl and topaz.

At the present level of erosion, the geometry of the intrusions indicates that the three early granites (G1-G3) are arranged within one another with a marked eccentricity towards the southwest. The granites were probably emplaced in a series of pulses of rising magma. Each pulse was introduced into an ever-widening sloping 'wall' fissure connected to a 'roof' fissure, the space created by the subsidence of a block or blocks of country rock bounded by outward-sloping ring fractures - the cauldron subsidence or ring dyke model of emplacement (Figure 15.5). In the Eastern Mournes Centre only roof pendants of G1 remain (hence the name G1 'Roof') and an original ring dyke for this granite cannot be inferred with any certainty. Outcrops of the Outer portion of G2 may represent relatively steeply sloping walls without any true roof connections. In contrast, exposures between and within G2 Inner and G3 show flat or gently sloping roof-type contacts. In the Western Mournes Centre

Photograph 5
Rhythmic layering in boulder (90 cms long) of G1 granite from the Eastern Mournes Centre.

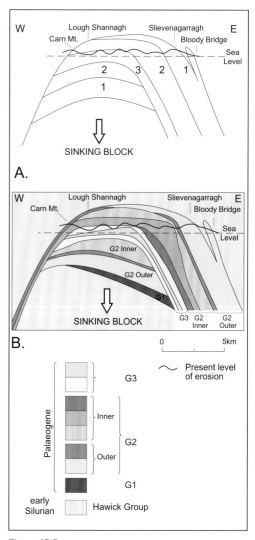

Figure 15.5
A. Mode of intrusion of the Mourne Granites (15) and B. revised interpretation based on the mapping of the Eastern Mournes Centre by Hood (12).

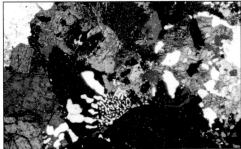

Photomicrograph No. 1
Typical G1 hornblende-biotite syenogranite from the Eastern Mournes Centre showing granophyric intergrowth of alkali feldspar and quartz. (Crossed polars, field of view 5mm wide).

Photomicrograph No. 2
Biotite granite from the G2 granites of the Eastern Mournes Centre showing granophyric intergrowth of alkali feldspar and quartz. (Crossed polars, field of view 5mm wide).

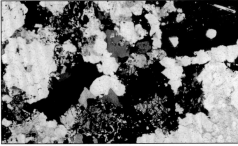

Photomicrograph Nos. 3 and 4
Mafic rich bands in the boulder of layered G1 granite from the Eastern Mournes Centre with clusters of aegirine-augite, epidote, biotite and isotropic iron ore set in a matrix of granophyric alkali feldspar and quartz. (3-Crossed polars and 4-Plane polarised light, field of view 5mm wide).

the same mode of intrusion has been proposed for G4 and G5, although at the present level of erosion only flat-lying roof contacts are exposed (15, 16). This emplacement mechanism allowed the granites to be intruded without causing significant uplift or doming of the country rocks.

Fragments of the Silurian country rocks that formed the 'roof' of the granite complex are exposed on several peaks in the eastern and western Mournes. Also, a screen of Silurian country rocks is exposed as a thin sliver wedged into G2 Outer at the eastern edge of the Eastern Mournes Centre at Slievenagarragh. During intrusion of the granites the country rocks were indurated and thermally metamorphosed to form diopside- and biotite-bearing hornfels extending several hundred metres from the contact. The hornfels is well exposed around the eastern edge of the Mourne Mountains in coastal cliffs, in the river above Bloody Bridge [J387 269] and in the Glen River [J370 299] southwest of Newcastle.

Slieve Gullion Complex

The Slieve Gullion Complex represents the 'root' zone of a now deeply eroded volcanic caldera (17) that intruded the southwest end of the Caledonian Newry Igneous Complex (Figure 15.1) at about 58-56Ma (18, 19). The highest point, Slieve Gullion (573m), lies at the centre of an 11km diameter, circular igneous complex intruded into a circular ring fault (Photograph 7). The Complex consists of three distinct units (Figure 15.6) with the earliest intrusion of silicic magma forming an almost complete ring that was associated with high level explosive activity. In the centre of the complex, and forming Slieve Gullion, a later, sheeted complex consists of flat-lying silicic and basic layers. The final intrusive phase is a granite stock that is confined to the southeast part of the complex.

Photograph 6
The Hare's Gap and Slieve Bernagh from the Diamond Rocks [J331 286] on the Brandy Pad, all formed of fine-grained granite of the G2 Inner facies.

The **Slieve Gullion Ring Dyke** marks the outer edge of the intrusive complex and forms a circle of hills up to 300m high (Photograph 8) composed mainly of porphyritic felsite and porphyritic granophyre (20). The ring dyke encloses two generations of earlier formed gabbro/dolerite intrusions and olivine basalt, trachyte and tuffs which were the earliest eruptive products of the Slieve Gullion 'volcano'. Evidence of subsequent explosive activity occurs near Forkill in the form of vents, containing agglomerate consisting mainly of fragments of brecciated granodiorite from the Newry Igneous Complex and Lower

Photograph 7
Slieve Gullion from west of Mullaghbane [H978 188].
Looking east-northeast the distance to the summit is 5km.

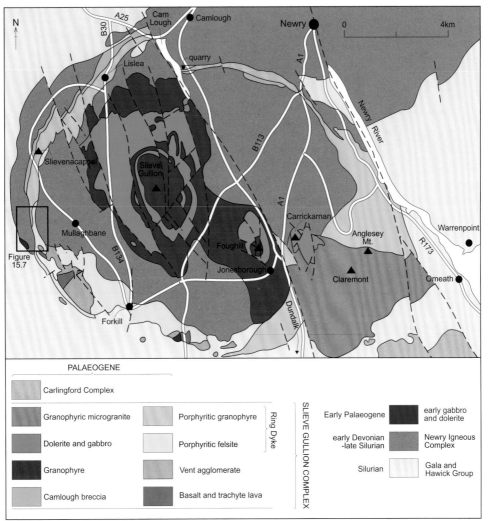

Figure 15.6
Geological map of the Slieve Gullion Complex (2).

Palaeozoic country rock together with large foundered rafts of the older basalt and trachyte lavas. In the main part of the ring dyke the **porphyritic felsite** pre-dates the **porphyritic granophyre** and cross-cuts the vent agglomerates. The felsite is restricted to the southwest part of the ring where its outcrop varies in width from 100m to 1.5km. Well-developed flow banding in the outer margins of the ring dyke indicates that it is a sheet structure which intrudes a pre-existing ring fracture dipping steeply to the southwest. The **porphyritic granophyre** forms a more pronounced ring structure and post-dates and intrudes the felsite west of Mullaghbane (Figure 15.7). Linear zones of crush brecciation, the **Camlough Breccias** (17) affect the Newry Granodiorite, porphyritic granophyre of the ring dyke and post-granophyre aplites in the northwest quadrant of the Slieve Gullion Complex. Cam Lough lies at the northern edge of the complex along a dextral strike-slip fault which displaces the porphyritic granophyre ring dyke horizontally for about 2km. East of the Camlough Fault the steeply inclined intrusive contact between porphyritic granophyre of the ring dyke and Silurian and Newry Granodiorite country rocks is exposed in Cam Lough quarry (Photograph 9) [J037 246].

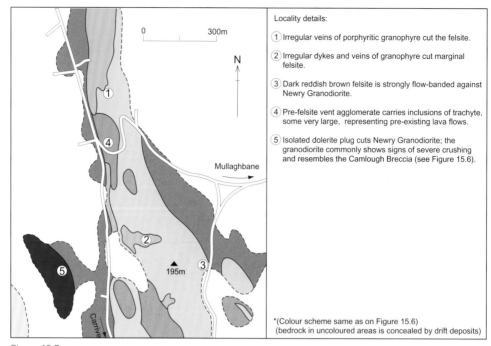

0   300m

N
↑

① Irregular veins of porphyritic granophyre cut the felsite.

② Irregular dykes and veins of granophyre cut marginal felsite.

③ Dark reddish brown felsite is strongly flow-banded against Newry Granodiorite.

④ Pre-felsite vent agglomerate carries inclusions of trachyte, some very large, representing pre-existing lava flows.

⑤ Isolated dolerite plug cuts Newry Granodiorite; the granodiorite commonly shows signs of severe crushing and resembles the Camlough Breccia (see Figure 15.6).

Mullaghbane

▲ 195m

*(Colour scheme same as on Figure 15.6)
(bedrock in uncoloured areas is concealed by drift deposits)

Figure 15.7
Detailed geological map of the western part of the Slieve Gullion ring dyke near Mullaghbane, Co. Armagh (after 20).

At the centre of Slieve Gullion, the **Layered Complex** post-dates the ring dyke and consists of at least 13 alternating units of silicic and basic rock (20). The layered nature of these rocks finds strong topographic expression on the west side of Slieve Gullion, and on Foughill [J042 181] and Carrickarnan [J080 181] straddling the Newry-Dundalk road. The Layered Complex was interpreted initially as a succession of rhyolitic and basaltic lava flows, sills, acid tuffs and agglomerates that accumulated on the floor of a caldera (21). Their subsequent transformation to the present assemblage, which includes rocks with gabbroic and granitic textures, was presumed to be the result of pneumatolytic and hydrothermal alteration during late-stage volcanic activity. A reinterpretation of these rocks now concludes that they represent a protolith of granodiorite of the late Caledonian Newry

Photograph 8
Looking west from the lower slopes of Slieve Gullion towards two isolated knolls forming part of the ring dyke with Slievenacappel in the background.

Photograph 9
Intrusive contact between pale brown granophyre of the Slieve Gullion ring dyke and country rock composed of pale to medium grey sheared and hornfelsed Silurian greywacke which has been intruded by microgranite, biotite granite and diorite of the southwest pluton of the late Palaeozoic Newry Igneous Complex. Cam Lough quarry [J037 246], 5km WSW of Newry, on the east side of Cam Lough, Co. Armagh.

Igneous Complex that was altered, first by intrusion of granophyre sheets and then by a more basic magma (22). This concept supported the fact that not all contacts between the acidic and basic sheets are flat-lying. On the north flank of Slieve Gullion they possess a steep, wall-like relationship and, in the north of the complex, the **Lislea Granophyre** is regarded as a peripheral ring dyke intrusion continuous with the upper (laccolithic) granophyre layers of the central complex.

The final major magmatic event at Slieve Gullion was the intrusion of a **granite stock** in the southeastern part of the complex. Exposures on Clermont [J098 171] and Anglesey Mountain [J104 176] are of greyish green granophyric microgranite with iron-rich clinopyroxene as the dominant mafic mineral. The stock cuts both the porphyritic granophyre of the ring dyke and layers of the sheeted complex but is cut by basaltic cone sheets associated with the Carlingford Complex.

Minor Igneous Intrusions
Dykes
Throughout the early Palaeogene (Palaeocene) the continental crust of Northern Ireland was in a state of tectonic extension (23). Magma, of mainly basaltic composition, was intruded into the dilated crust and formed linear **dyke swarms** in northwest Britain (24) and Northern Ireland (Figure 15.8). A small number of dykes in Co. Fermanagh are multiple intrusions up to 30m wide compared to the normal range of 1-5m. Some of these dykes clearly acted as long-term conduits for eruptive volcanism that was evidently more extensive than the present outcrop would indicate. Age dating of the Doraville Dyke in Co. Fermanagh at 69Ma raises the possibility that its intrusion occurred in the Late Cretaceous (25).

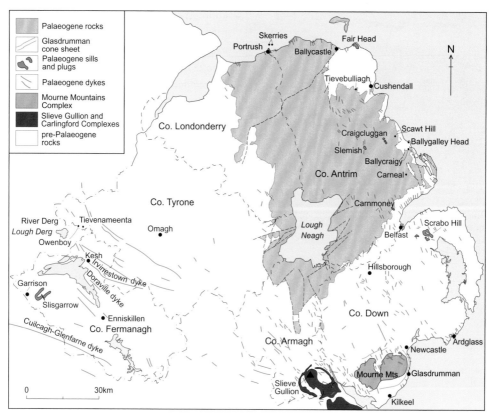

Figure 15.8
Distribution of Palaeogene minor intrusions in Northern Ireland.

Dyke intrusion took place throughout the period of early Palaeogene magmatism and pre- and post-dates the central complexes of Carlingford, Slieve Gullion and the Mourne Mountains. The basalt lavas of the Antrim Lava Group were erupted from linear fissures fed by major dykes which have mostly been eroded or remain concealed. Nevertheless, the Upper Basalt Formation is cut by a combination of dykes and elongate dyke-like plugs such as Slemish [D222 054] and Craigcluggan [D294 080] (26).

A major dyke swarm extends southeastwards across the north of Ireland (Figure 15.8) and represents a continuation of the **Donegal-Kingscourt dyke swarm** that reach from Rockall, through Ireland to Anglesey and North Wales and into the Midlands of England. Regional doming and rifting between Greenland and northwest Europe in the Late Cretaceous and early Palaeogene resulted in crustal dilation and the opening of fractures. Initially, the fractures lay parallel to a northeast-southwest trending rift zone and although followed by dykes in Greenland and the Faeroe Islands were unable to completely release tensional stresses caused by the doming.

In Ireland, the dyke swarm intruded a complementary set of northwest-southeast trending fractures that subsequently developed on the margin of the North European Plate. It is most likely that the source of these dykes was located northwest of Ireland. The dykes transect all major structural elements and only rarely are offset by contemporaneous or later faults. Dyke thickness is extremely variable and while thin examples may not be identifiable beyond one-exposure, mega-dykes, 10-100m wide, can be traced for tens of

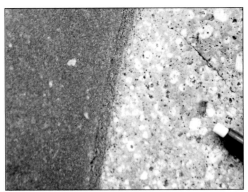

Photograph 10
The Glasdrumman Cone Sheet comprising a core of quartz-feldspar porphyry with basaltic margin. Glasdrumman Port [J380 225], 9km south of Newcastle, Co. Down.

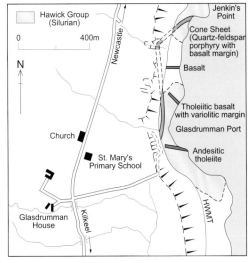

Figure 15.9
Detailed geological map of Glasdrumman Port, Co. Down [20].

kilometres at outcrop and on regional magnetic anomaly maps (27). Numerous examples in Counties Fermanagh and Tyrone intrude Devonian and Carboniferous rocks, such as the 27km long Cuilcagh-Glenfarne Dyke (28, 29) and the 30-35km long Irvinestown Dyke which transects the western end of the Fintona Block (30). Most of the mega-dykes are moderately fresh, feldsparphyric olivine basalt and dolerite. The multiple nature and gabbroic core of the Doraville Dyke is exposed in the quarry [H200 558] southwest of Irvinestown and illustrates a long history of intrusion.

The **minor dykes** in Counties Fermanagh and Tyrone are usually of olivine basalt or dolerite composition. Most have been altered in the zeolite facies, and contain saponite and carbonate, the most common alteration products, occurring in small circular vesicles. However, the vesicles occasionally contain silica (chalcedony) making these dykes unusually hard, such as the example intruding the Carboniferous Ballyshannon Limestone Formation in the quarry [H243 630] 6.4km east of Kesh.

Within the dyke swarm are rare examples of olivine-free basalt and olivine-rich picro-dolerite. A small number of dykes intruding the Dalradian rocks northeast of Lough Derg have relatively evolved trachybasalt or rhyolite compositions. They include a 2.5m wide quartz trachyte or rhyolite dyke in the River Derg [H096 765] and a 2.7m wide trachybasalt dyke with fresh andesine phenocrysts at Tievenameenta [H152 756]. On the east bank of the Owenboy Burn at Owenboy [H123 768] an intrusion of porphyritic rhyolite forms a 1.75m thick sheet inclined 40° to the southeast and has thin margins of pitchstone. The upper 1.5m is crudely columnar jointed while the lower part is flow-banded and intensely jointed.

In Co. Down, the Palaeogene dyke swarms follow a NNW-orientation and are localised around Slieve Gullion and the Mourne Mountains, between Ardglass and Hillsborough and in the Belfast area. There appears to be a discontinuity between the swarms in Co. Down and southeast Co. Antrim that may reflect late Palaeogene dextral strike-slip on the Southern Upland Fault (31). The dykes in north Co. Down consist predominantly of olivine basalt and olivine dolerite with examples of silica-rich, olivine-free tholeiitic basalt.

Dykes pre- and post-date the intrusion of the Mourne Mountains granites (32). The younger dyke swarm includes olivine-bearing and olivine-free (tholeiitic) basalt, andesite, dacite, quartz-feldspar and feldspar-rich porphyry and felsite. Dykes are well exposed on the coast south of Newcastle. A number of composite intrusions occur in this area, the most notable example being the **Glasdrumman Cone Sheet** (Photograph 10). The intrusion outcrops (Figure 15.9) on the shore at Glasdrumman Port [J380 225] and extends for over 20km along the east and southeast sides of the Eastern Mournes Centre. It is concentric to the margin of the Eastern Mournes Centre, dips to the north and west, and consists of quartz-feldspar porphyry with thin basaltic margins.

Plugs

The Antrim Lava Group is cut by dolerite plugs that in places form prominent landmarks rising above the surface of the Antrim Plateau. At least thirty of these intrusions are recognised and vary in diameter from 50m to 1km with a circular outline or are elongate in a NNW-SSE direction, parallel to the main dyke swarm. They consist mainly of olivine dolerite with local variations due to compositional zoning. This is particularly evident at **Slemish** [D222 054], a 1km long elliptical multiple plug that intrudes the Upper Basalt Formation (Figure 15.8). Slemish is the largest volcanic vent in Ireland (26) and consists of at least three separate magma pulses, the latest cutting through the two earlier pulses that form the lower part of the hill. The two earliest pulses contain platy cognate xenoliths representing fragments of the surface crust of the lava lake in the vent that were disrupted by convection currents and sank into the magma pool (33).

    Tievebulliagh [D193 268] near Cushendall, is an inclined, oval-shaped olivine dolerite plug with a marginal facies of olivine-rich picritic dolerite. This plug is notable for the presence of a slumped block of lateritised basalt of the Interbasaltic Formation. This has

Photograph 11
Scawt Hill [D337 091] on the eastern edge of the Antrim Plateau. Cretaceous chalk with flint nodules were hornfelsed by dolerite magma producing a calcsilicate mineral assemblage. 3.75km WNW of Ballygalley, Co. Antrim.

been metamorphosed to form **porcellanite**, an extremely resistant hornfels that was used by Neolithic people to manufacture axe heads (Chapter 18).

Many of the plugs in Co. Antrim have contact metamorphosed the rocks into which they were intruded. At **Scawt Hill** (Photograph 11), **Carneal** [J389 959] and **Ballycraigy** [D387 045] the Cretaceous chalk and flint nodules were hornfelsed by the dolerite magma producing calcsilicate mineral assemblage. Indeed, Scawt Hill is the type locality for minerals such as scawtite, larnite, hydrocalumite and portlandite (34-36). Flint nodules, around which many of these minerals developed, show a progressive marginal metasomatism to larnite-spurrite rock with a core of wollastonite and xonotolite. At the margins of the intrusion, assimilation of lime by the olivine dolerite has produced a lining on the conduit wall of black pyroxenite and titanaugite rocks with plagioclase or nepheline or melilite. At Carneal, south of Larne, P-T measurements indicate that metamorphism occurred at extremely high temperatures (1050-1100°C) and low pressure (*c.* 200 bars). In contrast other large dolerite plugs such as Ballygalley Head [D383 078] produced very little alteration in the Cretaceous chalk country rock. Carneal, like Carnmoney near Belfast [J333 825], is associated with agglomerate wedges, apparent relics of tuff-filled vents which were later filled with magma.

Sills

During the main phase of volcanic activity in the early Palaeogene, some rising magma failed to reach the surface and was injected sideways into the sedimentary strata to form **sills**.

The **Scrabo Sill** near Newtownards is the main component of a complex of linked olivine dolerite and gabbro sills intruding the Triassic Sherwood Sandstone Group (37). Other sills in this complex are exposed at Ballyrainey and Dundonald while the Ballyalton borehole penetrated a dolerite sill 160m thick (38, 39). At the south quarry, on the east face of Scrabo Hill, a vent agglomerate containing blocks of Triassic sandstone in a greenish yellow tuffaceous matrix is closely associated with the dolerite sill and feeder dykes. This is indicative of an early phase of explosive activity pre-dating emplacement of the Scrabo Sill (40).

Photograph 12
Fair Head [D180 438], the spectacular cliff formed by an 82m thick Palaeogene dolerite sill intruding coal-bearing Carboniferous rocks. 6km ENE of Ballycastle, Co. Antrim.

195

The 82m thick **Fair Head Sill** (Photograph 12) forms the prominent headland east of Ballycastle in the Carboniferous coalfield of northeast Co. Antrim and is the largest component in a complex of olivine dolerite sills (41). It dips gently to the south and thins to the southeast, where it cuts Carboniferous, Triassic and Cretaceous rocks. On the east side of Fair Head, the **Binnagapple Sill** intrudes the coal-bearing Murlough Shale Formation (Photograph 13). This sill, which occurs some 13m below the Fair Head Sill, consists of 15m of columnar-jointed olivine dolerite and forms the prominent cliffs to the south and west of Fair Head, reappearing on the shore at Farragandoo [D167 431].

The **Portrush Sill**, which forms Ramore Head [C852 415] and extends at least 2km offshore to form the islands of the Skerries, also underlies much of Portrush. It is 45m thick and intrudes and has hornfelsed the fossiliferous Jurassic Waterloo Mudstone Formation (Chapter 11) for at least 8m from the intrusion contact. The sill has a fine-grained chilled margin, and a middle consisting of massive, coarse dolerite with dark gabbroic 'clots' of olivine ± augite or feldspar-rich segregations. The dolerite also contains mudstone xenoliths and is cut by late-stage veins of pyroxene and plagioclase (42). The Ramore Head locality was central to the scientific debate in the 18th Century between "Neptunists" and "Vulcanists" who expressed opposing views about the origin of volcanic rocks. Neptunists believed that basalt was laid down under water and quoted the occurrence of ammonites in the hornfelsed Jurassic mudstone at Portrush in support of their argument. Although the Vulcanists, who favoured a volcanic origin for basalt, quickly demonstrated that the fossiliferous rock was marine shale, the controversy reached an international audience and, for a while, focussed the attentions of the scientific community on this locality in Northern Ireland.

In Co. Fermanagh, the olivine-dolerite **Garrison Sill** intrudes early Carboniferous strata in the core of a Variscan periclinal fold and outcrops over an area of about 15km^2 some 5km ENE of Garrison (28). The sill is 20-30m thick on the northern limb of the fold and 5-15m on the southern limb. The upper and lower margins of the sill are exposed in the disused quarry at Slisgarrow (H014 516). Here, contact metamorphism has resulted in a calcsilicate mineral assemblage in impure limestone of the Carboniferous Meenymore Formation (Chapter 7). Minerals present include grossularite garnet, diopside, wollastonite and plagioclase (43).

Photograph 13
Columnar jointed dolerite of the Binnagapple Sill intruding sandstone and coal seams of the Carboniferous Ballycastle Group, 4km ENE of Ballycastle, Co. Antrim.

References

1) Carruthers, R. M., Cornwell, J. D, Turnbull, G., Walker, A .S. D. and Bennett, J. R. P. 1987. Interpretation of the Bouguer gravity anomaly data for Northern Ireland. *Regional Geophysics Research Group, British Geological Survey* No. RG 87/5.

2) Geraghty, M. 1997. *A geological description of Monaghan - Carlingford to accompany the Bedrock Geology 1:100,000 Scale Map Series, sheet 8 and 9, Monaghan and Carlingford, with contributions by J. Farrelly, K. Claringbold, C. Jordan, R. Meehan and M. Hudson.* Geological Survey of Ireland, 60pp.

3) Mitchell, W. I., Cooper, M. R., Hards, V. L. and Meighan, I. G. 1999. An occurrence of silicic volcanic rocks in the early Palaeogene Antrim Lava Group of Northern Ireland. *Scottish Journal of Geology*, **35**, 179-85.

4) Preston, J. 1981. Tertiary Igneous Activity. *In*: Holland, C. H. (ed.). *A Geology of Ireland*. Scottish Academic Press, Edinburgh.

5) Le Bas, M. J., 1960. The Petrology of the Layered Basic Rocks of the Carlingford Complex, Co Louth. *Transactions of the Royal Society of Edinburgh*, **64**, 169-200.

6) Le Bas, M. J., 1967. On the origin of Tertiary granophyres of the Carlingford Complex, Ireland. *Proceedings of the Royal Irish Academy*, **65B**, 325-38.

7) Meighan, I. G., Fallick, A. E. and McCormick, A. G. 1992. Anorogenic granite magma genesis: new isotopic data for the southern sector of the British Tertiary Igneous Province. *Transactions of the Royal Society of Edinburgh; Earth Sciences*, **83**, 227-33.

8) Gibson, D., McCormick, A. G., Meighan, I. G. and Halliday, A. N. 1988. The British Tertiary Igneous Province; Young Rb-Sr ages for the Mourne Mountains Granites. *Scottish Journal of Geology*, **23**, 221-25.

9) Meighan, I. G., Gibson, D. and Hood, D. N. 1984. Some aspects of Tertiary acid magmatism in NE Ireland. *Mineralogical Magazine*, **48**, 351-63.

10) Cook, A. H. and Murphy, T. 1952. Gravity Survey of Ireland North of the line Sligo-Dundalk. *In: Measurements of Gravity in Ireland*. Dublin Institute for Advanced Studies, Geophysical Memoir No 2, Part 4, 17-20.

11) Tomkieff, S. I. and Marshall, C. E. 1935. The Mourne dyke swarm. *Quarterly Journal of the Geological Society of London*, **91**, 251-92.

12) Hood, D. N. 1981. *Geochemical, petrological and structural studies on the Tertiary granites and associated rocks of the eastern Mourne Mountains, Co. Down, Northern Ireland.* Unpublished Ph.D thesis, Queen's University, Belfast.

13) Gibson, D. 1984. *The petrology and geochemistry of the western Mournes granites, Co. Down.* Unpublished Ph.D thesis, Queen's University, Belfast.

14) Meighan, I. G. 1979. The acid igneous rocks of the British Tertiary Province. *Bulletin of the Geological Survey of Great Britain*, **70**, 10-22.

15) Richey, J. E., 1927. The structural relations of the Mourne Mountains (Northern Ireland). *Quarterly Journal of the Geological Society of London*, **83**, 653-88.

16) Emeleus, C. H. 1955. The granites of the Western Mourne Mountains, Co. Down. *Scientific Proceedings of the Royal Dublin Society*, **27**, 35-50.

17) Richey, J. E., 1932. The Tertiary Ring Complex of Slieve Gullion (Ireland). *Quarterly Journal of the Geological Society of London*, **88**, 776-849.

18) Meighan, I. G., McCormick, A. G., Gibson, D., Gamble, J. A. and Graham, I. J. 1988. Rb-Sr isotopic determinations and the timing of Tertiary central complex magmatism in NE Ireland. *In*: Morton, A. C. and Parson, L. M. (eds.). *Early Tertiary volcanism and the opening of the NE Atlantic*. Geological Society Special Publication No 39, 349-60.

19) Gamble, J. A., Wysoczanski, R. J. and Meighan, I. G. 1999. Constraints on the age of the British Tertiary Volcanic Province from ion microprobe U-Pb (SHRIMP) ages for acid igneous rocks from Northern Ireland. *Journal of the Geological Society, London*, **156**, 291-99.

20) Emeleus, C. H. and Preston, J. 1969. *Field Excursion Guide: The Tertiary Volcanic Rocks of Ireland*. Belfast.

21) Reynolds, D. L. 1951. The geology of Slieve Gullion, Foughill, and Carrickarnan: an actualistic interpretation of a Tertiary gabbro-granophyre complex. *Transactions of the Royal Society of Edinburgh*, **62**, 85-143.

22) Bailey, E. B. and McCallien, W. J. 1956. Composite minor intrusions and the Slieve Gullion Complex, Ireland. *Liverpool & Manchester Geological Journal*, **1**, 466-501.

23) Geoffroy, L., Bergerat, F. and Angelier, J. 1996. Brittle tectonism in relation to the Palaeogene evolution of the Thulean/NE Atlantic domain: a study in Ulster. *Geological Journal*, **31**, 259-69.

24) Speight, J. M., Skelhorn, R. R., Sloan, T. and Knapp, R. J. 1982. The dyke swarms of Scotland. *In*: Sutherland, D. S. S. (ed.). *Igneous Rocks of the British Isles*. Wiley & Sons, New York. 449-59.

25) Johnston, T. P. and Rundle, C. C., 1993. K-Ar results from dolerite intrusions in County Fermanagh, Northern Ireland. *Irish Journal of Earth Science*, **12**, 65-74.

26) Geological Survey of Northern Ireland 2001. Ballymena, Northern Ireland Sheet 20. Solid and Drift Geology. 1:50,000. (Keyworth, Nottingham: British Geological Survey).

27) Geological Survey of Northern Ireland. 1971. Magnetic anomaly map of Northern Ireland. 1:253,440. (Southampton: Ordnance Survey for the Geological Survey of Northern Ireland).

28) Legg, I. C., Johnston, T. P., Mitchell, W. I. and Smith, R. A. 1998. *Geology of the country around Derrygonnelly and Marble Arch*. Memoir of the Geological Survey of Northern Ireland, Sheet 44, 56 and 43 (Northern Ireland).

29) Brandon, A. 1973. Two new dolerite dykes intruding Carboniferous shales near Thur Mountain, County Leitrim. *Irish Naturalists' Journal*, **17**, 334-39.

30) Geological Survey of Northern Ireland 1997. Northern Ireland. Solid Geology (second edition). 1:250,000. (Keyworth, Nottingham: British Geological Survey).

31) Preston, J. 1982. The British Volcanic Province: Eruptive Rocks. *In*: Sutherland, D. S. S. (ed.). *Igneous Rocks of the British Isles*. Wiley & Sons, New York, 351-68.

32) Robbie, J. A. 1955. The Slieve Binnian Tunnel, an aquaduct in the Mourne Mountains. *Bulletin of the Geological Survey of Great Britain*, **8**, 1-20.

33) Preston, J. 1963. The dolerite plug at Slemish, Co Antrim. *Liverpool and Manchester Geological Journal*, **3**, 301-14.

34) Tilley, C. E. 1929. On Larnite and its associated minerals from the limestone contact-zones of Scawt Hill, County Antrim. *Mineralogical Magazine*, **22**, 77-86.

35) Tilley, C. E. and Harwood, H. F. 1931. The dolerite-chalk contact of Scawt Hill, County Antrim. *Mineralogical Magazine*, **22**, 439-68.

36) Tilley, C. E. and Alderman, A. R. 1933. Progressive metasomatism in the flint nodules of the Scawt Hill contact zone. *Mineralogical Magazine*, **24**, 513-18.

37) Smith, R. A., Johnston, T. P. and Legg, I. C. 1991. Geology of the country around Newtownards. *Memoir of the Geological Survey of Northern Ireland*. Sheet 37 and part of sheet 38 (Northern Ireland).

38) Geological Survey of Northern Ireland 1989. Newtownards, Northern Ireland Sheet 37 and part of 38. Solid Geology. 1:50,000. (Southampton: Ordnance Survey for the Geological Survey of Northern Ireland).

39) Bazley, R. A. B. 1975. The Tertiary igneous and Permo-Triassic rocks of the Ballyalton Borehole, Co Down. *Bulletin of the Geological Survey of Great Britain*, **50**, 71-101.

40) Preston, J. 1962. Explosive volcanic activity in the Triassic sandstone of Scrabo Hill, Co Down. *Irish Naturalists Journal*, **14**, 45-51.

41) Wilson, H. E. and Robbie. J. A., 1966. Geology of the country around Ballycastle. *Memoir of the Geological Survey of Northern Ireland*. Sheet 8 (Northern Ireland).

42) Wilson. H. E. and Manning, P. I., 1978. Geology of the Causeway Coast. *Memoir of the Geological Survey of Northern Ireland*. Sheet 7 (Northern Ireland).

43) Jones, K. A. and Galway, A. K. 1966. Size distribution, composition and growth kinetics of garnet crystals in some metamorphic rocks in the west of Ireland. *Quarterly Journal of the Geological Society of London*, **122**, 29-44.

Chapter 16

Late Palaeogene (Oligocene) Sedimentary Basins

W. I. MITCHELL

Introduction

The end of basaltic volcanism in Northern Ireland during the late Palaeocene (*c.* 58Ma), coincided with the end of Phase 1 of the two major phases of magmatism in the North Atlantic Igneous Province (1). At present, the greatest thickness of basalt lava recorded is 780m and 769m in the Langford Lodge and Ballymacilroy boreholes (Figure 16.1) respectively (2). By contrast, on the Island of Mull (Figure 14.3) it is estimated that up to 1000m of basalt lava had been eroded since the early Palaeogene (3).

After volcanism in the later Palaeocene and Eocene, northeast Ireland and the lava plateau were affected by a post-magmatic, wrench-dominated stress system which produced conjugate NNW-trending (dextral) and northeast-southwest (sinistral) shears and NNE-trending normal faults (4). The effects of Palaeogene sinistral strike-slip on reactivated Caledonian fractures such as the Tow Valley, Carnlough and Sixmilewater faults, resulted in the present compartmentalisation of the basalt lavas. At the margins of the lava outcrop, the impact of vertical movement was most severe in north Co. Armagh where the lavas were eroded and the Lough Neagh Group oversteps southwards onto Mesozoic, Carboniferous and early Palaeozoic 'basement'.

However, by the end of the Eocene waning tectonic activity and denudation led to the virtual peneplanation of the plateau surface, although the pattern of fault-bounded blocks of lavas of either the Lower Basalt or Upper Basalt formations was by then well established. During the Oligocene, non-marine sedimentary basins subsided in response to syndepositional faulting. As a result, the majority of the new basins developed above major fault lines on a basalt land surface. In the Ballymoney area, the Lough Neagh Group rests unconformably on the Upper Basalt Formation in the hanging wall of the Tow Valley Fault (Figure 16.1). Although a precursor of this fault probably influenced the location of depocentres in the basin, the absence of thick conglomerates suggests that growth faulting was the dominant control and that sedimentation extended southeast of the fault line. Basin subsidence is believed to have occurred in a sinistral transtensional regime with NNE-SSW extension (5). Dilation of the NNW-trending fractures at their intersection with a principal displacement zone, the Tow Valley Fault, promoted continued basin subsidence. At Ballymoney, over 500m of sediment filled the rapidly subsiding, pull-apart basin (Figure 16.1). Around Lough Neagh, the Lough Neagh Group is 353m thick in the Washing Bay borehole (6) and 381m in a borehole at Derryinver which did not penetrate the base of the Group.

Lough Neagh Group

Exposures of the Lough Neagh Group are not known in either of the main areas of outcrop around Lough Neagh or at Ballymoney (Figure 16.1). Nevertheless, detailed information on its stratigraphy and subsurface outcrop is available from the results of an extensive drilling programme that confirmed the presence of lignite seams and provided information on the lithostratigraphy, biostratigraphy, mineral composition and sediment provenance (7). The Lough Neagh Group comprises the **Dunaghy** and **Ballymoney** formations (Table 16.1).

Dunaghy Formation

The subsurface outcrop of sedimentary rocks of the Dunaghy Formation is confined to the Ballymoney and Agivey 'basins' (Figure 16.1). At Ballymoney, the rocks occupy three separate areas in the hanging wall of the Tow Valley Fault (Figure 16.2A) and range in thickness from 22m to a maximum of 276m in the Dunaghy borehole [C980 264]. In the Agivey 'basin', the formation comprises 66m of multicoloured clay and gritty clay, thin lignite beds and thin conglomerates. The prevalence of shearing in these rocks, and of faulted contacts at the top and base, is a reflection of more than 400m of post-Oligocene dip-slip on the Tow Valley Fault.

Basalt lava underlying the Lough Neagh Group at Ballymoney is weathered to a depth of up to 80m and is altered to a mixture of yellowish brown, reddish brown and purplish red, clay-rich lithomarge. Relict igneous textures include net veining, incipient brecciation, the outline of former zeolite-filled vesicles and spheroidal weathering. Clasts in 6m

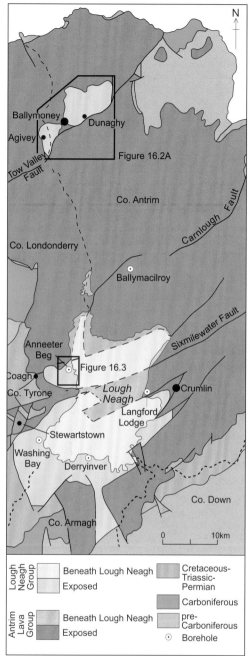

Figure 16.1
Simplified geological map illustrating the distribution of the Lough Neagh Group.

of yellow, pink, grey and brown conglomerate and breccio-conglomerate at the base of the Dunaghy Formation consist of decomposed basalt derived from the weathering profile in the underlying lavas. Higher strata consist mainly of reddish brown lateritic clay, mottled in shades of brown, blue, grey, purple and green. Thin sections of bluish grey mudstone include beds and small nodules of authigenic siderite, sandy clay, coarse-grained sand and rare beds

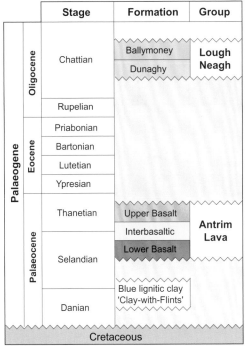

	Stage	Formation	Group
Oligocene (Palaeogene)	Chattian	Ballymoney	Lough Neagh
		Dunaghy	
	Rupelian		
Eocene (Palaeogene)	Priabonian		
	Bartonian		
	Lutetian		
	Ypresian		
Palaeocene (Palaeogene)	Thanetian	Upper Basalt	Antrim Lava
		Interbasaltic	
	Selandian	Lower Basalt	
		Blue lignitic clay 'Clay-with-Flints'	
	Danian		
Cretaceous			

Table 16.1
Palaeogene lithostratigraphical divisions in
Northern Ireland.

of brown lignitic clay and black lignite from 0.5-5m thick.

Organic residues are dominated by wood fragments and plant tissue but also contain sparse palynomorph assemblages of bisaccate pollen *Erecipites* spp., *Laevigatosporites* spp. and *Nyssapollenites satzveyensis* that are typical of the Late Oligocene of the British Isles (8) and of the SP8 zone (9). In particular, *Corsinipollenites oculusnoctis* and *Tricolpopollenites spinus* are confined to the Late Oligocene of western Britain. The flora in the Dunaghy Formation indicates a cool temperate, peat-forming, freshwater swamp environment dominated by ferns and mosses with a densely vegetated hinterland. Nearby upland/montane forests largely consisted of conifers.

Ballymoney Formation

This formation is restricted to the Ballymoney and Agivey areas, north of the Tow Valley Fault, and to the shores of Lough Neagh (Figure 16.1). It usually rests unconformably on the Antrim Lava Group, except where the Dunaghy Formation intervenes, and in the area southwest and south of Lough Neagh, where it oversteps onto Triassic and Lower Palaeozoic rocks. Multiple seams of lignite occur in the concealed basins at Ballymoney and near Coagh (7).

In the **Ballymoney** area, the Lough Neagh Group is concealed by up to 70m of glacial till (10). The Ballymoney Formation has a composite thickness of about 240m, but does not exceed 200m in any borehole. Within the succession are six lignite seam groups with a maximum total thickness of 177m. Near Ballymoney, lignite is concentrated in one seam which is 105m thick (Figure 16.2, Borehole 1); it comprises a bed 100m thick (Seam Groups B, C, D) and 5m of clay. Northeast of Ballymoney, the 100m bed of lignite is now represented by 120m of strata, but seam splitting has reduced the composite thickness of lignite to 38m (Figure 16.2, Borehole 2). Further to the east, this trend is reversed and seam thickening and merging results in an aggregate thickness of 70m with one lignite bed over 50m thick (Figure 16.2, Borehole 3).

Near **Coagh**, in east Co. Tyrone (Figure 16.1), the outcrop of the Lough Neagh Group is concealed by up to 36m of glacial deposits (7). The margins are unfaulted and the strata dip gently towards Lough Neagh. The Ballymoney Formation has a maximum thickness of 282m (base of formation not penetrated) in the borehole at Anneeter Beg.

The **lignite** consists of massive brownish black, woody and non-woody material grading into lignitic clay. Leaf and plant debris is rare but well-preserved specimens are common in the lignitic clay, with roots and stems in growth position. Grey and brownish grey, very stiff **clay** consisting mainly of kaolinite, **sandy clay** and thin **clayey sand** separate the lignite seams. Sedimentary structures such as laminations or bedding are rare. Grains of

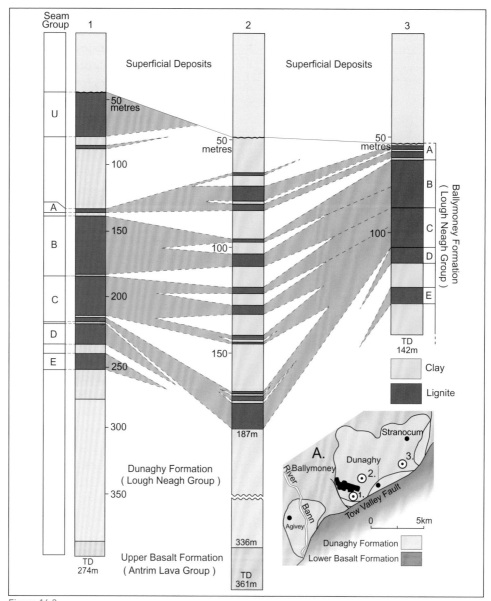

Figure 16.2
Comparative Lithostratigraphy of the Lough Neagh Group in boreholes in the Ballymoney area.
A - Location map of the Ballymoney area.

Unit (thickness)	Lithology	Palaeoenvironment
4 (80m)	**Clay, sandy,** pale to dark greenish grey and greyish brown, fining and coarsening-upwards sequences; thin lignite and lignitic clay	**Fluvial and deltaic;** caused by filling and shallowing of the basin
3 (18-65m)	**Clay,** dark to olive green, massive, plant debris, quartz sands and siderite bands	**Lacustrine;** open water and nearshore conditions created by rapid submergence of the peat swamp
2 (19-39m)	**Lignite,** one seam in north and west splitting and thinning to east and south	**Swamp and raised peat;** vegetable matter accumulating at margins
1 (100m)	**Clay,** bluish grey to dark brown, stiff, thin lignite seams; **conglomerate** with small pebbles and granules of multicoloured clay, quartz, cobbles of deeply weathered basalt	**Fluvial;** basal conglomerate derived by erosion of weathered basalt, overlain by **deltaic** facies with swamps developing at margins

Table 16.2
Detailed stratigraphy of the Ballymoney Formation in Co. Tyrone.

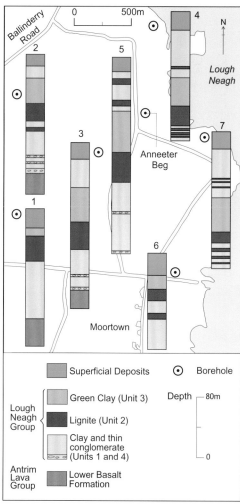

Figure 16.3
Lithostratigraphy of the Ballymoney Formation in selected boreholes in the area east of Coagh, Co. Tyrone.

authigenic siderite are common in the clay, with beds of hard, grey to yellowish grey sideritic ironstone up to 0.3m thick. The Coagh area is the only part of the outcrop of the Ballymoney Formation in which lithological units, other than lignite, can be correlated between boreholes (Figure 16.3). Distinctive clays of Unit 3 (Table 16.2) are also underlain by lignite in the boreholes at Derryinver and Washing Bay (Figure 16.1) and are referred to the "Middle Shales" (6).

Pollen assemblages confirm the Late Oligocene (Chattian) age of the Ballymoney Formation (8). Particularly important is *Cicatricosisporites chattensis*, which is restricted to the Chattian Stage, *Boehlensipollis*, which in France is restricted to the Oligocene and an association of the long-ranging forms *Arecipites, Dicolpopollis* and *Monocolpopollenites*, which are most common in the Oligocene. The assemblages indicate a warm temperate, frost-free climate and swamp environment with coniferous pollen derived from upland regions. Unit 3 contains the bivalve *Unio* and gastropod *Viviparus*, with ostracods and diatoms (11).

Sediment provenance in the Lough Neagh Group

Continuous movement on the Tow Valley Fault zone and other northeast-southwest trending fractures sustained basin subsidence in the Late Oligocene during deposition of both the Dunaghy and Ballymoney formations. Thus, in the Ballymoney-Agivey area, the margins of the Dunaghy Formation 'basin' were overstepped by the Ballymoney Formation in an areally more extensive, successor basin. Provenance studies of heavy minerals in the Lough Neagh Group indicate that the Palaeogene basalt lavas were the dominant source for the detritus, particularly at Ballymoney (11). However, in contrast at Crumlin, some coarse sediment was derived by erosion of unroofed Palaeogene granites of the Mourne Mountains Complex. At the base of Unit 4 (Table 16.2), in east Co. Tyrone, some detritus originated from the early Ordovician Tyrone Igneous Complex, the Devonian rocks of the Fintona Block and from Triassic rocks. This change was caused either by drainage systems eroding through the basalt into older rocks, or by the headward expansion to the west and northwest of the main drainage arteries.

203

Late Palaeogene (Oligocene) Sedimentary Basins / Chapter 16

References

1) Saunders, A. D., Fitton, J. G., Kerr, A. C., Norry, M. J. and Kent, R. W. 1997.
The North Atlantic Igneous Province. *In*: Mahoney, J. J. and Coffin, M. F. (eds.).
Large igneous provinces. American Geophysical Union Monographs, 100, 45-94.

2) Wilson, H. E. 1983. Deep Drilling in Northern Ireland since 1947. *Irish Naturalist's Journal,* **21,** 160-63.

3) Walker, G. P. L. 1971. The distribution of amygdale minerals in Mull and Morven (western Scotland). *In*: Murty,
T. V. V. G. G. R. K. and Roa, S. S. (eds.). *Studies in Earth Sciences.* W. D. West commemorative volume, 181-94.

4) Geoffroy, L., Bergerat, F. and Angelier, J. 1996. Brittle tectonism in relation to the Palaeogene evolution of the
Thulean/NE Atlantic domain: a study in Ulster. *Geological Journal,* **31,** 259-69.

5) Kerr, I. D. V. 1987. *Basement/Cover structural relationships in the north Antrim area, Ireland.*
Ph.D. Thesis, The Queen's University of Belfast.

6) Fowler, A. and Robbie, J. A. 1961. Geology of the country around Dungannon.
Memoir of the Geological Survey of Northern Ireland, **Sheet 35 (Northern Ireland).**

7) Geological Survey of Northern Ireland 1984. *Mineral Exploration Programme, volumes 2, 3, 5, 6, 8.*

8) Wilkinson, G. C., Bazley, R. A. B. and Boulter, M. C. 1980. The geology and palynology of the Oligocene Lough
Neagh Clays, Northern Ireland. *Journal of the Geological Society of London* **137,** 65-75.

9) Meyer, K. J. 1988. The description of the interregional zonation of the Palaeogene (SP zones 1-8).
Subgroup Palynology (pollen, spores). *Geologisches Jahrbuch,* **100,** 288-94.

10) Geological Survey of Northern Ireland. 1999. Coleraine, Northern Ireland Sheet 13. Solid and Drift Geology.
1:50,000. (Keyworth, Nottingham: British Geological Survey).

11) Parnell, J., Shukla, B. and Meighan, I. G. 1989. The lignite and associated sediments of the Tertiary Lough
Neagh Basin. *Irish Journal of Earth Sciences,* **10,** 67-88.

Chapter 17

Post-Variscan Deformation and Basin Formation

T. P. JOHNSTON

Introduction

From the Late Permian onwards, the separation of the European and North American continental plates led to the creation of the North Atlantic Ocean. As part of the European Plate, Northern Ireland experienced tensional tectonic stress, which caused crustal subsidence onshore and offshore and was a major factor in the development of two distinct groups of fault-bounded Mesozoic sedimentary basins (1, 2). An outer group of basins with a predominantly northeast-southwest orientation developed in the area referred to as the 'Marginal Belt', which stretches approximately 150km offshore to the edge of the continental shelf. Sedimentary basins that developed onshore in Northern Ireland and Great Britain are referred to collectively as the 'Clyde Belt', and belong to an inner group of basins typically with a northwest-southeast or NNW-SSE orientation (Figure 17.1). These onshore basins formed in response to ENE-WSW stretching, producing half grabens by dip-slip reactivation of existing Caledonian structures (3).

Development of Permo-Triassic basins in Northern Ireland

The present outcrop of Permian and Triassic strata in Northern Ireland is restricted to the periphery of the Antrim Plateau (Figure 9.2). However, regional gravity surveys and exploratory drilling have identified sedimentary basins concealed beneath the Palaeogene Antrim Lava Group of the Antrim Plateau (Chapters 14 and 19). Significant depocentres including the Lough Neagh and Larne basins are infilled mainly by Permian and Triassic rocks (4, 5, 6, 7). The presence of concealed Carboniferous lithologies has been confirmed in the Lough Foyle basin by the Magilligan borehole (8).

Rathlin and Lough Foyle basins

Both the Rathlin and Lough Foyle basins are post-Variscan transtensional half-grabens with a sedimentary fill consisting mainly of Permian and Triassic strata. The **Rathlin Basin** formed in response to extension along NNW-SSE trending faults in the area between the Tow Valley and Lough Foyle faults (9). The basin extends northwards offshore beneath Rathlin Island and southwards to the Tow Valley Fault. Gravity modelling suggests that the deepest part of the basin is located close to the Tow Valley Fault with an estimated 2000m of Mesozoic sediment (7). The **Lough Foyle Basin** is bounded by a northeast-southwest trending fault tracing the northwest shore of Lough Foyle while the basin extends and deepens to the southeast beneath the Lough. East of Lough Foyle, the basin is concealed

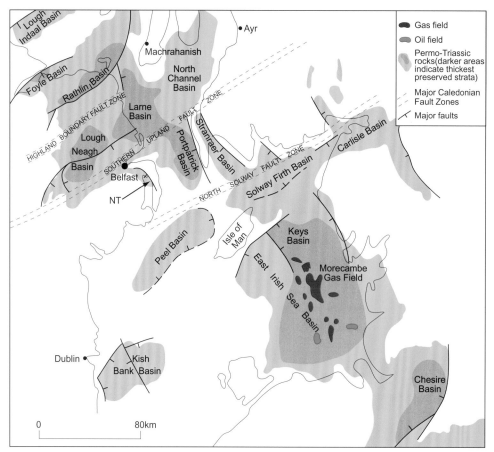

Figure 17.1
Permo-Triassic basins of Irish Sea and surrounding areas (NT-Newtownards Trough).

beneath the Antrim Plateau. The Magilligan borehole encountered 806m of Triassic strata overlying 350m of early Carboniferous coal-bearing strata. Gravity modelling suggests that the Carboniferous section may be in the order of 800m thick (4).

Lough Neagh Basin

In south central Co. Antrim, the Lough Neagh Basin is largely concealed by Palaeogene basalt lava of the Antrim Plateau. The asymmetric form of the basin is structurally controlled along its southern flank by northeast-southwest trending faults and resembles the southern part of the Rathlin Basin (4). Gravity modelling predicts a total basin depth of almost 4km. The stratigraphy of the basin has been tested in the Ballymacilroy and Langford Lodge boreholes (5, 10).

Larne Basin

Exploratory drilling in the Larne Basin in southeast Co. Antrim (Larne No.1 and No.2 boreholes) demonstrated 3000m of Permian and Mesozoic strata (6). Exposed rocks of Triassic-Cretaceous age occur in the Larne area, but the remainder of this basin is concealed beneath the Antrim Plateau. A gravity model has determined an oval geometry for the concealed basin with a depocentre located just north of Larne and extending offshore to the northeast. Although the basin initially subsided in the Permian along pre-existing northeast-southwest (Caledonian) fractures, the outcrop pattern of Triassic and younger rocks in the Larne area indicates that later subsidence was influenced primarily by NNW-SSE trending normal faults.

South Co. Antrim and north Co. Down

Triassic to Cretaceous rocks in this area dip regionally towards the northwest and are exposed along the north side of Belfast Lough and extend southwestwards beneath Belfast and the Lagan Valley. Although up to 1000m of Permian and Triassic rocks rest unconformably on the Southern Uplands-Down-Longford Terrane on the south side of Belfast Lough and the Lagan Valley, the location of the main depocentres is poorly constrained. The unconformity is modified and displaced by northwest-southeast trending faults.

Newtownards Trough

This basin lies between Comber and Newtownards and transects the Caledonian structural grain of the Southern Uplands-Down-Longford Terrane thus resembling the Permo-Triassic basins in the Southern Uplands of Scotland (3, 11). Subsidence was controlled by extension on northwest-southeast trending faults which developed in this terrane in both Northern Ireland and Scotland during an early phase in the opening of the Atlantic Ocean (12).

The Newtownards Trough is a half-graben that is believed to contain between 500-700m of Permian and Triassic rocks (13) although the oldest strata may be equivalent to the thin succession of early Carboniferous rocks exposed at Castle Espie in the northwest part of the basin (Chapter 7). The easterly-directed regional dip and asymmetrical nature of the Bouguer gravity anomaly indicate that basin subsidence was accommodated by syn-depositional movement on the Newtownards Fault (11).

Post-Mesozoic structural history

The post-Mesozoic structural development of Northern Ireland continued to be dominated by tensional tectonic forces related to the opening of the North Atlantic Ocean and separation of the North American and European plates. In north Co. Antrim, a reconstruction of the post-Carboniferous stress history, based on basement/cover relationships, revealed at least four separate tectonic phases (Tables 17.1 and 17.2) between the late Carboniferous and Palaeogene (9).

Period	Principal Stress Direction
Palaeogene	(See Table 17.2)
Late Jurassic to Early Cretaceous	ESE-WNW compression
Triassic	ENE-WSW transtension
Late Carboniferous (Variscan)	E-W to ESE-WNW compression

Table 17.1
Late Carboniferous to Palaeogene tectonic phases in north Co. Antrim (9).

	Period	Principal Stress Direction
Stage 2.	Mid-Eocene to mid-Miocene	NNE-SSW compression producing strike-slip faults and reactivation of Stage 1 structures.
Stage 1.	Late Palaeocene to early Eocene	ENE-WSW extension producing normal faults .

Table 17.2
Stages of Palaeogene and Neogene fracturing (9).

Opening of the North Atlantic Ocean

Regional deformation in the late Jurassic and Early Cretaceous created a sub-Late Cretaceous unconformity that increases in magnitude from east to west in Northern Ireland. Thus, in south and east Co. Antrim basal Cretaceous strata rest on either the Late Triassic Penarth Group or Early Jurassic Waterloo Mudstone Formation (Chapters 10 and 11). In contrast, at the western margin of their outcrop the unconformity is more pronounced and basal Cretaceous strata overstep both those units and older Triassic and Carboniferous rocks, and rest on the early

Palaeozoic Tyrone Igneous Complex on Slieve Gallion. However, tectonic activity continued into the Late Cretaceous and the effects of further uplift, faulting and gentle folding resulted in the minor unconformities and erosion surfaces that affect both the Hibernian Greensands and the Ulster White Limestone formations (Chapter 12). By the end of the Cretaceous period (65Ma) the continental crust in the North Atlantic region had stretched and thinned under the influence of a tensional regime. The separation of the North American and European continental plates was accomplished by a complex sequence of events which involved multiple spreading centres and culminated in the opening of the North Atlantic Ocean.

The creation of new oceanic crust at the mid-Atlantic ridge and increasing separation of the continental plates was accompanied by an upsurge of 'in-plate' magmatic activity as the thinned continental crust moved across hotspots (plumes) in the earth's upper mantle. In Northern Ireland and throughout the North Atlantic Igneous Province, the Palaeocene (65-52Ma) was a period of intense intrusive and extrusive igneous activity (14). Graben and half-graben sedimentary basins formed in Northern Ireland and particularly offshore on continental crust at the northwest margin of Europe as sea-floor spreading and plate rotation set up a tensional regime. In many of these basins, the sedimentary fill contains stratigraphical evidence of contemporaneous volcanic activity (14).

At this time, the crust was also subjected to localised doming and uplift as magma from the upper mantle and lower crust forced a path to the surface. In Northern Ireland, two phases of extensional deformation are recognised in the Late Cretaceous and early Palaeogene rocks (15). Both structural phases are characterised by a particular stress regime but have similar trends for the maximum component of horizontal stress.

In Northern Ireland, several types of structural features are associated with early Palaeogene magmatic activity.

Intrusions controlled by ring fractures

Wide-diameter annular fractures are closely associated with the intrusion of the central igneous complexes in Northern Ireland. The Mourne Mountains granites (Chapter 15) were emplaced in five separate phases of magma injection at two centres comprising the eastern Mournes (G1-G3 granites) and the western Mournes (G4-G5 granites). Successive phases of granite intrusion are believed to have followed the same ring fractures and were accommodated by continuing subsidence of the central block of Silurian country rocks (16).

In the Slieve Gullion Complex (Chapter 15), where some igneous activity reached the surface, granophyre and porphyritic felsite dykes were emplaced in concentric ring fractures, with a diameter of about 11km, at the southwest end of the late Caledonian Newry Igneous Complex (Chapter 5).

In southeast Co. Down a cone-sheet system intrudes the Silurian rocks around the eastern centre of the Mourne Mountains Complex. These intrusions were emplaced in inward-dipping, conical fractures that were generated by the emplacement of the rising granite magma. The best example of a composite acid cone-sheet is exposed at Glasdrumman Port (Chapter 15).

Doming associated with magmatism

In Northern Ireland there is limited evidence of doming associated with magmatism during the Palaeogene. Along the eastern contact of the Mourne Mountains Complex, eg. at Ballagh Park [J385 289], there is evidence of structural drag and strike swing in the Silurian country rocks.

Crustal dilation

Swarms of northwest-southeast trending dykes occur in Northern Ireland. The number of dykes increases in the vicinity of intrusive centres such as Slieve Gullion and the Mourne Mountains and in parts of Co. Fermanagh. In general, the dykes in Northern Ireland were intruded along fractures that are orientated normal to the direction of major rifting between Greenland and Northern Europe (Figure 15.8) (14).

Late to post-Palaeogene faulting

The outcrop pattern of the Palaeogene Antrim Lava Group (Chapter 14) and the Oligocene Lough Neagh Group (Chapter 16) indicates that major faulting continued in Northern Ireland after the cessation of magmatic activity and that there are two distinct groups of late to post-Palaeogene faults. This pattern has been confirmed by regional geophysical surveys and satellite imagery which supports the occurrence of the mapped faults together with many hitherto unmapped structures.

NNW-SSE trending faults

An early group of late to post-Palaeogene faults trending NNW-SSE is responsible for the compartmentalisation of the basalt outcrop in Co. Antrim. Similar faults also transect Palaeogene intrusive centres of the Mourne Mountains and Slieve Gullion and, in general, pre-date the northeast-southwest trending faults.

Northeast-southwest trending faults

The second group of faults in Northern Ireland that were active in the late Palaeogene include most of the northeast-southwest trending major normal faults and include the Tow Valley, Sixmilewater and Carnlough faults. These faults are parallel to earlier, Caledonian, structures and developed in the Palaeogene stress systems. Many of these faults were reactivated in the Neogene (late or post-Oligocene; 38-12Ma) and, in conjunction with NNW-trending splays, may have been responsible for basin subsidence associated with deposition of the Lough Neagh Group adjacent to the Tow Valley Fault in north Co. Antrim. The three basins at Ballymoney, Coagh and Crumlin all contain thick deposits of lignite (Chapter 16).

References

1) Kent, P. E. 1978. Mesozoic vertical movements in Britain and the surrounding continental shelf. *In*: Bowes, D. R. and Leake, B. E. (eds.). *Crustal evolution in northwestern Britain and adjacent regions.* Geological Journal Special Issue No. **10**, 309-24.

2) McLean, A. C. 1978. Evolution of fault-controlled ensialic basins in northwestern Britain. *In*: Bowes, D. R. and Leake, B. E. (eds.). *Crustal evolution in northwestern Britain and adjacent regions.* Geological Journal Special Issue No. **10**, 325-46.

3) Anderson, T. B., Parnell, J. and Ruffell, A. H. 1995. Influence of basement on the geometry of Permo-Triassic basins in the northwest British Isles. *In*: Boldy, S. A. R. (ed.). *Permian and Triassic rifting in Northwest Europe.* Geological Society Special Publication No. **10**, 103-22.

4) Carruthers, R. M., Cornwell, J. D., Turnbull, G., Walker, A. S. D. and Bennett, J. R. P. 1987. Interpretation of the Bouguer gravity anomaly data for Northern Ireland. *Report of the Regional Geophysics Research Group British Geological Survey*, No. 87/5.

5) Thompson, S. J. 1979. Preliminary report on the Ballymacilroy No. 1 borehole, Ahoghill, Co. Antrim. Geological Survey of Northern Ireland, Open File Report No. 63, Belfast.

6) Penn, I. E., Holliday, D. W., Kirby, G. A., Kubala, M., Sobey, R. A., Mitchell, W. I., Harrison, R. K.and Beckinsale, R. D. 1983. The Larne No. 2 Borehole: discovery of a new Permian volcanic centre. *Scottish Journal of Geology*, **19**, 333-46.

7) Bennett, J. R. P., 1983. *The sedimentary basins in Northern Ireland*. Institute of Geological Sciences, London.

8) Geological Survey of Northern Ireland, 1981. Limavady, Northern Ireland Sheet 12 and part of Sheet 6. Solid. 1:50,000. (Southampton: Ordnance Survey for the Geological Survey of Northern Ireland).

9) Kerr, I. D. V. 1987. *Basement/Cover structural relationships in the north Antrim area, Ireland.* Ph.D. Thesis, The Queen's University of Belfast.

10) Manning, P. I., Robbie, J. A. and Wilson, H. E. 1970. Geology of Belfast and the Lagan Valley. *Memoir of the Geological Survey of Northern Ireland.* Sheet 36 (Northern Ireland).

11) Smith, R. A., Johnston, T. P. and Legg, I. C. 1991. Geology of the country around Newtownards. *Memoir of the Geological Survey of Northern Ireland*, Sheet 37 and part of sheet 38 (Northern Ireland).

12) Bott, M. H. P. 1978. The origin and development of the continental margins between the British Isles and southeast Greenland. *In:* Bowes, D. R. and Leake, B. E. (eds.). *Crustal evolution in northwestern Britain and adjacent regions.* Geological Journal Special Issue No. 10, 377-92.

13) Geological Survey of Northern Ireland 1989. Newtownards, Northern Ireland Sheet 37 and part of sheet 38. Solid Geology. 1:50,000. (Southampton: Ordnance Survey for the Geological Survey of Northern Ireland).

14) Preston, J. 2001. *In:* Holland, C. H. (ed.). *The Geology of Ireland.* Dunedin Academic Press, Edinburgh, 353-73.

15) Geoffroy, L., Bergerat, F. and Angelier, J. 1996. Brittle tectonism in relation to the Palaeogene evolution of the Thulean/NE Atlantic domain: a study in Ulster. *Geological Journal*, **31**, 259-69.

16) Richey, J. E., 1927. The structural relations of the Mourne Mountains (Northern Ireland). *Quarterly Journal of the Geological Society of London*, **83**, 653-88.

Chapter 18

Quaternary

R. A. B. BAZLEY

Introduction

The Quaternary era commenced about 2.5Ma ago and completes the geological history of Northern Ireland. It's deposits, which cover most of the older rocks, are unconsolidated, relatively soft and contribute directly to modern soils. They are shown on the detailed maps of the Geological Survey of Northern Ireland and have special significance for engineering, agriculture and the environment. The final glacial episode had an important influence on the landscape of today and the variable climate through the era probably has implications for future climate change.

The oscillating nature of the global climate during the Quaternary is reflected in Ireland where conditions fluctuated many times from glacial to temperate (1). The record of these climatic changes is preserved in the oxygen isotope levels in oceanic sediments and is defined by the stages that have been established (Table 18.1). However, the age and correlation of most Quaternary deposits in Ireland is still problematical especially when considered in a British or wider context, although a meaningful time frame within a circum-North Atlantic context is now being developed (2). In Ireland there are no deposits representing the first 2Ma of the Quaternary era. Even after this period, the evidence is fragmentary but it permits the construction of local stratigraphies and the recognition of regional climate changes and events (Table 18.1).

Northern Ireland has a wide range of spectacular glacial features of late Pleistocene age and Irish words, such as *drumlin* and *esker* are now used internationally in glacial geology. It has been written, "....the drumlins of North-East Ireland belong to .... the most remarkable drumlin assemblage in the world" (3) and the famous 'basket-of-eggs' topography of Co. Down makes a strong case for the claim (Photograph 1). Spectacular eskers are found at Causeway End [J245 646] near Lisburn, Muntober [H740 810] northwest of Cookstown, Eskermore [H525 678] near Beragh and north of Bellaghy [H970 989]. Ice-smoothed and striated surfaces, kettle-holes, ice-wedge casts, deeply cut channels, moraines and many other glacial and deglacial features can be seen in Northern Ireland. All help interpret what happened in our most immediate past.

The remains of plants and animals in Quaternary deposits indicate the climatic conditions of their time by reference to the habitat occupied by the same or similar species today. Plants (especially pollen), insect remains, mammal bones and marine organisms like foraminifera are important climatic indicators. Age estimates, of varying reliability because of contamination problems, may be determined for Quaternary deposits that contain wood, shells or bones. Several methods of dating include radiocarbon (reliable to about 30,000BP) and amino acid (reliable to around 200,000BP*) (* BP means Years **B**efore **P**resent).

211

Photograph 1
Drowned drumlins in Strangford Lough looking SSW to the Mourne Mountains, Co. Down.

A continuous record of seasonal climatic change combined with accurate dating of sediments containing tree remains has been established from tree-ring growth patterns (dendrochronology) and covers the past 7,300 years (4).

Most important is the establishment of reliable correlation between sites and the development of a stratigraphy. The following account catalogues events from the earliest to the latest but the reader should note that understanding of the epoch in Ireland is still developing and parts remain controversial. Particularly, the story of changing sea levels has yet to be satisfactorily understood and linked to the climatic events.

The Quaternary is divided into the **Pleistocene** and **Holocene**, the latter covering the last 10,000 years. Most local names used in the following text are shown on Figure 18.2.

Pleistocene

The Pleistocene commenced with an episode of global cooling that led to vast accumulations of snow and ice in northern latitudes. The resulting polar ice sheet (Figure 18.1) expanded and contracted many times, on occasions engulfing Britain and Ireland and most of northern Europe (5). During repeated cold episodes the landscape in Ireland was subjected to severe weathering and erosion, particularly during the last major glaciation which removed or substantially modified the pre-existing regolith. In the south of Ireland, older Pleistocene deposits include evidence of the Gortian Interglacial, a Middle Pleistocene warm period dated to about 365,000BP, which is succeeded by glacigenic sediments (tills) ascribed to the **Munsterian Stage** (1). However, in Northern Ireland most glacial deposits are of Upper Pleistocene age, with at the base, evidence of a warm temperate stage here referred to the **Last Interglacial (Ipswichian) Stage**. The climate during the succeeding **Midlandian Cold Stage** was mainly made up of cold periods **(stadials)**, interspersed with cool phases **(interstadials)**. The last major glaciation peaked between about 24,000-18,000BP and engulfed all but the most southerly parts of Ireland and Britain.

	Approx. Age (BP)	Stages British *European*	Climate	North of Ireland deposits and events	Pollen Zones	O₂ Isotope Stages	North of Ireland Stages/Substages	
Holocene	1000	Flandrian *Flandrian*	Cool and wet		X	1	Littletonian (Postglacial)	
	2000			Volcanic dust from Iceland eruption	IX			
	3000							
	4000				VIII			
	5000		Temperate	Forest clearance				
	6000				VII			
	7000		Warm and Dry	Belfast estuarine clays	VI			
	8000			Marine transgression	V			
	9000		Warming	Human settlement	IV			
Pleistocene	10000	Devensian *Weichselian*	Arctic	Mountain glaciers/corries Woodgrange deposits	III		Nahanagan Stadial	**Midlandian**
	11000		Mild	Giant Irish deer	II		Woodgrange interstadial	
	12000		Sub-Arctic	Ice wedges	I			
	13000		Glacial	Ice readvance, Co. Down drumlins, Armoy moraine			Killard Point event	
	14000							
	15000		Warming	Ice decay. Marine transgression. Outwash deposits, eskers, moraines		2	Glenavy Stadial	
	16000							
	17000			Malone sands, kettle holes				
	18000		Sub-Arctic					
	19000							
	20000		Glacial	Major glaciation. Ice sheet cover complete. Gelvin, Maguiresbridge, Glenavy tills formation; Belfast lower till				
	21000							
	22000							
	23000							
	24000							
	25000							
	30000			Derryvree/Greenagho beds			Derryvree Interstadial	
	40000		Sub-Arctic with short, warm periods			3		
	50000			Hollymount Bed				
				Aghnadarragh Bed		4	Aghnadarragh Interstadial	
	60000							
	70000		Glacial	Fermanagh, Bovevagh, and Lackagh tills formation			Fermanagh Stadial	
	80000		Cooling			5		
	90000							
	100000							
	110000							
	120000	Ipswichian *Eemian*	Temperate to Subtropical	Benburb Bed		5e	Last Interglacial	

Table 18.1
A timescale of Quaternary events during the late Pleistocene in Northern Ireland. (Blues are cold climate: Greens are moderate climate).

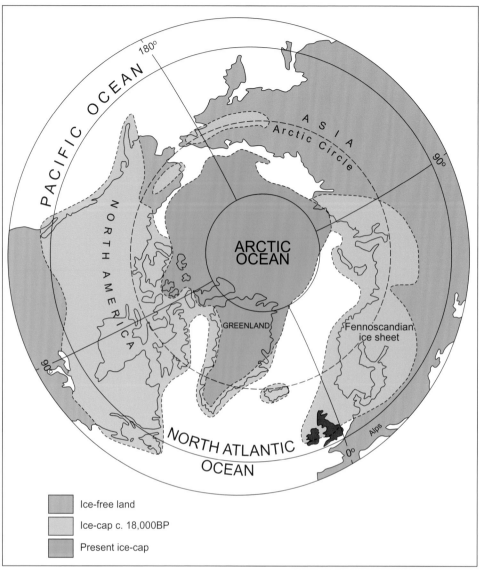

Figure 18.1
Distribution of ice sheets during the late Pleistocene and at present in the Northern Hemisphere (5).

Last Interglacial (Ipswichian) Stage

The oldest known fossiliferous Quaternary deposits in the north of Ireland are located at Benburb [H810 520], Co. Tyrone. The strata, which are overlain by glacial till, consist of at least 4m of dark brown peat and grey lacustrine clay with assemblages of pollen and spores and plant macrofossils including seeds and angiosperm and conifer leaves. The pollen spectrum is indicative of a warm climate with forests of yew *(Taxus)*, pine *(Pinus)*, silver fir *(Abies)*, alder *(Alnus)*, hazel *(Corylus)*, oak *(Quercus)* and holly *(Ilex)* (6). Benburb is the first interglacial site to be recognised in Northern Ireland. The age of the deposit is uncertain. It was initially correlated with the Gortian (Hoxnian) Interglacial but the pollen assemblages may not be diagnostic of that interglacial and a correlation with the Ipswichian Interglacial is favoured here (7).

214

Figure 18.2
Location map of the main Quaternary sites in Northern Ireland.

Midlandian Cold Stage

Prior to the last glaciation in the north of Ireland, climatic conditions ranged from cold glacial episodes to relatively short warmer phases with intervening cold periods characterised by permafrost. A tentative sequence of climatic changes associated with distinctive sediments including tills, stratified deposits and organic layers has been defined at a few sites in Northern Ireland. The correlation of sediments between sites is however, problematical and their assignment to **early, middle** or **late** episodes of the Midlandian is largely unsubstantiated by accurate dates. Nevertheless, this tripartite division of the Midlandian cold-climate period is convenient for descriptive purposes. The stadials are recognised by tills/diamicts and interstadials by organic remains.

Early Midlandian
Fermanagh Stadial

The earliest glacigenic deposits in Northern Ireland probably date from the early part of the Midlandian Stage. They include glacial tills deposited by ice from an Irish centre and from a Scottish source. The latter moved onshore along the east and north coastal fringes of Northern Ireland as well as sweeping across Counties Down and Armagh. Evidence of ice flowing to the south and southwest from the Irish Sea and North Channel is found in the

215

distribution of clasts of Cretaceous chalk and flint and in the concentration of distinctive erratics of riebeckite-microgranite derived from Ailsa Craig in the Firth of Clyde (3).

The slopes south of Lough Foyle, Co. Londonderry have three tills demonstrably one above the other. The basal two tills are probably from this early glaciation and the highest is from the late final glaciation. South of Ballykelly [C612 191], at the base and in contact with bedrock, is the 2m thick **Lackagh Till** (8). Erratics indicate deposition from an Irish ice source to the south. The overlying **Bovevagh Till** is about 7m thick and is widely exposed between Eglinton and Limavady. This till is present up to a height of 200m above sea level and erratics show that it was deposited by an ice sheet moving southwards from Scotland. It is a brown, calcareous lodgement till with clasts of basalt, chalk, flint, Triassic and Carboniferous sandstone, and Dalradian lithologies. It also includes in some places grey mud with numerous shells of marine bivalves, gastropods and foraminifera that probably originated as offshore deposits picked-up by the ice sheet and transported inland. At some localities the glaciomarine deposits are distinct clasts within the till. However, at Sistrakeel [C626 213] near Ballykelly, it has been suggested that the glaciomarine deposit lies beneath the Bovevagh Till and has not been moved. The section consists of 3m of stratified diamict and cobble gravel and a 2m thick mud unit. The mud contains a microfauna of foraminifera and ostracods of high boreal to arctic aspect and broken shells of marine molluscs that give amino acid dates around 90,000BP (9). It is also now suggested that the type section of the Bovevagh Till at Bovevagh Old Church [C668 140] includes *in situ* marine muds (9).

The basal lodgement tills at Derryvree, Aghnadarragh, Hollymount and Greenagho (Figure 18.2) are ascribed to the Fermanagh Stadial (Table 18.1). The presence of a suite of erratics common to all these localities indicates an origin from one ice sheet that moved radially from central northern Ireland, blocking the on-shore movement of Scottish ice thereby restricting its till to the coastal fringe (Figure 18.3A). However, further south the Scottish ice pressed inland for tens of kilometres. Near Crossmaglen (Figure 18.2), glacial gouges on roches moutonnées were produced by ice flowing to the southwest, and probably date from this time (10).

Aghnadarragh Interstadial

Evidence for the stratigraphical position and age of the **Aghnadarragh Interstadial** occurs in Unit 6 in the stratotype section at Aghnadarragh [J125 735] (11). The lowest part of the succession, represented by Units 2-6 (Table 18.2), is typical of a low-angle, prograded delta infill and records a gradual climatic transition from glacial-deglacial-interstadial at the end of the early Midlandian. Organic material from Unit 6 gives a minimum ^{14}C age of 48,180BP. After climatic amelioration during the Aghnadarragh Interstadial, conditions deteriorated and the upper peat horizon (Unit 8) gave a minimum ^{14}C age of 46,850BP for the ensuing cold phase.

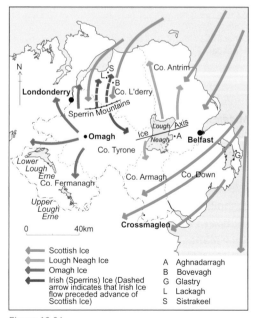

Figure 18.3A
Ice-flow directions during the early Midlandian (Fermanagh Stadial).

Unit (thickness)	Lithology	Palaeo-environment	Flora and Fauna (Climate)	Interpretation	
10 (4-7m)	Massive till facies Stratified till facies	Lodgement till deposited beneath and directly from an ice mass; abundant ice-faceted clasts	**Barren** (severe cold initially, becoming glacial)	**GLENAVY STADIAL**	
9 (3m)	Sand	Ephemeral flood deposits in distal parts of a sandur		**Cold Phase**	
8 (*c.* 0.15m)	Detrital organic mud	Transitory shallow lakes	**Treeless landscape with sedges (*Cyperaceae*) and grasses (*Gramineae*); insects of northern aspect** (cold, non-glacial)		
7 (2m)	Interbedded pebbly sand and gravel	Large scale infill of channels by debris flows	**Barren**		
6 (1.5m)	Organic woody detritus peat and interbedded sand and gravel	Woodlands with areas of swamp; deposition in water on a shallow delta	**Woodlands of birch (*Betula*), pine (*Pinus*) and spruce (*Picea*)** (cool, temperate)	**AGHNADARRAGH INTERSTADIAL**	
5 (4-5m)	Interbedded gravel, sand and diamicton lenses	Deposition from gravelly debris flows; growth of ice wedges	**Teeth, tusks and leg bones of mammoth (*Mammuthus primigenus*) and Musk-ox (*Ovibus*)** (cold, non-glacial)	**Cold (Periglacial) Phase**	**FERMANAGH STADIAL**
4 (2-3m)	Parallel laminated and rippled sand with dropstones	Ice withdrawal and formation of pro-glacial lakes	**Barren** (severe cold, non-glacial)	**Deglacial Phase**	
3 (>1.5m)	Massive mud				
2 (5m)	Massive till (diamicton) facies	Lodgement till deposited beneath and directly from an ice mass	**Barren** (glacial)	**Glacial**	
1	Glaciotectonised lignite beds	Deformation beneath easterly-moving ice sheet			

Table 18.2
Lithostratigraphy, fossil content and climatic interpretation of the Midlandian section at Aghnadarragh, Co. Antrim (11).

Middle Midlandian

Evidence for cold, non-glacial climatic conditions during the middle Midlandian is found at three sites in Co. Fermanagh. Freshwater organic mud occurs at **Hollymount** [H356 403], near Maguiresbridge (12) and at **Greenagho**, near Belcoo (13). Pollen assemblages indicating open countryside conditions of northern aspect at Hollymount gave a minimum ^{14}C age of 41,500BP. No pollen was found at Greenagho and the ^{14}C date of 32,460BP is regarded with caution as a minimum date. It is not possible to correlate the peat in Unit 8 at Aghnadarragh with either the Hollymount or Greenagho deposits because of the absence of reliable dates.

At **Derryvree** in Co. Fermanagh [H361 390], a lower till, deposited during the early Midlandian Fermanagh Stadial, is separated from a late Midlandian upper till by organic-rich layers with a flora of freshwater mosses and sedges and an insect fauna of cold northern aspect (14). A ^{14}C age of 30,500±1170-1030BP was obtained for the organic-rich layers.

Late Midlandian

The late Midlandian period started about 25,000BP and continued up to 10,000BP (Table 18.3). It is the final, predominantly glacial, episode of the Midlandian Stage. The ice mass was retreating significantly before 16,000BP (2) so in Northern Ireland deglaciation features like eskers, glacial lakes, subglacial channels and outwash deposits were forming and maybe continued through to the end of the drumlin re-advance episode (Killard Point event) at about 13,000BP.

Glenavy Stadial

The Glenavy Stadial (Last Glacial Maximum) reached a maximum around 24,000-20,000BP and the 'upper tills' in Northern Ireland derive from this episode. Ice cover was virtually complete and extended beyond the present coastline in most areas. Strong ice flows moved radially from the Omagh and Lough Neagh ice dispersal centres (Figure 18.3B) depositing thick glacial diamicts (tills). At Aghnadarragh (Table 18.2), the Glenavy Stadial is represented by a thick till (Unit 10) that has been termed the Glenavy Formation (9). The till is termed the Gelvin Till in the north and the Maguiresbridge Till in the west (9). These lodgement tills largely reflect the local bedrock in erratic content and can be around 10m thick. Extensive northeast-southwest trending rogen moraine formed between the Erne Basin and Co. Armagh (10).

It was at this time that crustal depression caused by the weight of ice reached a maximum so at about 18,000BP, when deglaciation probably started, sea levels were much higher than at the present time compared to the land. There is a raised beach platform at 14.5m above sea level [C601 223] near Ballykelly, Co. Londonderry (8). Hence the extensive glacial outwash deposits pouring into the sea from the Roe and Foyle/Faughan valleys were planed to an elevation of just over 14m above present sea level. These deltaic deposits (Fruitfield Formation) (9) form an extensive terrace that rises in height southwards up the valleys, reaching 24m south of Limavady.

Deglaciation was probably a complex process with ice retreats, standstills and even minor readvances in different areas at different times. Evidence of retreat moraines can be seen along the valleys of the River Foyle (15) and River Roe (8). Just south of Carlingford Lough, at Cooley Point, there is evidence that the ice margin had withdrawn by around 15,800BP (16) confirming that major deglaciation of the Irish Sea basin had started before 16,000BP (2).

Meltwater deposits such as the Malone Sands in Belfast probably formed in ice marginal lakes at this time. It is likely that the diamict which covers these sands in the Lagan Valley between Belfast and Lisburn, is the product of debris flow and was not a till deposited directly from an ice mass. Overflow meltwater from 'Lake Lagan' initially drained

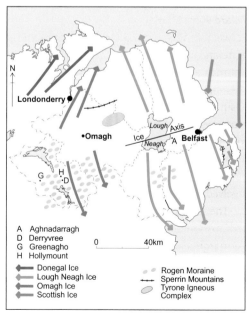

Figure 18.3B
Ice-flow directions and glacial features during the late Midlandian (Glenavy Stadial).

Time Period (^{14}C kyr BP)	Glacial/sedimentary signature	Climatic signature	Substage
11.0-?10.5	Extensive periglacial activity; restricted corrie glaciers in upland areas	Cooler, wetter climate	**Nahanagan Stadial**
13.0-11.0	Late-glacial organic sequences. Stagnation zone retreat in eastern Ireland;	Climate warming /oscillations	**Woodgrange Interstadial**
15.0-13.0	Ice streaming; morainal bank formation. Temporary withdrawal of ice margins (Cooley Point)	Cooling in Northern hemisphere	**Killard Point event**
25.0-17.0	Rogen moraine formation; deposition of till	Last Glacial Maximum	**Glenavy Stadial**

Table 18.3
Summary of the main characteristics of the late Midlandian substages in Ireland.

northeastwards along the course of the present River Lagan. When that route became blocked, maybe by ice during a later readvance, the water instead flowed west to Lough Neagh, through the Soldierstown Gap at Moira. It was probably at this time, when the ice support withdrew, that the major block landslides occurred along steep margins of the Antrim Plateau, from Cave Hill and northwards along the Antrim coast to Binevenagh in the west, near Limavady. Particularly catastrophic was the huge slip at Sallagh Braes, north of Larne.

Another feature that developed at the time of the decay of the ice sheets, with the release of vast quantities of meltwater below the ice, are the deeply incised glacial channels. Fine examples occur at Bernisk Glen [H605 675] 3.5km east of Sixmilecross, Butterlope Glen [H492 950] 4km north of Plumbridge, south of Loughaveema [D207 354] near Ballycastle and Gortin Gap [H490 850] in Co. Tyrone.

Killard Point Stadial

Between 14,500-14,000BP ice re-advance and a major drumlin-forming episode in the north of Ireland is correlated with the episode of iceberg discharge in the North Atlantic known as **Heinrich event 1** (2). Initially, ice flow was largely erosive and was responsible for the streamlining, remoulding or removal of bedforms in the area of rogen moraine in the Erne Basin and central Co. Armagh (which were created during the Glenavy Stadial). Linear moraines which extend from Kells in Co. Meath to Killard Point in Co. Down (17) define the southeastern margin of the ice mass (Figure 18.3C). Calving of icebergs into the sea (at the higher level mentioned above) instigated the propagation of faster ice flow streams northwards from Dundalk Bay through Co. Armagh to the south side of Lough Neagh and involved the headward (north to northwestward) erosion of pre-existing transverse ridges.

The stadial is especially associated with the formation of drumlins and ice-moulded bedforms in Counties Down and Armagh (Table 18.3). At Killard Point [J613 435], there was ice-marginal deposition of gravel deposits that prograded south from the ice front into the sea (17). The deposits consist of reworked glacigenic diamict interbedded with the gravel and beds of red marine mud containing *in situ* marine microfaunas. The melting of icebergs into the sea produced the dropstones that occur in the muds.

Regional evidence now indicates that ice flowed west and north from the Omagh area and, with much greater effect than hitherto, from the Lough Neagh ice axis (Figure 18.3C). Here, as elsewhere, drumlins occur on low ground mainly below 200m, but other

Photograph 2
The Munville esker [H371 355], 2km NNE of Lisnaskea, Co. Fermanagh. The ridge, which rises towards the viewer, originated during north-south flow of the ice sheet and is composed of glacial diamict.

streamlined rock-cored ridges occur at higher altitudes. Towards the end of the period, linear ridges of moulded till formed in the Clogher Valley beneath ice moving to the southwest from Lough Neagh and by southeasterly ice flow in the area south of Lisnaskea, perpendicular to the orientation of rogen moraine in that area (Photograph 2). In Co. Antrim, ice from Lough Neagh advanced northwards, moulding drumlins across the Antrim Plateau, including the valleys of the Rivers Bann and Main. In north Co. Antrim a slightly later southward advance of ice from Scotland reached the line of the Armoy Moraine. It rode over the pre-existing drumlins without destroying their form, advancing into outwash deposits that were thrust into a series of sub-parallel ridges. The Armoy Moraine, up to 50m thick, is composed of gravel, diamict, clay, silt, sand and is notable for its glaciotectonic deformation features (18). Sandwiched between the margins of the two ice masses, extensive sand and gravel was deposited at the edge of the Scottish ice in a lake system fringing the breached, southern margin of the Armoy Moraine (19). Concurrently, as the ice wasted southwards, north-south trending eskers developed in meltwater channels under the ice sheet. They extend for 15km from Cullybackey [D055 058] in the south, to the west of Glarryford [D055 130] and end at The Isles [D023 204] near Dunloy.

After the ice readvance, deglaciation would have continued in earnest. As the ice retreated southward across northwestern Co. Londonderry and Co. Tyrone to the ice centres in Lough Neagh and the Omagh Basin it became confined to low ground south of the deglaciated Sperrin Mountains. Glaciofluvial deposits on their flanks, such as in the Lough Fea and Pomeroy-Draperstown areas, record positions of the ice margin during retreat (20). On the north side of the Sperrin Mountains deep lakes formed in long narrow valleys that were dammed by ice flowing from the Omagh and Lough Neagh centres (Figure 18.3C). Gilbert-type deltas and glaciolacustrine sediments were deposited in these ice-marginal lakes which, in the Murnee Hills, created a high level shoreline up to 450m above present sea level (Photographs 3A, 3B).

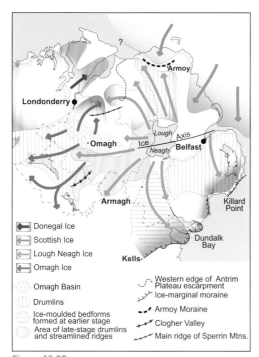

Ice-flow directions and glacial features during the Killard Point event of the late Midlandian.

Map legend:
- Donegal Ice
- Scottish Ice
- Lough Neagh Ice
- Omagh Ice
- Omagh Basin
- Drumlins
- Ice-moulded bedforms formed at earlier stage
- Area of late-stage drumlins and streamlined ridges
- Western edge of Antrim Plateau escarpment
- Ice-marginal moraine
- Armoy Moraine
- Clogher Valley
- Main ridge of Sperrin Mtns.

Woodgrange Interstadial

In the marine environment evidence for ameliorating climatic conditions some 13,000-11,000BP is found at Rough Island, Co. Down. This tiny island in Strangford Lough has, resting on a glacial till, a composite deposit of late-glacial marine laminated mud and sand that has been eroded by tidal currents into a ridge overlain by post-glacial gravel. The mud contains foraminifera dated to 12,700BP (2). Sea levels during the period must have dropped to below the present day levels. However, the best record of conditions during the time between the disappearance of the ice and the present, is preserved in the vegetation.

A complete record of the changes mentioned above is found in the complex of raised lowland peat at Sluggan Bog [J099 921] in Co. Antrim (Figure 18.2), 3km northeast of Randalstown (21). As well as cut sections in the peat, boreholes encountered 5.2m of raised bog peat, fen peat and lacustrine mud in a shallow, concealed basin. The section is divided into ten pollen zones (Table 18.4) and has a radiocarbon date of 12,500BP for organic detritus at the base of the section, which lies on till.

The Murnee Hills delta showing the two main levels of the deposit [C705 057], 4km SSE of Dungiven, Co. Londonderry. The lower level is covered by up to 1m of peat which conceals at least 10m of cross-stratified sand and gravel.

In the wake of the disappearing ice sheets, initial colonisation was by vegetation of Arctic tundra affinity. The oldest pollen assemblages from Sluggan Bog (Zone S:I) are dominated by dwarf willow *(Salix herbaceae)* and sorrel *(Rumex)* indicating a cool climate. In Zone S:II the increasing domination of poplar *(Populus)*, juniper *(Juniperus)* and birch is indicative of warmer conditions at the start of the **Woodgrange Interstadial**. It was at this time that Ireland witnessed the arrival of the Giant Irish Deer *(Megaceros giganteus)* whose antlers have been found in deposits in Larne Lough, Co. Antrim.

Nahanagan Stadial

Climatic deterioration then led to the onset of the **Nahanagan Stadial**, the final glacial episode in Ireland. Ice accumulation was confined to ice fields and local corrie glaciers in the Mourne and Sperrin mountains. Major ice sheets did not advance across Ireland and evidence for the cold episode is limited to protalus ramparts, fossil rock glaciers and soliflucted material (1). Once again juniper, mosses and sedges typical of the open tundra dominated the treeless landscape and indicated a temperature depression of up to 8°C.

Holocene

The Holocene Series in Ireland represents the final 10,000 year post-glacial period and is termed the Littletonian Stage (Table 18.1). After the end of the glacial Nahanagan Stadial (Zone S:III) the vegetation history of Ireland evolved through phases of open-tundra and birch woods (Zone S:IV) to the hazel forests of the early Boreal period (Zone S:V) which were gradually invaded by oak *(Quercus)* and elm *(Ulmus)*. The establishment of the first high forests only occurred in the succeeding late Boreal period (Zone S:VI) and pollen spectra are dominated by oak and elm and, eventually, pine.

Photograph 3B
The Murnee Hills delta. Foresets of loose sand with thin beds of gravel, dipping at up to 25°, and a topset bed of flat-lying gravel about 1m thick. (Hammer length 35cm).

Photograph 4
Temporary section in Holocene deposits composed mainly of sleech at the Lincoln Centre [J335 374], at the junction of Sandy Row and Hope Street, Belfast. (Section about 5m high.)

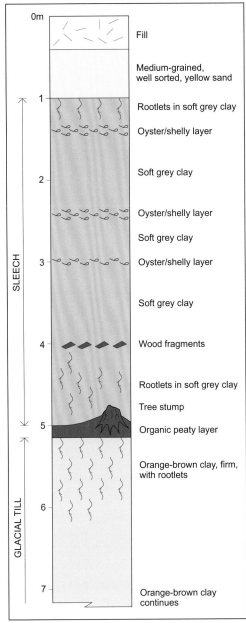

Figure 18.4
Detailed log of Holocene deposits in a temporary excavation at the Lincoln Centre (J 335 374) at the junction of Sandy Row and Hope Street, Belfast.

A notable marine transgression **(Flandrian Transgression)** occurred at about 8,500BP in the early part of the late Boreal period (Table 18.1). Rising sea level inundated Strangford Lough, Larne Lough and Lough Foyle and covered thin peat (dated to 9,100BP) in the estuaries of the River Lagan and River Bann with grey mud, silt and sand. In the Belfast area this estuarine deposit is known as 'sleech' and contains oysters, mussels and gastropods (Figure 18.4; Photograph 4). The combination of very low bearing strength and thickness of up to 17m presents engineering problems and large buildings are generally founded on a forest of piles to transfer the weight down to stronger material (Chapter 23). During the transgression maximum, Lough Neagh expanded and diatomite, up to 1m thick, was deposited in the Bann Valley, south of Portglenone. This white deposit is formed of the siliceous skeletons of some forty species of diatom (alga) which flourished in a Boreal climate 2.5°C warmer than today. The climate also encouraged the formation of white calcareous clay, the *Chara* Marl, containing freshwater bivalves and gastropods.

In Ireland, the boundary between the S:VI and S:VII zones is recognised by the changing composition of the forests from the warm, dry Boreal climate to a wetter and cooler Atlantic regime. This change is also reflected in the spread of alder, the decline of pine forests and the accumulation of peat in raised bogs. The pine stumps that occur at the base of most peat bogs in Northern Ireland represent this transition. At Sluggan Bog, the first evidence of the influence of Neolithic man on the natural vegetation is found at the end of S:VII.

Around the coast of Northern Ireland the impact of successive phases of marine low-stand and of transgression are evident in the development of post-Glacial raised beaches a few metres above present sea level. There are 8m high bay-head gravel ridges at Cushendun, Co. Antrim. Gravel barriers at Magilligan, Co. Londonderry, although partly concealed by aeolian sand, consist of at least thirty swash-aligned beach ridges that developed some 7,000BP (22). Post-glacial beach levels are also shown by the height of caves at The Gobbins and Cushendun, in Co. Antrim. Extensive areas of windblown coastal sand at Dundrum, Co.

Zone	Age BP	Period	Vegetation History		
S:X	1,560 BP–present day	Historic	Clearance of secondary forest in stages		POST-GLACIAL (Littletonian)
S:IX	3,880-1,560	later Prehistoric	Secondary forest	Neolithic	
			Forest with increasing Bronze Age clearances		
S:VIII	4,900-3,880	early farming	Forest disturbed by Neolithic farming		
S:VII	7,020-4,900	Atlantic	'Climax' forest		
S:VI	8,570-7,020	late Boreal	Mixed forest with oak and elm and lastly pine		
S:V	9,200-8,570	early Boreal	Hazel woodland invaded by oak and elm	Mesolithic	
S:IV	9,700-9,200	early Post-glacial	Open birch woodland		
			Birch woodland		
			Open tundra with juniper		
S:III	11,000-9,700	Nahanagan (Roddansport) Stadial	Open tundra		LATE GLACIAL (late Midlandian)
S:II	12,350-11,000	Woodgrange Interstadial	(Some birch?)		
			Birch woodland		
S:I	Ends 12,350	Older *Salix herbacea*	Open - ? some birch and juniper		

Table 18.4
Summary of the Holocene vegetation history in Northern Ireland based on the pollen zone scheme from Sluggan Bog, Co. Antrim (21).

Down and at Portstewart Strand and Magilligan, in Co. Londonderry date from the early Atlantic Period (7,000-6,000BP).

The coincidence between accurate dates for times of narrow tree-ring growth and acid layers in Greenland ice cores suggests that the Irish oaks were reacting to, and thus recording, times of environmental stress. Recent studies of layers of volcanic dust (tephrochronology) in Irish peat have proved the influence of at least nine eruptions within the last 10,000 years, several of which are attributed to the Icelandic volcano Hekla (23). The Hekla 4 eruption is dated to between 4,395 and 4,279BP and the possible correlation with narrow tree-rings in 4,345BP is compelling evidence for the influence of volcanism in the north Atlantic region on the climate of Ireland at that time.

The influence of people in Northern Ireland

Neolithic people arrived in Ireland, probably from Scotland, before the Flandrian Transgression in the middle Boreal period (Zones S:V and S:VI). They left traces of their existence around the coast of Counties Antrim and Down in the form of kitchen middens and collections of flint tools. In the earliest period of human occupation, Northern Ireland would have been ranked as exceptionally well endowed in the essential natural resources of the day. Rock types such as flint, chert, porcellanite, dolerite/basalt and mudstone were exploited (and in some cases exported) for the manufacture of polished stone axe heads and implements such as flint knives, scrapers and arrowheads. There was an abundant supply of clay suitable for making pottery. Large rock blocks (some glacial erratics) were available for

use in dolmens, passage graves and stone circles such as Ballynoe, near Downpatrick. Although there are known occurrences of copper, gold and tin in Northern Ireland their use in manufacture remains unproven. Nor has the prehistoric exploitation of gold in Northern Ireland yet been proven. Occurrences of iron ore include the laterite of the Palaeogene Interbasaltic Formation and bog iron ore but there is no firm evidence for specific exploitation in Iron Age times. Thus with the advent of metal working, Northern Ireland's strength in terms of natural resources declined from its exporting status in Neolithic times.

Porcellanite axe heads from Co. Antrim exceed 10,000 in number and are the most numerous of all the sourced axe lithologies in Britain and Ireland. The porcellanite is a mullite-cordierite-corundum-spinel hornfels that formed by contact metamorphism between degraded basalt lava in the Interbasaltic Formation and olivine dolerite plugs. Occurrences are restricted to two known localities at Tievebulliagh [D193 268] near Cushendall and Brockley on Rathlin Island (24). The products of the ensuing axe factories were distributed throughout but not, it seems, beyond Ireland and Britain. The Malone Hoard comprises 19 beautifully finished, probably ceremonial, porcellanite axes, which were found at Danesfort, Belfast (Photograph 5).

The impact of people on the Irish landscape cannot be underestimated. In particular, their use of peat as the primary fuel and, more recently major drainage schemes, has now reduced the area of raised bogs to about 20% of their former extent.

The survival of people in Ireland has, however, largely relied on agricultural practices that are dependent on that thinnest of deposits, the soil. Due to the erosive effects of glaciers soil profiles only started to develop about 10,000BP on the new glacigenic materials and younger deposits. Nevertheless, 308 varieties of soil have been identified in Northern Ireland and reflect the influence of bedrock geology, drift deposits, climate and groundwater chemistry (25). Artificial and improved natural drainage has expanded the area available for agriculture in particular the reclaimed land, similar to the Dutch polders, at Ballykelly on the south side of Lough Foyle. In modern times, it is the capital city that is extending into Belfast Lough by means of landfill, in the process producing the youngest superficial layer of all.

References

1) Coxon, P. 1997. Pleistocene climate change: the evidence from Irish sequences. *In*: Sweeney, J. (ed.). *Global change and the Irish environment*. Royal Irish Academy, Dublin, 17-35.

2) McCabe, A. M. and Clarke, P. U. 1998. Ice sheet variability around the North Atlantic Ocean during the last deglaciation. *Nature, London*, **392**, 373-77.

3) Charlesworth, J. K. 1939. Some observations on the glaciation of north-east Ireland. *Proceedings of the Royal Irish Academy*, **45B**, 11, 255-95.

4) Baillie, M. G. L. 1993. Palaeoecological Research. *The Biochemist. The Bulletin of the Biochemical Society*, **15 (4)**, 23-26.

5) Osborne, R. and Tarling, D. H. 1995. *The Historical Atlas of the Earth (A Visual Exploration of the Earth's Physical Past)*. Viking. Penguin Books Ltd., London

6) Boulter, M. and Mitchell, W. I. 1977. Middle Pleistocene (Gortian) deposits from Benburb, Northern Ireland. *Irish Naturalists Journal*. **19**, 2-3.

7) Gennard, D. E. 1984. A palaeoecological study of the interglacial deposit at Benburb, Co. Tyrone. *Proceedings of the Royal Irish Academy*. **84B**, 43-55.

8) Bazley, R. A. B., Brandon, A. and Arthurs, J. W. 1997. Geology of the country around Limavady and Londonderry. *Geological Survey of Northern Ireland. Technical Report GSNI/97/1*

9) McCabe, A. M. 1999. Ireland. *In*: Bowen, D. Q. (ed.). *A revised correlation of Quaternary deposits in the British Isles*. Geological Society, London, Special Report, **23**, 113-24.

10) McCabe, A. M., Knight, J. and McCarron, S. G. 1999. Ice-flow stages and glacial bedforms in north central Ireland: a record of rapid environmental change during the last glacial termination. *Journal of the Geological Society, London*. **156**, 63-72.

11) McCabe, A. M., Coope, G. R., Gennard, D. E. and Doughty, P. 1987. Freshwater organic deposits and stratified sediments between Early and Late Midlandian (Devensian) till sheets, at Aghnadarragh, County Antrim, Northern Ireland. *Journal of Quaternary Science*. **2**, 11-33.

12) McCabe, A. M., Mitchell, G. F. and Shotton, F. W. 1978. An inter-till freshwater deposit at Hollymount, Maguiresbridge, County Fermanagh. *Proceedings of the Royal Irish Academy*, **78**, 77-89.

13) Dardis, G. F., Mitchell, W. I. and Hirons, K. R. 1985. Middle Midlandian interstadial deposits at Greenagho, near Belcoo, County Fermanagh, Northern Ireland. *Irish Journal of Earth Sciences*, **7**, 1-6

14) Colhoun, E. A., Dickson, J. H., McCabe, A. M. and Shotton, F. W. 1972. A Middle Midlandian fresh-water series at Derryvree, Maguiresbridge, County Fermanagh, Northern Ireland. *Proceedings of the Royal Society of London*, **180B**, 273-92.

15) Colhoun, E. A. 1972. The deglaciation of the Sperrin Mountains and adjacent areas in counties Tyrone, Londonderry and Donegal, Northern Ireland. *Proceedings of the Royal Irish Academy*, **72B**, 8, 91-147.

16) McCabe, A. M. and Haynes, J. R. 1996. A late Pleistocene intertidal boulder pavement from an isostatically emergent coast, Dundalk Bay, Eastern Ireland. *Earth Surface Processes and Landforms*, **21**, 555-72.

17) McCabe, A. M., Dardis, G. F. and Hanney, P. 1984. Sedimentology of a Late Pleistocene submarine moraine complex, County Down, Northern Ireland. *Journal of Sedimentary Petrology*, **56**, 716-30.

18) Shaw, J. and Carter, R. W. G. 1980. Late Midlandian sedimentation and glaciotectonics of the North Antrim End Moraine. *Irish Naturalists' Journal*, **20**, 67-69.

19) Geological Survey of Northern Ireland 1999. Coleraine, Northern Ireland Sheet 13. Solid and Drift Geology. 1:50,000. (Keyworth, Nottingham: British Geological Survey).

20) Geological Survey of Northern Ireland 1995. Draperstown, Northern Ireland Sheet 26. Solid and Drift Geology. 1:50,000. (Keyworth, Nottingham: British Geological Survey).

21) Smith, A. G. and Goddard, I. C. 1991. A 12500 year record of vegetational change at Sluggan Bog, Co. Antrim, N. Ireland (incorporating a pollen zone scheme for the non-specialist). *New Phytologist*. **118**, 167-87.

22) Carter, R. W. G. 1982. Sea-level changes in Northern Ireland. *Proceedings of the Geologists Association*. **93 (1)**, 7-23.

23) Pilcher, J. R., Hall, V. A. and McCormac, F. G. 1996. An outline tephrochronology for the Holocene of the north of Ireland. *Journal of Quaternary Science*. **11 (6)**, 485-94.

24) Meighan, I. G., Jamison, D. D., Logue, P. J. C., Mallory, J. P., Simpson, D. D. A., Rogers, G., Mandal, S. and Cooney, G. 1996. Trace Element and Isotopic Provenancing of North Antrim Porcellanites: Portrush-Tievebulliagh-Brockley (Rathlin Island). *Ulster Journal of Archaeology*. **56**, 25-30.

25) Cruickshank, J. G. 1997. Soil and environment: Northern Ireland. *The Queen's University of Belfast*. Newforge Lane, Belfast. 1-214.

Chapter 19

Geophysics and Concealed Geology

D. M. REAY

Introduction

The distribution and structure of the rocks mapped at the land surface can be extrapolated to elucidate the geological structure at depth. Boreholes can sample the rocks below the surface at discrete locations. GSNI holds records for over 30,000 boreholes but of these only 482 are more than 100m deep and only 18, mainly oil and gas exploration wells, are deeper than 1000m.

Geophysical data provide further valuable indirect evidence about the nature of the sub-surface rocks and geological structure. These data are related to particular physical properties of the rocks such as density, magnetic susceptibility, seismic velocity and electrical conductivity. The geophysical data can be interpreted in terms of the sub-surface distribution of the rocks from which they originate although there will never be a single 'correct' interpretation.

Seismic refraction and seismic reflection surveys yield information about the gross crustal structure and more detailed upper crustal structure, respectively. There are no useful refraction data in Northern Ireland and seismic reflection coverage from petroleum exploration activity is sparse and limited to sedimentary basins. The COOLE refraction line and deep seismic data from the WINCH survey line provide information about crustal structure in Ireland and offshore between Northern Ireland and Scotland respectively. The data cannot be extrapolated along strike into Northern Ireland with any confidence.

The main geophysical datasets acquired on a regional scale over Northern Ireland are based on measurements of the earth's gravity and magnetic fields. Observations about the structure and nature of the concealed rocks below Northern Ireland are based largely on the interpretation of regional gravity and aeromagnetic surveys [1]. Gridded data has been used to generate colour and shaded-relief images that 'convey information on both anomaly amplitude (as colour) and anomaly gradient (as relief) and highlight structural trends, lineaments and textural contrasts not easily discernible on standard contour maps' [2]. Integrated gravity and magnetic anomaly models give further insight into the geological structure of Northern Ireland. Additional information has been derived from the results of seismic reflection surveys, deep-sounding electromagnetic experiments and local ground magnetometer surveys.

This account relies heavily on the work of Richard Carruthers, who led a series of BGS projects that greatly increased our understanding of the gravity and magnetic anomalies of Northern Ireland, and who died in a tragic accident in 2001.

Survey	1959-1960: Canadian Aero Service Ltd. N-S Flight lines, 2km spacing, E-W Tie-Lines every 10km. Terrain clearance 1000 ft (305m) except in areas of sharp relief	
Processing	Digitisation along flight lines. Anomalies calculated by subtracting background field (1)	
Gridding	Interpolated directly onto a 200m grid; interim points added to reduce 'string of pearls' appearance of linear anomalies orthogonal to flight lines	
Image Processing	Colour-filled anomaly Horizontal gradients Upward continuation (regional/residual separation) Reduction-to-pole Remanence of basalts	**Highs**: metamorphic basement, mafic and ultramafic intrusions, contact aureole to felsic intrusions **Lows**: sedimentary rocks, some granitic intrusions **Linear features**: faults, basin or intrusion margins, dykes, deep-seated lineaments **Regional trends**: deep sources **Residual trends**: local or shallow features Re-positions anomaly above causative body Re-displays reversely magnetised basalts as normally magnetised (positive anomalies)

Table 19.1
Aeromagnetic data acquisition, processing and display.

Aeromagnetic data

The Government of Northern Ireland funded a regional aeromagnetic survey of Northern Ireland, flown in 1959, as part of a UK-wide programme. Data from the survey was manually contoured and an aeromagnetic anomaly map of Northern Ireland produced in 1971 (3). Later the flight line profiles were digitised, anomalies calculated, gridded and computer-generated images produced (Table 19.1).

Gravity data

The first regional gravity survey in Ireland in 1950 included 350 gravity stations in Northern Ireland (Table 19.2). The Bouguer gravity anomaly map produced from these observations revealed the general form of the most significant anomalies in Northern Ireland (4). Gravity surveys during 1959-60 by the BGS provided a detailed coverage for Northern Ireland. A lake-bottom survey, using an underwater gravity meter, provided coverage for Lough Neagh and led to the publication of a revised gravity map of Northern Ireland (5). Additional data have subsequently been acquired in Co. Antrim and integrated into the regional dataset.

Surveys	1959-1960: 10,488 stations, mean station density $c.$ 1 per 1.25km^2 1984: 400 stations over Lough Neagh, 1km grid 1990: 107 stations from north Co. Antrim infill Additional data for adjacent areas supplied by Dublin Institute of Advanced Studies, British Geological Survey, Hydrographic Office and the Western Geophysical Company for offshore areas of the North Channel and Malin Sea	
Data Reduction	Bouguer anomalies derived using standard procedures with correction densities of 2.7Mg/m^3 for land and 2.4Mg/m^3 for sea (1)	
Gridding	1km grid generated and interpolated to 200m spacing.	
Image Processing	Colour-filled anomaly Horizontal gradients Upward continuation (Regional/residual separation)	**Highs**: metamorphic basement, mafic and ultramafic intrusions **Lows**: sedimentary rocks, granitic intrusions **Linear features**: faults, basin or intrusion margins, dykes, deep-seated lineaments **Regional trends**: deep sources **Residual trends**: local or shallow features

Table 19.2
Gravity data acquisition, processing and display.

Image processing

Shaded relief has been added to many images to enhance subtle local gradients in the field values thereby creating a topographic surface that is 'illuminated' by a point source with a specific inclination and azimuth, thus generating a shadow effect. Although a single grey scale presentation usually provides the highest resolution of the topographic surface gradients, the addition of colours enhances variations in amplitude of the parameter displayed and gives a more informative picture. This process enhances anomalies orthogonal to the direction of illumination so a range of illumination angles is used to highlight different structural trends.

Rock properties

Information on the physical properties of the main rock types found in Northern Ireland is limited, although some systematic results are available from outcrop samples and from geophysical logs in deep boreholes.

Density

In Northern Ireland the measured density of sedimentary rocks and of granitic intrusions is less than average while the density of most metamorphic and mafic rocks is higher than average. The density of basalt lava of the Antrim Lava Group (Chapter 14) as derived from borehole logs is anomalously low (<2.55Mg/m^3) compared to the expected mean value of 2.85Mg/m^3. However, this may be explained by the presence of features such as inter-flow weathering zones, fracturing and tuffaceous layers, which will all act to reduce the overall bulk density of the lava pile. A representative value of 2.66Mg/m^3 has therefore been used for modelling purposes. The sedimentary rocks also show a wide range of density values, with younger sedimentary rocks in general being less dense than older rocks. These values are dependent on the original lithology and subsequent diagenetic and burial history of the rocks.

Magnetic properties

In general, most magnetic anomalies in Northern Ireland are associated with igneous rocks and, to a lesser extent, with meta-igneous and volcaniclastic rocks. Sedimentary rocks

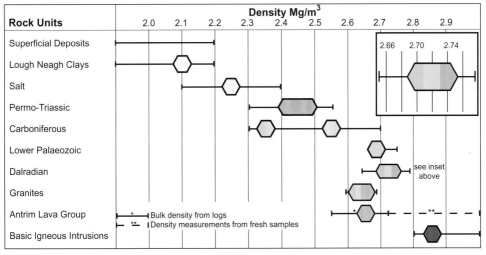

Table 19.3
Densities of rocks found in Northern Ireland.

Age	Potential sources of magnetic anomaly		Susceptibility (SI) *remanence vector*
Palaeogene	Basic lavas and tuffs	(M)	0.02 (mean value) (6) *D=194, I=-60*
	Lavas (M) and intrusive rocks (H)		*D=188, I=-62.8* (7) 0.015 - 0.15
	Basalt lavas	(M)	*D=198.5, I=-59.7* (8)
	Acid igneous intrusions	(L-M)	0.010 - 0.017 0.005 (mean value) (9)
	Basic igneous intrusions	(M)	0.005 - 0.014 (10)
Permian	Lavas		
Carboniferous	Basic lavas and tuffs		
Devonian	Andesitic lavas and tuffs	(L-M)	
	Acid igneous intrusions	(L-M)	0.005 (mean value) (9)
Ordovician	Basic lavas and tuffs	(M)	
	Acid igneous intrusions	(L-M)	0.005 (mean value) (9)
	Basic igneous intrusions	(M-H)	
Neo- and Mesoproterozoic	Basic igneous intrusions	(H)	
	Metamorphic basement	(M)	

Table 19.4
Summary of magnetic properties of igneous rocks in Northern Ireland. (L- low magnetisation (susceptibility $<10^{-3}$ SI) (anomalies unlikely); M- mixed magnetisation (variable response); H- significant magnetisation ($>10^{-2}$ SI) (anomalies likely)).

usually have very low magnetic susceptibilities, unless they contain significant amounts of ferromagnetic minerals, and give a low or, if their diamagnetic component is high enough, even a slightly negative response. The only systematic examination of the magnetic properties (susceptibility and remanent magnetisation) of rock types in Northern Ireland has concentrated on the palaeomagnetic studies of the basalt lava of the Antrim Lava Group (Table 19.4).

The magnetisation of the basalt lava and associated intrusive rocks has been examined in palaeomagnetic studies (6, 7, 11, 12). Its dominant component is a natural remanent magnetisation (NRM) acquired under the influence of the geomagnetic field at the time of cooling of the lava. The NRM is almost invariably aligned in the opposite direction to that of the present day geomagnetic field. This is consistent with results from other palaeomagnetic studies which revealed that only about 20% of 717 Palaeogene dykes examined in the UK were normally magnetised (13). The stable bulk magnetisation of the basalt lava is now found to show a declination of about 190° and an inclination of -60°, with variations from the mean of up to 20° in both parameters.

In general, for the basalt lavas and minor intrusions, the NRM (acquired during cooling) is expected to exceed the induced magnetisation component (acquired from the present-day geomagnetic field). However, given the variable nature of these properties, the relationship between them, the Koenigsberger ratio (Q), which is defined as the ratio of remanent to induced magnetisation, may be close to 1, or locally <1. This implies that significant magnetic anomalies may arise from variations in the magnetisation of a lava sequence as well as from variations in the shape and thickness of the lava pile. In addition to the basalt lavas and associated rocks, there is clear evidence of other rock types in Northern Ireland with distinctive magnetic signatures based on an interpretation of the magnetic anomaly maps and the surface geology.

Geophysical domains

The shaded relief images of the aeromagnetic and gravity anomalies can be divided into major geophysical anomaly domains and interpreted qualitatively. The magnetic anomaly data yield information about relatively magnetic basement and igneous rocks, whereas the gravity anomalies reflect the contrast between less dense sedimentary and silicic rocks and more dense metamorphic rocks and basic igneous rocks.

Anomalies on the aeromagnetic image (Figure 19.1) range from -700 to +700nT, with most of the variation caused by the highly magnetic basalt lavas of the Antrim Plateau. The colour scale on the image has been stretched to show the lower amplitude anomalies that characterise less magnetic rocks in Northern Ireland (Table 19.5).

The negative anomaly **MD1**, associated with Pre-Dalradian Basement rocks of the Lough Derg Inlier, extends north of the Lough Derg Slide thus confirming their extension below this shallow structure (Chapter 2). **MD2** is a less well-defined belt of moderately positive anomalies extending from Ballybofey (Co. Donegal) into the Sperrin Mountains. They probably reflect a higher proportion of metabasic rocks in the Dalradian compared to **MD3** where quartz-rich Dalradian and Carboniferous rocks around and under Lough Foyle give slightly negative anomalies. The strong positive anomalies of **MD4** offshore from Malin Head in Co. Donegal may indicate high-density Lewisian basement rocks beneath the Dalradian in this area.

Positive anomalies extend from the Dalradian inlier in northeast Co. Antrim (**MD5a**) southwestwards under the basalt lavas of the Antrim Plateau to the Sperrin Mountains, the Lack Inlier and Fintona Block (**MD5b - c**). Strong positive anomalies coincide with mafic rocks in the Tyrone Igneous Complex (Chapter 3) (**MD5d**). The extension to the northeast of similar anomalies may indicate the presence of these rocks at shallow depths. A lozenge-shaped negative anomaly coincides in part with tonalite intrusions in the Tyrone Igneous Complex and may reflect the extension of these bodies at depth, beneath the Omagh Thrust Fault (**MD5e**).

In the southwest there is a prominent WNW-ESE belt of three positive anomalies (**MD6a-c**). Magnetic basement, possibly early Palaeozoic volcanic rocks, below the Carboniferous sedimentary basin is the probable source of these anomalies. **MD7** is an area of negative magnetic anomaly over the Devonian and Carboniferous rocks between the Tempo-Sixmilecross and Clogher Valley faults (Chapter 8).

The southern margin of the Midland Valley Terrane in Scotland is marked by a strong positive anomaly over the Ballantrae (Ophiolite) Complex and late Ordovician magnetite-bearing greywacke. This anomaly can be traced southwestwards from Scotland across the North Channel (**MD8a**) into Northern Ireland between Larne and the north shore of Belfast Lough. However, its character is masked by the strong magnetic response of the basalt lavas of the Antrim Plateau, although a similar positive anomaly (**MD8b**) emerges along strike southwest of Lough Neagh. The anomaly amplitude decreases to the southwest until this belt intersects the WNW-ESE Fermanagh Highlands zone to produce the Slieve Rushen magnetic high (**MD6c**). It can be inferred that ultramafic rocks, similar to those of the Ballantrae Complex, lying at relatively shallow depths, are the source of this magnetic anomaly (**MD8a-b**). South of magnetic high MD8, the early Palaeozoic sedimentary rocks of the Southern Uplands-Down-Longford Terrane are characterised by negative anomalies (**MD9**).

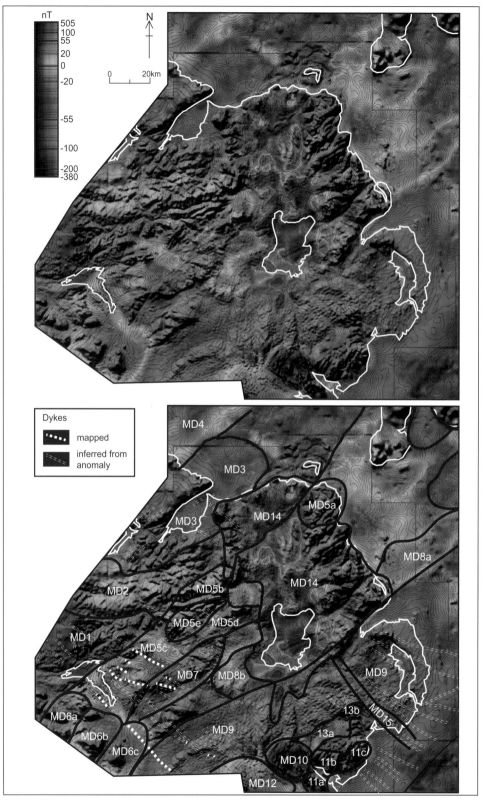

Figure 19.1
Aeromagnetic anomalies (reduced to pole) on ground topography. Shaded relief illumination from NNW.
Topographic image based on digital elevation data supplied by the Ordnance Survey of Northern Ireland.

232

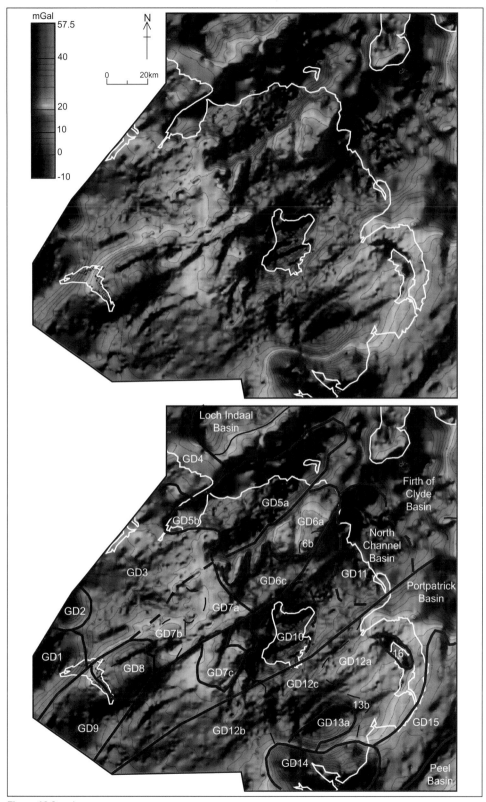

mGal
57.5
40
20
10
0
-10

N

0   20km

Loch Indaal
Basin

GD4

GD5a

GD5b

GD6a

6b

Firth of
Clyde
Basin

North
Channel
Basin

GD3

GD6c

GD11

Portpatrick
Basin

GD2

GD7a

GD7b

GD10

GD1

GD8

GD7c

GD12a

16

GD12c

GD9

GD12b

13b

GD13a

GD15

GD14

Peel
Basin

Figure 19.2
Bouguer Gravity Anomaly Data: Colour-filled/line contours of the observed values. Shaded-relief illumination from north west.

Magnetic	Gravity	Feature Name	Anomaly source
MD1	GD1	Lough Derg Inlier (Moine Supergroup)	Low density, low susceptibility quartz-rich rocks
	GD2	Barnesmore Complex (Co. Donegal)	Low density granite
MD2		Central Highlands (Grampian) Terrane (Dalradian)	Medium to high density basement with occasional moderately magnetic lithologies
MD3	GD3	Dalradian	Low susceptibility basement rocks
MD4	GD4	Central Highlands (Grampian) Terrane (Dalradian)	High susceptibility Lewisian basement concealed beneath Dalradian rocks
(MD3)	GD5a	Foyle and Rathlin basins	Low density and low susceptibility Permo-Triassic and Carboniferous rocks
MD5a	GD6a-b	Dalradian Inlier (northeast Co. Antrim) and Highland Border Ridge	High density, high susceptibility mafic metamorphic rocks
	GD6c	Maghera and Kilrea basins (MKB) Loughguile Basin (LGB)	Low density Carboniferous to Triassic sedimentary rocks in small fault bounded basins on high density Dalradian basement, concealed beneath Antrim Lava Group
MD5b	GD7a-b	Sperrin Mountains (Dalradian)	High density, high susceptibility metamorphic rocks
MD5c	GD7a-b	Lack Inlier (Dalradian) Dromore High (concealed)	High susceptibility, very high density ultrabasic rocks buried at depth under Fintona Block. Source under Lack Inlier closer to surface
MD5d	(GD7a)	Tyrone Igneous Complex	High susceptibility, high density mafic igneous rocks
MD5e	(GD7a)	Early Palaeozoic arc-related intrusives	Low susceptibility, medium density tonalite and granodiorite
MD6a-c	GD9	Fermanagh Highlands	Thick, low density Carboniferous sedimentary rocks overlying high susceptibility early Palaeozoic volcanogenic basement rocks?
MD7		Clogher Valley (Counties Fermanagh and Tyrone)	Low susceptibility Devonian and Carboniferous sedimentary rocks
MD8a		S. Antrim-Ballantrae (southwest Scotland) magnetic high	High susceptibility rocks (ophiolite and early Ordovician magnetite-bearing greywackes?), underlying sedimentary strata
MD8b	GD7c	Magnetic High	Extension of MD8a to SW, thin sedimentary cover
	GD10	Lough Neagh Basin	Deep sedimentary basin
	GD11	Larne Basin	Deep sedimentary basin extends offshore into North Channel Basin
MD9	GD12a-c	Southern Uplands-Down Longford Terrane	Low susceptibility, moderate density Lower Palaeozoic greywackes
MD10	GD14	Slieve Gullion Central Complex	High density, high susceptibility mafic igneous intrusion
MD11a-c	GD14	Carlingford and Mourne Mountains Central Complexes	Separate culminations to intrusive centres
MD12		Magnetic High (Co. Louth)	High susceptibility rocks of Central Belt of Southern Uplands-Down-Longford Terrane
MD13a MD13b	GD13a GD13b	Newry Igneous Complex	(a) Low density, low susceptibility granodiorite with moderate susceptibility margins; (b) moderate density, high susceptibility ultramafic and intermediate intrusive rocks
MD14		Antrim Lava Group (Antrim Plateau)	High susceptibility basalt lava and minor intrusions usually dominated by remanent magnetisation in a reversed magnetic field
MD15		Co. Down-Co. Antrim magnetic high	Linear magnetic high caused by high susceptibility of dyke/fracture zone
	GD15	Offshore Co. Down	High density, low susceptibility basement
	GD16	Newtownards Basin	Low density, low susceptibility Permo-Triassic and Carboniferous rocks

Table 19.5
Characteristics of magnetic and gravity anomaly domains in Northern Ireland.
(Colour scheme as for Figures 19.1 and 19.2).

low ▮▮▮▮ high

In the southeast of Northern Ireland the image is dominated by a high amplitude positive anomaly over the Slieve Gullion Central Complex (Chapter 15) (**MD10**). Subsidiary positive anomalies also occur over the Carlingford Central Complex and over both the western and eastern centres of the Mourne Mountains Central Complex (**MD11a-c**). Zone **MD12** in Co. Louth (Republic of Ireland) represents the northeastern end of an anomaly that resembles positive anomalies across the Central Belt of the Southern Uplands-Down-

Longford Terrane in Scotland. Granodiorite associated with the Newry Igneous Complex show a lower amplitude positive anomaly (**MD13a**), with a small high amplitude anomaly associated with the Ultramafic-Intermediate Complex at Slieve Croob (Chapter 5) (**MD13b**).

The magnetic anomaly field of the Antrim Plateau (**MD14**) is characterised by large amplitude negative anomalies which reflect the dominance of the NRM acquired by the basalt lava during a period of reversal of the Earth's magnetic field. In many areas the plateau margin is defined by positive anomalies which may, in part, be an edge effect. These are often most pronounced where zones of positive magnetic anomalies disappear beneath the plateau but may be poorly developed when adjacent areas, such as around Lough Foyle, have low or negative anomalies.

Areas of the Antrim Plateau with positive anomalies occur over the concealed Dalradian rocks of the Highland Border Ridge, an arcuate anomaly around the Tardree Rhyolite Complex (Chapter 14), and as several small areas covered by the subsurface extension of the Ballantrae magnetic anomaly (between MD6a and MD6b).

Dyke swarms

At least three main dyke swarms are recognised in Northern Ireland. Late Palaeozoic lamprophyre dykes in the Southern Uplands-Down-Longford Terrane do not have a significant magnetic expression (Chapter 5). Two major Late Cretaceous to Palaeogene dyke swarms occur in Northern Ireland (Figure 15.8); the northwest to southeast Donegal-Kingscourt dyke swarm and the NNW-SSE trending dykes crossing Counties Antrim and Down. The larger dykes of the former swarm commonly have characteristic reverse anomalies that can be traced through Counties Fermanagh, Tyrone and Armagh although not all dykes have strong anomalies and their magnetisation patterns can be complex. A broader linear positive anomaly (**MD15**) running northwest-southeast across Co. Down is associated with the St. John's Point – Lisburn dyke swarm but may also represent an older major crustal fracture zone (the Antrim – Down Lineament).

Bouguer gravity anomaly values in Northern Ireland range from -10 over Lough Neagh to +57 mGal at Slieve Gullion, against a regional or background level of 20-23 mGal. The main structural elements of Northern Ireland are clearly evident on the gravity images, with blue and purple negative anomalies representing sedimentary basins and granitic intrusions and red positive anomalies representing high-density basement and mafic intrusions (Figure 19.2).

A negative anomaly (**GD1**) over the Lough Derg Inlier reflects the relatively low density of those predominantly quartzose rocks. **GD2**, just to the north, coincides with the Barnesmore granite which has been modelled as a batholith at least 5km deep (4). The area from eastern Co. Donegal to the northern part of the Sperrin Mountains (**GD3**) is characterised by Bouguer anomaly values of +20-23mGal reflecting high density Dalradian rocks. The overlapping gravity high (**GD4**) and positive magnetic anomaly MD4 in the north of Inishowen, Co. Donegal also indicates higher density basement rocks.

The Rathlin (**GD5a**) and Foyle (**GD5b**) sedimentary basins are characterised by strong negative anomalies, separated by a ridge of shallow Dalradian basement rocks extending northeastwards from the Sperrin Mountains. The gravity anomaly minima, adjacent to the Tow Valley and Foyle faults, indicate the areas of thickest preserved sedimentary rocks in these basins and demonstrates their half-graben profile.

The Dalradian inlier in northeast Co. Antrim is characterised by a high positive anomaly (**GD6a**) although higher values do occur to the southwest beneath the basalt lavas of the Antrim Plateau (**GD6b**), possibly reflecting metabasic Dalradian rocks at shallow depths.

To the southwest, beneath the Antrim Plateau, the presence of small Carboniferous and Permo-Triassic basins on the Highland Border Ridge, with north-south orientated bounding faults, can be inferred from the anomaly pattern (**GD6c**).

The south Sperrin Mountains show small elongated anomalies >+25mGal (**GD7a-c**) superimposed on a background field of +20-23mGal which correlate with outcrops of basic rocks of the Tyrone Igneous Complex but also occur beneath the Pomeroy Inlier (Chapter 3) and Devonian rocks to the south (Chapter 6).

At the southwest end of the Fintona Block is the 'Dromore High' (**GD8**). This prominent 35 x 25km positive anomaly has a maximum of +37mGal in the vicinity of Dromore, Co. Tyrone. The subsidiary high on its northwest flank coincides with Dalradian rocks of the Lack Inlier. The rocks at surface across most of the Dromore High are low-density Devonian and Carboniferous sedimentary rocks that cannot be the source of the anomaly. In order to account for the anomaly two main models have been proposed (1, 4). The preferred model envisages the anomaly as reflecting an extension of ophiolitic rocks similar to those in the Tyrone Igneous Complex. The other model is based on the occurrence of a Palaeogene gabbroic intrusion similar to that beneath the Slieve Gullion Central Complex. However, in contrast to Slieve Gullion, the magnetic anomaly associated with the Dromore High is low frequency and low amplitude. Seismic reflection data across the northwest flank of the anomaly show high amplitude reflectors between 0.9-1.5secs TWT, equivalent to a depth of 2.3-4km, using the seismic stacking velocities. The southwesterly-dipping reflectors are almost planar and fit a model of an obducted ophiolite sheet better than a pluton of basic igneous rocks.

The thick succession of Carboniferous sedimentary rocks southwest of Lower Lough Erne is marked by a Bouguer anomaly low (**GD9**). The major gravity lows **GD10** and **GD11** reflect low-density sedimentary rocks in the Larne and Lough Neagh basins respectively. The Lough Neagh Basin extends northeastwards offshore (into the North Channel and Firth of Clyde basins) and the gravity anomaly indicates that the thickest onshore sequence occurs near Larne. The lowest Bouguer anomaly values in the Lough Neagh Basin occur beneath the northeast and southwest corners of the present day Lough Neagh. These gravity minima probably reflect the greatest thickness of both the Oligocene Lough Neagh Group and Carboniferous to Early Jurassic sedimentary rocks.

The Southern Uplands-Down-Longford Terrane (**GD12a**) is characterised by Bouguer anomaly values of +20-22mGal in north Co. Down and +15-18mGal in south Co. Armagh (Chapter 4). The Caledonoid Newry Igneous Complex is marked by the low anomaly values (**GD13**) expected from the granodiorite rocks. Northwest of the Complex, lower than usual values of +12-15mGal over the early Palaeozoic envelope rocks may reflect a subsurface extension of the pluton (**GD12c**).

The major feature in the southeast of Northern Ireland is the gravity high (**GD14**) associated with the Slieve Gullion and Mourne Mountains central complexes. The coincidence of the gravity anomaly (maximum of +55mGal) and aeromagnetic anomaly with Slieve Gullion indicates that a massive mafic body is concealed beneath the exposed granitic and gabbroic rocks. Using a density contrast of +0.28Mg/m3 with the early Palaeozoic country rocks the anomaly can be modelled as a basic body *c.* 10km thick with its top at a depth of about 2-3km. Large positive gravity anomalies characterise a number of the basic intrusive centres of the North Atlantic Igneous Province (Chapter 14). Bouguer anomaly values rise southeastwards towards the Co. Down coast and an offshore high with values up to +30mGal (GD15). In the southeast corner of the image Bouguer anomaly values decrease towards the Peel sedimentary basin between Co. Down and the Isle of Man.

236

Geophysical lineaments: faults and terrane boundaries

Linear features are imaged best on displays of anomaly gradients, such as Figures 19.3 and 19.4. Terrane boundaries, major faults, dykes and other steep-sided intrusions can often be recognised on these plots and may be traced beneath younger cover rocks. The strongest gradients (red on Figures 19.3 and 19.4) are associated with major basin-bounding faults or where the density and magnetic contrasts are greatest. Many other linear features that do not coincide with known structures can also be recognised. For clarity, in Figures 19.3 and 19.4, not all known geophysical lineaments are indicated.

Terrane boundaries

The number and nature of basement suspect terranes in Northern Ireland, and their boundaries, is still a controversial issue (Chapter 1) (14-17). The Central Highlands (Grampian), Midland Valley and Southern Uplands-Down-Longford terranes are all recognised geophysically (Chapters 2-4). The boundaries between these terranes in Scotland are the Highland Boundary Fault and the Southern Upland Fault respectively. In Northern Ireland the Southern Upland Fault is concealed but the geophysical signature associated with the Ballantrae Complex on the north side of the fault trace can be recognised. The **Highland Boundary Fault** (HBF), which in western Scotland may act as a double terrane boundary between the Midland Valley and the Highland Border and Central Highland (Grampian) terranes, cannot be traced with any certainty west of Arran and its character almost certainly changes as it continues into Northern Ireland. The trace was originally located south of the inlier of Dalradian rocks in northeast Co. Antrim. As on the east coast of Scotland at Stonehaven, the Dalradian is overlain in northeast Co. Antrim by conglomerates, putatively of Devonian age. However, if the HBF is located south of the northeast Co. Antrim Dalradian inlier then it does not have a distinctive geophysical signature commonly associated with major crustal features. Gravity anomalies across the Dalradian-Devonian contact at Cushendun are more easily reconciled with an unconformity, or a stepped, normal fault zone than with a single, steeply inclined, normal fault zone comparable to the HBF in Scotland. Therefore a magnetic lineament, the **Fair Head-Clew Bay Line** (FH-CBL), was subsequently proposed as the continuation of the HBF into Ireland (14). In this model Dalradian rocks lying to the south of the FH-CBL, in northeast Co. Antrim and the Sperrin Mountains, are considered to be thrust southeastwards over rocks of the Midland Valley Terrane. At the southern limit of the Dalradian outcrop in the Sperrin Mountains the Omagh Thrust Fault is the surface expression of a ramp zone that dips northwest to join the steeper FH-CBL structure at depth (15). This model also places the surface trace of the HBF southeast of the FH–CBL, along the Omagh Thrust Fault and continuing northeastwards on the south side of the concealed Highland Border Ridge to the coast of Co. Antrim near Cushendun. There is no evidence that the Dalradian inlier in northeast Co. Antrim is an overthrust slice and therefore the terrane boundary at depth may also lie southeast of the inlier, rather than along the Tow Valley Fault. The magnetic anomalies between the Omagh Thrust Fault and FH-CBL (MD5b), believed to represent concealed Tyrone Igneous Complex, are very similar to anomalies from Dalradian rocks northwest of the FH-CBL between Castlefinn and Stranorlar in Co. Donegal (MD2). Indeed, the gravity anomaly between the Omagh Thrust Fault and the FH-CBL shows no evidence of an extension of the high-density basic rocks of Tyrone Igneous Complex beneath the Mullaghcarn Formation (Figure 2.4). In contrast, to the southwest, the northwest flank of the Dromore High may indicate basic rocks at depth beneath the Dalradian rocks of the Lack Inlier.

The recognition of the FH-CBL as the extension of the HBF into Ireland is problematical (16, 17). In an attempt to reconcile the difficulties the **Antrim-Galway Line** (AGL) was proposed as the boundary between a 'Northwestern terrane' and the Midland Valley Terrane.

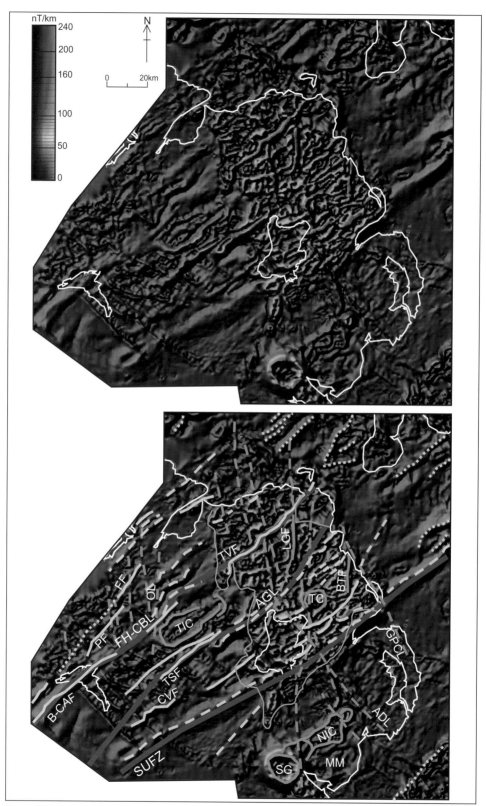

Figure 19.3
Horizontal gradient of RTP magnetic field after upward continuation by 800m. Shaded-relief illumination from the northwest. (See page 240 for key).

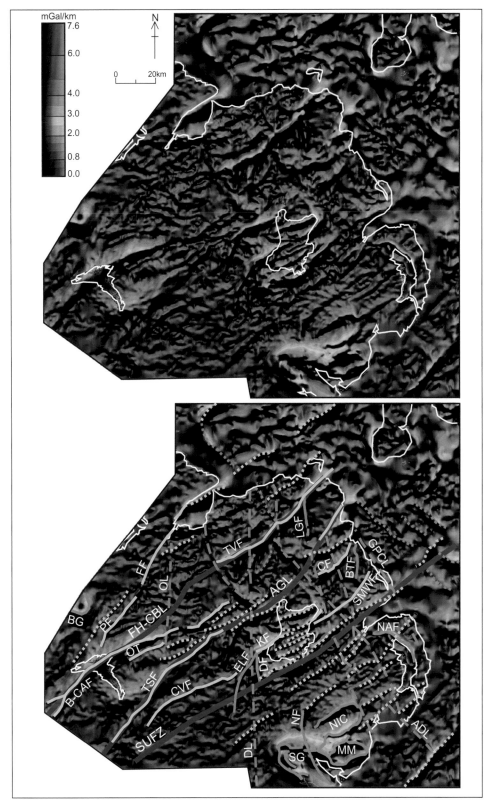

Figure 19.4
Horizontal gradient of Bouguer gravity anomaly after upward continuation by 500m.
Shaded-relief illumination from the north.

The former terrane lies between the Central Highlands (Grampian) and Midland Valley terranes and includes the 'Highland Border Ridge' and the Tyrone Igneous Complex, with the FH-CBL and the AGL as its terrane boundaries. The concealed (AGL) lineament trends from Cushendun in Co. Antrim southwestwards through the Tyrone Igneous Complex, appearing at the surface as the Tempo-Sixmilecross Fault from north of the Pomeroy Inlier (Chapter 3) through the Fintona Block to Galway on the west coast of Ireland. This model proposes that the AGL was the line along which the Midland Valley Terrane docked with a 'Northwestern terrane', by sinistral movement, while in Scotland this occurred along the HBF. However, because the magnetic lineament corresponding to the AGL is difficult to trace across the Antrim Plateau the originally defined surface trace of the Highland Boundary Fault is taken here as the demonstrable terrane boundary between the Central Highlands (Grampian) and Midland Valley terranes. The complex patterns of magnetic anomalies in the northern part of the Midland Valley Terrane in Northern Ireland may reflect the composite nature of this terrane.

Other major Caledonoid lineaments and faults

Many aeromagnetic and gravity lineaments of Caledonoid trend can be correlated with known faults and may be used to delineate these faults where they are not exposed. The interpretation of aeromagnetic and gravity horizontal gradient images is particularly helpful in tracing the Tow Valley Fault on the Antrim Plateau where it juxtaposes identical basalt lavas of the Upper Basalt and Lower Basalt formations.

In addition to mapped faults and their extensions other faults and structures may be inferred from lines with high gravity gradients. For example, there is a suite of small faults beneath Lough Neagh and a number of lineaments in the Southern Uplands-Down-Longford Terrane which may be correlated with tract boundaries.

NNW-SSE to NNE-SSW trending faults and lineaments

In addition to the dominant Caledonoid trending features there are a significant number of NNW, north-south and NNE-SSW trending geophysical lineaments, some of which may be

Symbol	Description
	Terrane Boundary (Postulated)
	Fault mapped / inferred
	Geophysical Lineament
	Margins of Intrusions
	Margin of Antrim Lava Group
	Caledonoid Trends
	NNW-SSE to NNE-SSW trend

	Symbol	Description
Terrane Boundary	AGL	Antrim-Galway Line
	FH-CBL	Fair Head-Clew Bay Line
	SUFZ	Southern Upland Fault Zone
Margins of Intrusions	BG	Barnesmore Granite
	MM	Mourne Mountains Complex
	NIC	Newry Igneous Complex
	SG	Slieve Gullion Complex
	TC	Tardree Rhyolite Complex
	TIC	Tyrone Igneous Complex
NNW-SSE to NNE-SSW trend	ADL	Antrim-Down Lineament
	BTF	Ballytober Fault
	DF	Drumkee Fault
	DL	Draperstown Lineament
	ELF	Elm Lodge Fault
	GPCL	Garron Point-Conlig Lineament
	KF	Killeen Fault
	LGF	Loughguile Fault
	NAF	Newtownards Fault
	NF	Newry Fault
	OL	Omagh Lineament
Caledonoid Trends	B-CAF	Belhavel-Castle Archdale Fault
	CF	Carnlough Fault
	CVF	Clogher Valley Fault
	FF	Foyle Fault
	OT	Omagh Thrust Fault
	PF	Pettigoe Fault
	SMWF	Sixmilewater Fault
	TSF	Tempo-Sixmilecross Fault

Table 19.6
Key to Figures 19.3 and 19.4.

correlated with mapped faults and their concealed extensions. The alignment of four Irish base metal deposits along a north-south trend led to the hypothesis that major north-south geofractures may have controlled the siting of some mineral deposits (18). Four such geofractures, linking mineral deposits and abutting pre-Carboniferous inliers, were identified. This theory has been modified and extended into the north of Ireland where the alignment of geological features and geophysical lineaments has been used to define major deep crustal fractures (19). The geophysical characteristics of these and other lineaments are discussed below.

Omagh Lineament
This lineament, which trends NNE from Tempo in Co. Fermanagh to Drumahoe, south of Lough Foyle, is a rather weak feature on both gravity and magnetic anomaly images but is recognised by its dislocation of other Caledonoid anomalies. It is coincident with two mapped faults and is associated with an increase in the number of mantle-derived tholeiitic sills and mineralised veins and causes an abrupt change in the orientation of bedding and the dominant foliation in Dalradian rocks at the eastern end of the Lack Inlier (20). It is interpreted as one of a series of ancient basement structures, maybe as old as 1800Ma (21), which have been reactivated on several occasions and may be associated with mineralisation. Recent high resolution data have delineated a persistent, narrow, low amplitude aeromagnetic anomaly coincident with the northern part of the originally defined lineament.

Draperstown Lineament
The Draperstown Lineament trends from Portrush on the north coast of Co. Antrim south past Draperstown towards the mineral deposits in south Co. Armagh and Co. Monaghan (22). It was recognised from an alignment of faults and intrusions, and the orientation of minor structures. In this case a zone of sub-parallel geological and geophysical features (the Draperstown Lineament corridor) is interpreted as lying above a major deep crustal discontinuity and are genetically related to episodic reactivation of this structure. It also forms the northern section of a proposed geofracture that passes south through the Kingscourt Fault and abuts the Kildare Inlier in the Republic of Ireland. Although originally identified as a linear gravity feature it is poorly defined on the gravity horizontal gradient image where it forms a zone of discontinuous linear gradient segments. Unlike the Omagh Lineament it does not have an obvious magnetic signature, although this may be because it extends mostly through cover, rather than basement, rocks.

Antrim-Down Lineament
A major linear anomaly extends northwest from St John's Point on the southeast coast of Co. Down to Lisburn in Co. Antrim and can be traced continuously to the Sixmilewater Fault. It is unusual in that it is a positive anomaly and has been attributed to the presence of the St John's Point-Lisburn Palaeogene dyke swarm (3, 23) that is most evident in coastal outcrop. An alternative interpretation is that the magnetic anomalies caused by the dykes are superimposed on a longer wavelength positive anomaly representing an older, major fault or fracture zone (21). Although the anomaly is discontinuous north of the Sixmilewater Fault the lineament may continue along a NNW or northerly trend and terminate against the Tow Valley Fault near Ballymoney.

Garron Point - Conlig Lineament
The most easterly of the defined geofractures was taken to run N6°W through the Conlig - Whitespots Mines (Chapter 21) and follow a 40km long Palaeogene dyke just off the

east coast of Co. Antrim (19). On the aeromagnetic and gravity horizontal derivative images, however, the most prominent lineament trends NNW, is marked by dykes on the Ards Peninsula, follows the east coast of Co. Antrim past Garron Point and offsets the gravity gradient associated with the southeast flank of the 'Highland Border Ridge' at Cushendun.

However, a caveat must be added to this lineament analysis in that most of the linear features are quite short and the selection of continuous lineaments is a subjective process, influenced by factors such as the scales and processing parameters used to generate the images, and personal bias in the interpreter. It is equally possible to pick features that cross-cut or intersect the above lineaments – for example, the north-south lineament from Dundrum, Co. Down, to Armoy, Co. Antrim that cuts the Antrim-Down Lineament (Figure 19.4).

Other trends
There are few examples of east-west trending structures in the geology of Northern Ireland. In north Co. Antrim, near the Giant's Causeway, the WSW-ENE trending Portbradden Fault is marked by a magnetic anomaly and is accompanied by several other short, parallel anomalies offshore.

Intrusive bodies
The margins of major intrusive centres such as the Newry Igneous Complex and the Palaeogene Mourne Mountains, Slieve Gullion and Carlingford complexes are picked out by

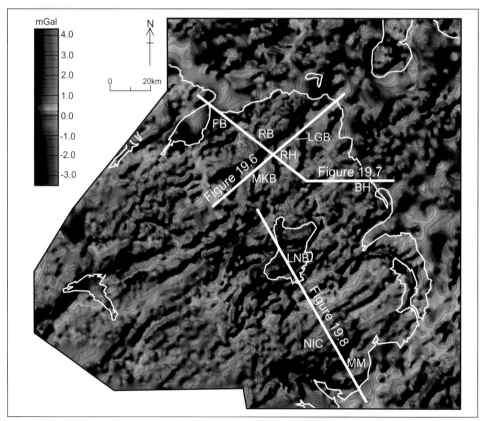

Figure 19.5
Location of gravity and aeromagnetic model profiles overlain on residual gravity anomaly image.

high gravity gradients. The gravity and magnetic gradients developed over the latter two centres are consistent with the model of a horizontal cylindrical basic intrusion with a WNW-ESE oval cupola beneath Slieve Gullion and a subsidiary cupola beneath Carlingford (4). In the Newry Igneous Complex interpretation of the aeromagnetic image identifies the three main granodiorite intrusions (Figure 5.1) but also indicates that the main batholith may be composed of two separate intrusions. Minor igneous intrusions such as dykes produce a significant response on the magnetic image but not on the gravity image except for the St John's Point swarm on the Antrim-Down Lineament.

Modelling

Gravity and magnetic data can be used to model the deep structure of Northern Ireland and may be constrained by additional information from the surface geology and borehole and seismic data. From a series of 2.5D models (2D models corrected for width:length ratio) that have been constructed across Northern Ireland (1) three examples are used to illustrate the general structure of basement and sedimentary basins in Northern Ireland (Figure 19.5).

Highland Border Ridge (Figure 19.6)

Profile A trends southwest-northeast along the Highland Border Ridge which, at surface, is mostly concealed by basalt lava of the Antrim Lava Group, although Dalradian rocks crop out in the Sperrin Mountains at the southwest end and in the inlier in northeast Co. Antrim. Based on the occurrence of gravity anomaly lows it is possible to recognise the presence of two concealed sedimentary basins, the Loughguile and Kilrea-Maghera basins, the latter itself sub-divided by a basement ridge. Both basins are fault-bounded with a sediment fill up to 1000m that thickens towards the margins. The thickening may be either syn-depositional or the result of later movement along the northeast-southwest and NNW-SSE trending marginal faults. The sedimentary fill of the Kilrea-Maghera Basin comprises Carboniferous and Triassic rocks, which are exposed near Maghera, and the Loughguile Basin contains Triassic and Cretaceous rocks, which outcrop near Armoy.

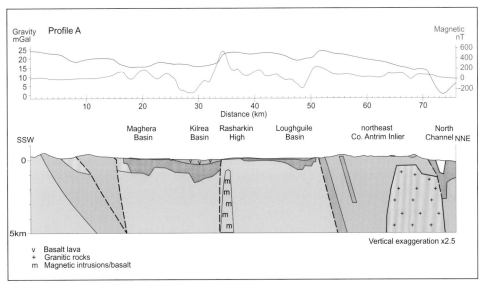

Figure 19.6
Gravity and magnetic model along the Highland Border Ridge.

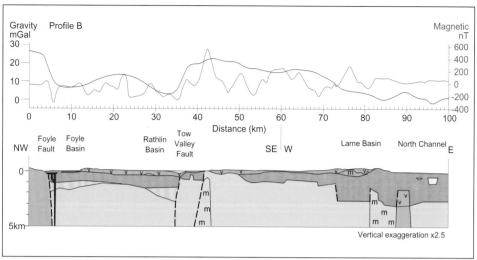

Figure 19.7
Gravity and magnetic model across Foyle, Rathlin and Larne basins.

The model also demonstrates the presence of a vertical intrusion, up to 2km wide, of highly magnetic, dense mafic rocks at Rasharkin. The gravity low near the Antrim coast has been modelled as a granitic intrusion, the concealed extension, to the northeast, of the early Caledonian Cushendun Granodiorite and associated quartz-porphyry intrusions. In the North Channel the presence of a gravity low is modelled as a narrow, *c.* 3km deep, fault-bounded basin containing low density sedimentary rocks.

Foyle, Rathlin and Larne sedimentary basins (Figure 19.7)

Profile B extends from the Inishowen Peninsula in Co. Donegal, southeastwards across the Foyle and Rathlin basins towards Ballymena in Co. Antrim and then eastwards to the Larne Basin. The surface geology is dominated by basalt lava of the Palaeogene Antrim Lava Group, with Triassic to Cretaceous rocks exposed in the Foyle Basin and on the east coast of Co. Antrim. High gravity values in Co. Donegal probably indicate that the Dalradian rocks are more dense than elsewhere, although the presence of high density Lewisian basement at depth is a possibility. The gravity profile includes a bi-polar anomaly low corresponding to the Foyle and Rathlin basins, and anomaly values that decrease eastwards over the Larne Basin. The Foyle and Rathlin basins show maximum sediment thickness adjacent to the Foyle and Tow Valley faults, respectively. Densities of 2.5Mg/m³ and 2.35Mg/m³ have been adopted for the Permo-Triassic and Carboniferous rocks respectively. The abnormally low density used for the Carboniferous rocks is based on measurements from the Magilligan borehole. Although this may be appropriate for the Carboniferous in the Foyle Basin a higher density might be expected in the Rathlin Basin, resulting in a corresponding increase in maximum sediment thickness from 2.75 to *c.* 4km. After crossing the Highland Border Ridge near the Rasharkin High the sedimentary rocks beneath the basalt lavas thicken to *c.* 1km along strike from the outcrop of the Cross Slieve Group (Chapter 6) between Cushendun and Cushendall. The gravity high near Ballymena may be interpreted either as a slight thinning of those sedimentary rocks, or the combined gravity high and positive magnetic signature may indicate a buried mafic intrusion or lithologies similar to the Tyrone Igneous Complex (Chapter 3).

244

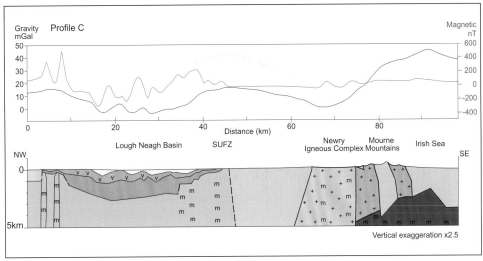

Figure 19.8
Gravity and magnetic model across Lough Neagh Basin, Newry Igneous Complex and Mourne Mountains Central Complex.

East of Slemish in Co. Antrim (Figure 15.8), a major fault downthrows strata to the east and about 3km of sedimentary rocks are modelled adjacent to the Ballytober Fault. The Ballytober Fault downthrows Permo-Triassic strata by more than 800m to the west and defines the western margin of a major horst, according to interpreted seismic data. The eastern flank of the horst is less clearly defined by a series of normal faults stepping down to the east towards the coastline of east Co. Antrim. The structure was modelled using a magnetic basement block located beneath the horst and density variations in the shallow section to improve the fit to the observed gravity anomaly. The significant gravity low east of the horst was modelled by adding thick beds of low density halite. Although halite has not been proven in this part of the basin north of the Sixmilewater Fault, it can be inferred from offshore seismic data.

Modelling of Profile B also demonstrates that the distinctive negative magnetic anomaly under Lough Foyle is best interpreted as a dyke/sill complex, rather than as an extension of the Magilligan sill or as a single major dyke. The magnetic anomaly high east of Slemish can be modelled as a normally magnetised block within the basalt lava pile, possibly reflecting an igneous centre or caldera. In contrast, the Palaeogene dolerite plug and volcanic vent of Slemish has a weak magnetic signature.

Lough Neagh Basin, Newry Igneous Complex and Mourne Mountains Central Complex (Figure 19.8)

Profile C extends from the northwest corner of Lough Neagh southeastwards to the Co. Down coast near Kilkeel. At the northwestern end the Carboniferous rocks around Draperstown are separated from the main Lough Neagh Basin by a basement ridge. This gravity high is associated with high amplitude, positive, magnetic anomalies and is likely to be an extension of the mafic rocks of the Tyrone Igneous Complex on Slieve Gallion. At the southern end of Lough Neagh, the thickness of sedimentary rocks in the Lough Neagh Basin is calculated at 2.5km, using a density of 2.5Mg/m³. Short wavelength anomalies are modelled as variations in the thickness of near-surface, low density rocks of the Lough Neagh Group (Chapter 16). Southeast of Lough Neagh and beyond the southern margin of

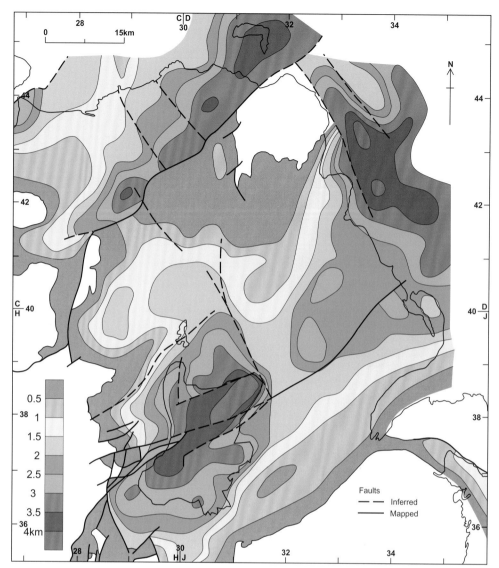

Figure 19.9
3-D gravity model: depth below sea-level to base Permo-Triassic.

the concealed Lough Neagh Basin, Lower Palaeozoic greywackes of the Southern Uplands-Down-Longford Terrane are modelled with a lower density (2.68Mg/m³) than expected. The lower density may be caused by the presence of granitic rocks of the late Caledonian Newry Igneous Complex at depth which is modelled as a large batholith with a density of 2.65Mg/m³. The margin of the batholith is inclined northwestwards and extends for 3km beyond the outcrop at surface, consistent with the presence of small isolated outcrops of granodiorite that occur within the greywacke. The gravity anomaly at the southeast end of the profile rises steeply to +46 mgals and reflects the presence of the large mafic igneous body beneath the low density granites of the Palaeogene Mourne Mountains Central Complex. The depth to the contact between the granite and the top of the underlying basic igneous body varies from 2.5-4km.

3D model of the Antrim Plateau (Figure 19.9)

3D modelling can be used to predict the shape of concealed sedimentary basins and the configuration of basement beneath basalt lavas of the Antrim Plateau. An initial model of the lavas was produced which matched the observed magnetic response by varying the depth to their base, assuming constant magnetisation. The model reproduced the general features of the observed anomaly pattern although short wavelength anomalies were not resolved. The grid derived for the base of the lava pile was used as an input into the gravity model, along with a constant background field of +25mGal and a 'basement' layer at a depth ranging from 5-8km. Other interfaces, in particular the base of the Lough Neagh Group and the base of Permo-Triassic strata, were allowed to vary. The model was adjusted against the observed gravity data by varying the parameters, one at a time, with a total of ten iterations. A mask was used to constrain the parts of the grid over which values were allowed to vary, to take into account the limits of the Permo-Triassic subcrop, for example.

The depth to the base of the Permo-Triassic succession from the 3D gravity model shows a good fit to borehole data, with the exception of Langford Lodge (Figure 9.2). This borehole is located on a narrow basement ridge adjacent to the outcrop of the lignite-bearing Lough Neagh Group at Crumlin, in an area of steep anomaly gradients poorly resolved by the model. It also shows the gross internal geometry of the Foyle, Rathlin, Lough Neagh and Larne basins but probably underestimates the total thickness of sedimentary rocks in the basins. This is because the lower part of the modelled Permo-Triassic succession may be replaced by a greater thickness of higher density Carboniferous strata. Detailed basin structure should not be inferred from the gravity modelling alone but from the integrated interpretation of all available geological and geophysical information, especially seismic reflection data.

References

1) Carruthers, R. M., Beamish, D., Heaven, R. E., Legg, I. C., Mitchell, W. I., Reay, D. M. and Walker, A. S. D. 1999. Regional interpretation of gravity and aeromagnetic data from Northern Ireland. GSNI Technical Report 99/1.

2) Lee, M. K., Pharaoh, T. C. and Soper, N. J. 1990. Structural trends in central Britain from images of gravity and aeromagnetic fields. *Journal of the Geological Society, London*, **147**, 241-58.

3) Geological Survey of Northern Ireland. 1971. Magnetic anomaly map of Northern Ireland. 1:253,440. (Southampton: Ordnance Survey for Geological Survey of Northern Ireland.).

4) Cook, A. H. and Murphy, T. 1952. Measurements of gravity in Ireland. Gravity Survey north of the line Sligo-Dundalk. Geophysical Memoirs No. 2, Part 4, Dublin Institute of Advanced Studies.

5) Geological Survey of Northern Ireland. 1984. Bouguer gravity anomaly map of Northern Ireland. 1:250,000. (Southampton: Ordnance Survey for Geological Survey of Northern Ireland.).

6) Hospers, J. and Charlesworth, H. A. K. 1954. The natural remanent magnetization of the Lower Basalts of Northern Ireland. *Monthly Notices of the Royal Astronomical Society, Geophysical Supplement*, **7**, 32-43.

7) Wilson. R. L. 1959. Remanent magnetism of late Secondary and early Tertiary British rocks. *Philosophical Magazine*, Vol. 4, 750-55.

8) Løvlie, R., Gidskehaug, A. and Storevedt, K. M. 1972. On the magnetization history of the Northern Irish basalts. *Geophysical Journal of the Royal Astronomical Society*, **27**, 487-98.

9) King, R. F. 1966. The magnetic fabric of some Irish granites. *Geological Journal*, **5**, 43-66.

10) Evans, R. B. and Evans, D. 1987. Geophysical investigations around Lough Foyle. *Regional Geophysics Research Group of the British Geological Survey*, **Report No. RG 87/4.**

11) Wilson. R. L. 1959. Palaeomagnetism in Northern Ireland. Part I: The thermal demagnetization of natural magnetic moments in rocks. *Geophysical Journal of the Royal Astronomical Society*, **5**, 45-58.

12) Wilson. R. L. 1970. Palaeomagnetic stratigraphy of Tertiary lavas from Northern Ireland. *Geophysical Journal of the Royal Astronomical Society*, **20**, 1-9.

13) Mussett, A. E., Dagley, P. and Eckford, M. 1976. The British Tertiary Province: Palaeomagnetism and ages of dykes, Lundy Island, Bristol Channel. *Geophysical Journal of the Royal Astronomical Society*, **31**, 505-13.

14) Max, M. D. and Riddihough, R. P. 1975. The continuation of the Highland Boundary Fault in Ireland. *Geology*, **3**, 206-10.

15) Hutton, D. H. W. 1987. Strike-slip terranes and a model for the British and Irish Caledonides. *Geological Magazine*, **124**, 405-25.

16) Murphy, F. C., Anderson, T. B., Daly, J. S., Gallagher, V., Graham, J. R., Harper, D. A. T., Johnston, J. D., Kennan, P. S., Kennedy, M. J., Long, C. B., Morris, J. H., O'Keefe, W. G., Parkes, M., Ryan, P. D., Sloan, R. J., Stillman, C. J., Tietzsch-Tyler, D., Todd, S. P. and Wrafter, J. P. 1991. An appraisal of Caledonian suspect terranes in Ireland. *Irish Journal of Earth Sciences*, **11**, 11-42.

17) Ryan, P. D., Soper, N. J., Snyder, D. B., England, R. W. and Hutton, D. H. W. 1995. The Antrim-Galway Line: a resolution of the Highland Border Fault enigma of the Caledonides of Britain and Ireland. *Geological Magazine*, **132**, 171-84.

18) Russell, M. J. 1968. Structural controls on base metal mineralisation in Ireland in relation to continental drift. *Transactions of Institue of Mining and Metallogeny*, **77**, B117-28.

19) Russell, M. J. and Haszeldine, R. S. In: Bowden, A. A., Earls, G., O'Connor, P. G. and Pyne, J. F. (eds.). *The Irish Minerals Industry 1980-1990. Irish Association for Economic Geology*, Dublin. 135-42.

20) Earls, G., Hutton, D. H. W., Wilkinson, J., Moles, N., Parnell, J., Fallick, A. and Boyce, A. 1996. The gold metallogeny of north-west Northern Ireland. *GSNI Technical Report 96/6*.

21) Hutton, D. H. W. and Alsop, G. I. 1996. The Caledonian strike swing and associated lineaments in northwest Ireland and adjacent areas: sedimentation, deformation and igneous intrusion patterns. *Journal of the Geological Society, London*, **153**, 345-60.

22) Earls, G., Hutton, D. H. W., Wilkinson, J. and Boyce, A. 2000. The mineral potential of the Draperstown lineament. *GSNI Technical Report*.

23) Carruthers, R. M., Cornwell, J. D., Turnbull, G., Walker, A. S. D and Bennett, J. P. R. 1987. Interpretation of the Bouguer gravity anomaly data for Northern Ireland. *Regional Geophysics Research Group of the British Geological Survey Report No. RG 87/5*.

24) Gibson, P. J. and Lyle, P. 1992. The interpretation of a major non-Caledonian structural lineament in northeast Ireland. *Irish Journal of Earth Sciences*, **11**, 181-85.

Chapter 20

Hydrogeology

M. R. COOPER and P. McCONVEY

Introduction

Water that occurs below ground and within the saturated zone of the strata is known as **groundwater** (Figure 20.1). Bedrock and superficial deposits that store and transmit useful quantities of groundwater are referred to as **aquifers**. The study of groundwater and aquifers is the multidisciplinary subject of hydrogeology (1). Groundwater constitutes the largest volume of freshwater in the United Kingdom, and as such is an important national asset. In Northern Ireland, groundwater fulfils two significant roles. First, it augments bulk public supplies and provides private water sources to domestic, agricultural and industrial users. In recent years, groundwater has provided up to 11% of the public water supply (2). However, recent rationalisation has led to a reduced groundwater contribution estimated to be 6% of the 740 million litres currently used on a daily basis (3). Second, groundwater makes an important contribution to flows in rivers (baseflow) helping to sustain their resource, ecological and amenity value.

The content of this chapter is based largely on the results of long-term investigations and a modern and practical understanding of regional groundwater distribution, potential and vulnerability. Much of the data depicts the hydrogeology and groundwater vulnerability of bedrock and superficial deposits in Northern Ireland (4, 5, 6). Compared to other parts of the United Kingdom, investigation of groundwater in Northern Ireland has been limited, due partly to the dominant role of surface water for water supply. This is now changing due to greater environmental awareness and the requirements of European legislation.

Groundwater in Northern Ireland is generally under utilised, leaving scope for future development in most areas. Under existing legislation, controlled water (including groundwater) must be protected both from pollution and over exploitation.

Northern Ireland's Aquifers

The wide range of aquifer types present reflects the diverse bedrock and superficial geology. Potential for groundwater abstraction at a particular location will depend on the nature of the underlying strata (Figure 20.2), their potential to receive recharge, their ability to transmit water and the local structural complexity.

Three broad aquifer classes in bedrock and superficial deposits, with respect to their potential for water supply, are defined (5):
1) Those in which intergranular flow is significant.
2) Those in which flow is dominantly in fissures and other discontinuities.
3) Those with limited potential, without significant groundwater.

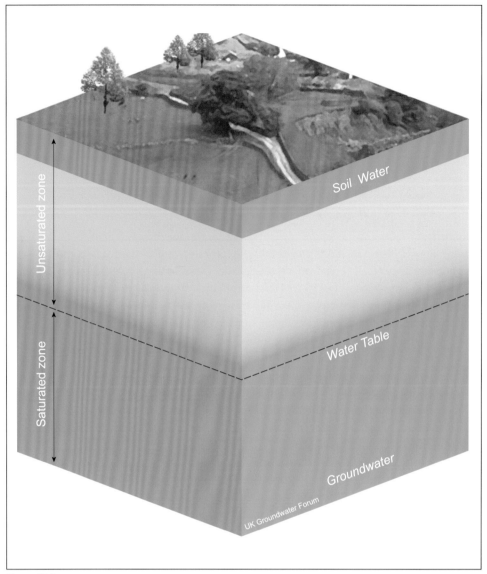

Figure 20.1
Underground profile showing the occurence of groundwater.

Class 1 includes highly productive and regionally important aquifers such as sandstones of the Triassic Sherwood Sandstone Group (Chapter 10). These sandstones have interconnected pore systems allowing significant intergranular flow although investigations have shown that fissure flow also plays a major role in groundwater transport. The potential of these rocks as a significant source of groundwater was first recognised around Belfast (7). In the Lagan Valley and around Newtownards, groundwater is abstracted for public water supply from both the Sherwood Sandstone Group and underlying Permian breccia and sandstone (8, 9, 10).

Deposits of glacial sand and gravel that occur mostly in river valleys are represented in this class and constitute locally important aquifers where sufficient saturated thickness is present. Such deposits have supported yields sufficient for public water supply adjacent to waterways such as the Oona Water in Co. Tyrone and the River Main in Co. Antrim.

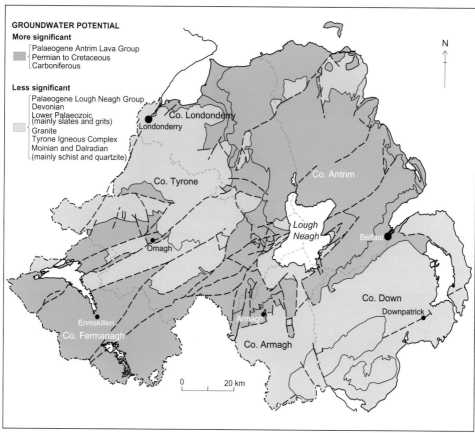

GROUNDWATER POTENTIAL

More significant
- Palaeogene Antrim Lava Group
- Permian to Cretaceous
- Carboniferous

Less significant
- Palaeogene Lough Neagh Group
- Devonian
- Lower Palaeozoic (mainly slates and grits)
- Granite
- Tyrone Igneous Complex
- Moinian and Dalradian (mainly schist and quartzite)

Co. Londonderry
Londonderry
Co. Tyrone
Co. Antrim
Lough Neagh
Belfast
Omagh
Co. Down
Downpatrick
Enniskillen
Co. Fermanagh
Armagh
Co. Armagh

0   20 km

N

Figure 20.2
Bedrock groundwater potential map of Northern Ireland.

Class 2 includes highly productive aquifers of limited extent and regionally extensive aquifers of local importance. Groundwater discharging from springs located at the base of the Cretaceous Ulster White Limestone Formation (Chapter 12) has been exploited for public supply. Investigations have shown that some of these are karstic conduits restricted to limited areas of exposure around the edge of the Antrim Plateau (11). In the outcrop of the lower Carboniferous rocks in the western part of Northern Ireland karstification of limestones and underground cave systems support major spring discharges (12) that also have been used for local public supply. This class also includes the basalt lavas of the Palaeogene Antrim Lava Group (Chapter 14) that form an extensive aquifer system with low to moderate groundwater potential. Within the lavas, groundwater is contained primarily in fractures and joints whose interconnection generally determines the yield of a particular borehole (Chapter 14, Photograph 3).

Class 3 strata are those with limited or no groundwater potential, such as the Devonian and Carboniferous red beds in the Fintona area of Co. Tyrone (Chapters 6 and 7). Indurated metamorphic and igneous rocks also fall within this class and include the Dalradian rocks of the Sperrin Mountains and northeast Co. Antrim (Chapter 2) and the outcrop of Ordovician and Silurian greywacke and mudstone that extends southwest from the Ards Peninsula through Counties Down and Armagh (Chapter 4). Water movement through these strata is often restricted to near-surface discontinuities such as open fractures, faults, joints or bedding planes. Although their groundwater potential is minimal a significant number of wells and boreholes are located within them. Under favourable local conditions such wells can satisfy demand from domestic and agricultural users.

Aquifer Potential

The availability of groundwater in Northern Ireland is controlled by four important factors:

1) A relatively high effective rainfall of about 500mm/annum which is distributed throughout the year.
2) The widespread distribution of clay-based till and gley soils.
3) Potentially productive aquifers are often concealed by low permeability strata.
4) Small, compartmentalised aquifer units.

Although the permeability of gley soils and glacial till is low, as soil moisture is at or near field capacity for a significant part of the year, some recharge of underlying bedrock aquifers can still occur. The last two factors combine to limit the regional resource value of groundwater (2).

Three measurable properties provide a gauge of aquifer potential as follows (Table 20.1):

1) Hydraulic conductivity (K) - the measure of the ability of a rock to transmit water.
2) Sustainable average borehole yield (Q)
3) Specific capacity (SC) - the measure of the efficiency of a borehole to deliver water.

The most favourable hydraulic properties are found in Quaternary deposits and in the Sherwood Sandstone Group. In contrast the Palaeogene basalt lavas, Permian, Carboniferous and Devonian rocks are all limited by low hydraulic conductivity and specific capacity which reduces aquifer potential. Although fossil soils or boles in the basalt lava succession can provide significant hydraulic conductivity for lateral transport of groundwater, they have little potential for storage. In the Lagan Valley, hydrogeological studies and more recently a combined geochemical and groundwater modelling investigation identified a complex regional aquifer system in the Sherwood Sandstone Group, with groundwater flow influenced by the presence of faulting and Palaeogene dykes (8, 13).

Groundwater Chemistry

A baseline hydrogeochemical survey of major ions in groundwater in Northern Ireland has demonstrated enrichment in calcium and bicarbonate, with slightly raised levels of sulphate (14). Most groundwater is weakly to moderately mineralised and oxygenated, although reducing conditions do occur locally. All groundwater tested was in the pH range of 4.7 to 9.0 with most samples between 6.8 and 7.8. Alkaline groundwater is invariably associated with limestone bedrock and with carbonate-cemented rock types. There is a general regional

	(K) (md^{-1})	(Q) (ls^{-1})	(SC) $(ls^{-1}m^{-1})$
Quaternary	1-100	3-45	<8
Palaeogene basalt	0.01-1.0	0.5-20	<1
Triassic	0.8-4.0	5-40	0.1-3.0
Permian	<1	5-25	>0.1
Carboniferous	0.1	5-12	0.1-1.0
Devonian	<<1	1.0-1.5	<0.1

Table 20.1
Hydraulic properties of Northern Ireland's principle aquifers (4).

consistency in the chemistry of groundwater from aquifers in different rock types. It is believed that the water-rock reaction processes are incomplete and that most groundwater in Northern Ireland is relatively immature and subject to active recharge (15). In the Sherwood Sandstone Group of the Lagan Valley geochemical investigation using isotopes indicate the existence of 'compartments' within the aquifer containing groundwater around 3-4000 years old (13).

Groundwater Vulnerability

Groundwater contamination, whether by point source or diffuse pollution, can represent a serious threat to human health and can impact on associated surface water ecosystems. Typical incidents of point source pollution include chemical spillages (Figure 20.3), discharges from poorly sited or maintained septic tanks, and leakage of leachate from landfill sites. Diffuse pollution is a much more insidious threat and includes long term, over-application of agricultural fertilisers, uncontrolled use of pesticides and leakage from sewerage systems. Because the migration of contaminants into aquifers can be measured by time-scales from hours to tens or even hundreds of years, an understanding of the

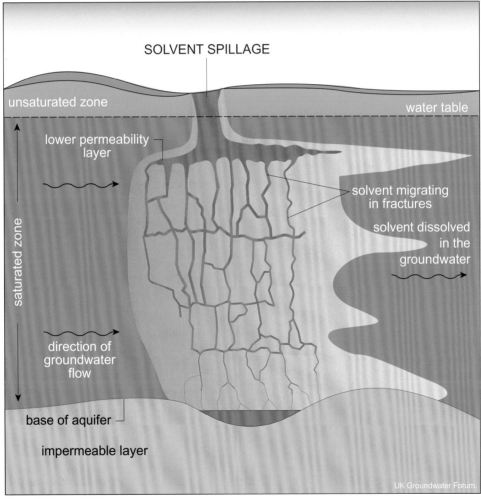

Figure 20.3
Example of impact on groundwater from point source pollution incident.

properties of all aquifers and overlying strata is important in helping to predict the movement and distribution of that pollution. The increasing use of nitrate as an agricultural fertiliser has resulted in its occurrence in some private and public groundwater supplies. Regional groundwater monitoring has also identified microbiological contamination at certain boreholes probably arising from poor wellhead protection measures and inappropriate siting of septic tanks and waste storage/disposal areas. The groundwater vulnerability map for Northern Ireland (6) provides baseline information on aquifers, superficial deposits and soil types that help in defining the measures required for the protection of aquifers (16).

In Northern Ireland, the most productive aquifers are also the ones that are considered to be at most risk, particularly where they are close to the surface. Recharge of water is usually greatest to such strata. However, the presence of soil cover and thick layers of low permeability deposits such as clayey till can protect these aquifers, but the natural variability of such deposits makes understanding their influence problematical. Groundwater in less productive aquifers can also be affected when the dominant fracture flow and shallow nature of the groundwater systems transmits contaminants rapidly to nearby wells and waterways. Although the role of groundwater for water supply is less extensive in Northern Ireland than for other parts of the United Kingdom and Ireland, it remains an important resource that requires sustainable management and protection from polluting activities.

References
1) Price, M. 1996. *Introducing Groundwater* (Second Edition). Chapman & Hall. London.

2) Robins, N. S. 1997. The Role of Groundwater as a Strategic and Economic Asset in Northern Ireland. The Journal of the Chartered Institution of Water and Environmental Management. 11, 246-50.

3) Water Service. 2002. WATER providing for THE FUTURE. Northern Ireland Water Resource Strategy 2002-2030.

4) Robins, N. S. 1996. Hydrogeology of Northern Ireland. (London: HMSO for the British Geological Survey).

5) British Geological Survey. 1994a. *Hydrogeological map of Northern Ireland.* 1:250 000. (Keyworth: British Geological Survey).

6) British Geological Survey. 1994b. *Groundwater vulnerability map of Northern Ireland.* 1:250 000. (Keyworth: British Geological Survey).

7) Hartley, J. J. 1935. The underground water resources of Northern Ireland. The Institute of Civil Engineers, Belfast District Association pamphlet. p.31.

8) Bennett, J. R. P. 1976. The Lagan Valley hydrogeological study. Geological Survey of Northern Ireland Open File Report No. 57.

9) Smith, A. 1985. Geological results of the Lagan Valley Groundwater Development Programme 1977-1984. Geological Survey of Northern Ireland Open File Report No. 71.

10) Kalin, R. M. and Roberts, C. 1997. Groundwater Resources in the Lagan Valley Sandstone aquifer, Northern Ireland. The Journal of the Chartered Institution of Water and Environmental Management 11, 133-39.

11) Barnes, S. and Worden, R. H. 1998. Understanding groundwater sources and movement using water chemistry and tracers in a low matrix permeability terrain: the Cretaceous (Chalk) Ulster White Limestone Formation, Northern Ireland. *Applied Geochemistry*, **13**, 143-53.

12) Karst Working Group. 2000. The Karst of Ireland; Limestone Landscapes, Caves and Groundwater Drainage Systems. Geological Survey of Ireland, Dublin.

13) McNeil, G. W., Cronin, A. A., Yang, T., Elliot, T. and Kalin, R. M. 2000. The Triassic Sandstone aquifer in Northern Ireland: constraint of a groundwater flow model for resource management. *In*: Robins, N. S. and Misstear, B. D. R. (eds.). *Groundwater in the Celtic Regions: Studies in Hard Rock and Quaternary Hydrogeology.* Geological Society, London, Special Publication **182**, 179-90.

14) Robins, N. S., Trafford, J. M. and McKenzie, A. A. 1994. Hydrochemical survey of Northern Ireland with particular regard to major ions. British Geological Survey Report, WD/94/62.

15) Robins, N. S. 1998. The Quality of Shallow Groundwaters in Northern Ireland. The Journal of the Chartered Institution of Water and Environmental Management. **12**, 163-69.

16) Environment and Heritage Service. 2001. A Policy and Practice for the Protection of Groundwater in Northern Ireland. Belfast.

Chapter 21

Minerals

J. W. ARTHURS and G. EARLS

Introduction

Northern Ireland has a varied mineral heritage with over 2,000 abandoned mine workings, dating mostly from the 18th to early 20th Century. Historical mining was mostly for iron ore, coal, lead and salt. However, since the 1970s, potentially economic deposits of lignite, gold and a variety of industrial minerals have been identified (Figure 21.1). Modern exploration technology makes it likely that new discoveries will be made in the future.

Northern Ireland is unlike the rest of the United Kingdom in that its minerals are mostly state owned, allowing mineral exploration companies to acquire exclusive rights to prospect over large tracts of land while also enabling government to manage the associated

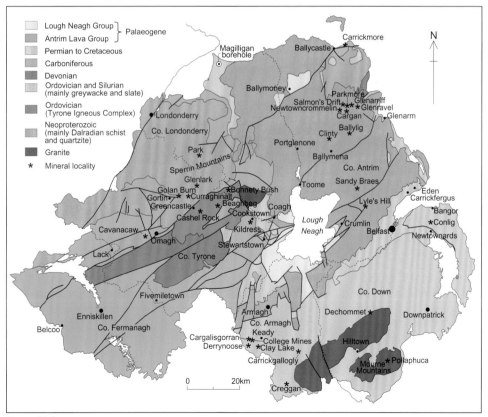

Figure 21.1
Generalised geological map of Northern Ireland with metalliferous mineral localities.

economic development on behalf of the wider community in Northern Ireland. The Mineral Development Act (Northern Ireland) 1969 vests all minerals in the Department of Enterprise, Trade and Investment (DETI), with three classes of exception. First, gold and silver which is owned by the Crown and administered by the Crown Estates Commission. Second, construction minerals described in the Act as "Common stone, sand and clay", and third, three small mineral properties that were active at the time of the enactment of the legislation (e.g. salt and perlite). The GSNI maintains a large library of exploration company reports which companies submitted to DETI under the terms of each prospecting licence.

Currently, only a restricted range of deposits, mostly aggregate and salt, are worked. Compared to other mineralised regions in Western Europe, Northern Ireland is relatively under-explored for predominantly non-geological reasons.

Precious Metals (Gold and Silver)

As displays of gold artefacts in Ireland's museums testify, gold occurrences have been known in Ireland since prehistoric times. The earliest historical reference to gold in Northern Ireland is by Gerald Boate in 1652, which referred to alluvial gold in the Moyola River (1). Nevertheless, although there was clear evidence of potential, there were no workings in historical times and gold was not explored for in Northern Ireland until the early 1980s. The catalysts that promoted increased gold exploration at this time were a dramatic rise in the gold price and the application locally of the then recently developed plate tectonic theory. As a result of this surge in exploration, at least two potentially economic deposits of gold have been discovered at Curraghinalt and at Cavanacaw in Co. Tyrone.

Gold (Au) always occurs alloyed with silver (Ag) and other elements. As deposits of silver ore alone are not known in Northern Ireland, gold and silver are discussed together. Four styles of gold mineralisation occur in Northern Ireland.

Photograph 1
Drilling at the Curraghinalt gold deposit, Sperrin Mountains.

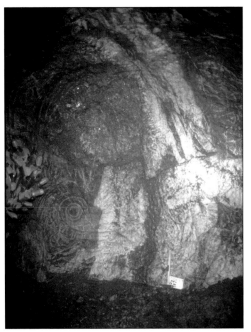

Photograph 2
Underground working at Curraghinalt showing quartz veins with pyrite. Cutting head of roadheader is on left.

Mesothermal quartz vein-hosted gold

Gold occurs in quartz veins ranging from a few mm to several metres in width and is often associated with pyrite and base metals. The veins were formed by high temperature mineralising fluids which filled space created by tectonism. Gold-bearing quartz veins have been found in two geological settings in Northern Ireland, in the Central Highlands (Grampian) Terrane and in the Southern Uplands-Down-Longford Terrane.

Central Highlands (Grampian) Terrane (Dalradian Supergroup)

Auriferous veins occur in the Neoproterozoic **Dalradian Supergroup**. It comprises a thick succession of metagreywacke and pelite, with minor carbonate, quartzite, graphite and basic igneous rocks that were deformed in the Grampian and Caledonian orogenies (Chapters 2 and 3). Although gold-bearing quartz veins occur throughout the Dalradian outcrop, most occurrences have been discovered close to the southern boundary, the Omagh Thrust Fault, on which Dalradian rocks are thrust southeastwards over the Ordovician Tyrone Igneous Complex (Figure 2.4).

The two main gold deposits in the Dalradian are at Curraghinalt [H570 860] and Cavanacaw [H401 708] in Co. Tyrone. The multi-vein deposit at Curraghinalt, about 5km east of Gortin, Co. Tyrone, was discovered in 1983 as a result of prospecting around a shallow soil arsenic anomaly (2). The resource has been calculated at 470,000t at a grade of 17g/t Au (Photographs 1 and 2).

The Curraghinalt deposit is interpreted to overlie a positive relief feature or 'ramp' in the Ordovician footwall of the Omagh Thrust Fault. Accommodation structures in the Dalradian overlying the ramp are believed to control the locus of quartz veining and gold mineralisation. The deposit consists of a swarm of WNW-trending, northeast-dipping veins in pelites, semi-pelites and psammites (Figure 21.2). Veins vary in width from a few mm up to 3m. Two K-Ar model ages on gouge from mineralised shear zones give dates of 315.5±6.5 and 325±6.7Ma. These dates indicate that the last structural movement associated with the veins occurred during the Variscan Orogenic Cycle (3).

Measurements of liquid-gas inclusions in the quartz veins, allied with studies of quartz growth, indicates that four distinct fluids (Q1-Q4) contributed to the formation of the vein system at Curraghinalt (Figure 21.3, Photograph 3). Q1 is interpreted as a metamorphic fluid and Q2 is probably related to intrusive intermediate igneous activity. Q3 has characteristics associated with derivation from surface and probably represents connate or formational water, while Q4 is basinal brine that may have been derived from the inversion of the Carboniferous Newtownstewart Basin to the west. Tectonism associated with the Q2 and the Q4 fluid phases brecciated earlier quartz and probably reflect the Caledonian Orogenic and Variscan Orogenic cycles respectively.

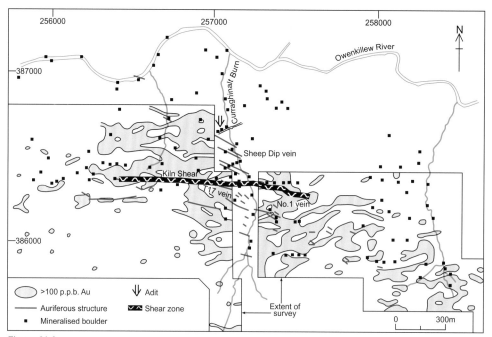

Figure 21.2
The geochemical distribution of gold in the Curraghinalt area based on trenching and/or drill testing of bedrock (2).

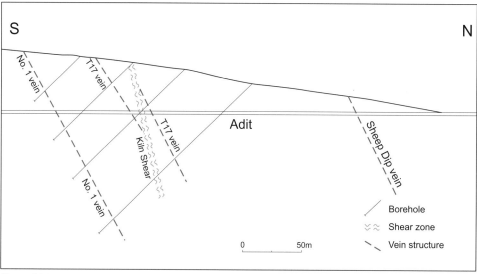

Figure 21.3
Schematic cross-section of the Curraghinalt gold deposit (3).

Gold mineralisation at Curraghinalt is related to the Q2 and Q4 fluid phases and tectonic events. Gold associated with the Q2 phase of mineralisation occurs within pyrite and is typically in the order of 90% Au and 10% Ag (Photograph 4). The second phase of gold mineralisation associated with the Q4 brine is of lower fineness, typically containing about 80% Au and 20% Ag (Photograph 5). However, although reducing the fineness of the gold present, the Q4 phase locally increases the gold grade in areas of increased fluid flow in the deposit. Gold at Curraghinalt occurs as electrum, in Au-bearing telluride (hessite) and as

Photograph 3
Iron stained, mineralised quartz vein (pyrite) in drill core from the Curraghinalt gold deposit. (Note bladed style of quartz). Coin diameter is 22mm.

Photograph 4
Early stage gold (bright, arrowed) in euhedral pyrite cubes (grey) in quartz veins (dark). In this case gold is telluride; in other cases it occurs as electrum. Curraghinalt, x480.

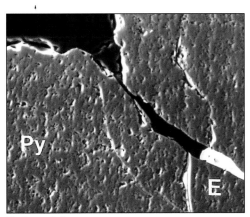

Py

E

Photograph 5
Secondary electron image showing crack in grey pyrite (Py) containing quartz (dark, known to be Q4) and late-stage electrum (E—bright phase, bottom right), Curraghinalt, x250.

trace substitutions in pyrite. Associated sulphides in the veins include pyrite, arsenopyrite, chalcopyrite, galena, sphalerite and sulpharsenides. Bismuth (Bi) and antimony (Sb) also occur. The gangue is dominantly quartz with minor calcite, dolomite, siderite and barite.

Gold-bearing quartz veins at Golan Burn [H524 873], 2km northeast of Gortin, Co. Tyrone, have also been explored and may represent the northwestern strike extent of the Curraghinalt vein swarm (4).

The Cavanacaw deposit occurs in Dalradian rocks of the Lack Inlier (Figure 2.1), west of Omagh. Since the discovery by prospecting in 1985 of outcropping mineralisation a geological resource of 2 million tonnes grading 6.9g/t Au has been quoted by the company (5). Several auriferous quartz veins have been identified, all of which are steeply dipping and trend generally north-south (Figure 21.4). Cavanacaw, and other occurrences of veins with this trend are interpreted as being related to a deep crustal structure, the Omagh Lineament (6). The veins at Cavanacaw are internally complex and heavily fractured and it has not been possible to determine the fluid history of the deposit. Cavanacaw is broadly mineralogically similar to Curraghinalt, although the relative abundance of certain elements differ. Where Curraghinalt is Cu dominant, Cavanacaw is Pb-Zn dominant and Au:Ag ratios are lower.

Numerous other vein-related bedrock occurrences of gold in the Dalradian have been recorded in Counties Londonderry and Tyrone by exploration programmes.

Southern Uplands-Down-Longford Terrane (Leadhills Supergroup)

Ordovician and Silurian rocks of the Leadhills Supergroup in Northern Ireland are an extension of the Southern Uplands Terrane of Scotland into Ireland (Chapter 4). Gold in quartz veins has long been known at Clontibret, Co. Monaghan, in the

Republic of Ireland, close to the border with Co. Armagh. The Clontibret mineralisation includes stibnite and is part of the same vein swarm that includes the lead veins of the South Armagh-Monaghan Mining District (7).

Gold occurrences have been identified in two areas of Co. Armagh in the Southern Uplands-Down-Longford Terrane. At Cargalisgorran [H803 333], drilling has proved vein widths of 3.03m grading 2.16g/t Au. Initial interpretations indicate that the auriferous veins are associated with subsidiary fracturing along the northeast-trending Orlock Bridge Fault, a major shear zone extending through the entire terrane.

Stratabound gold occurrences

Stratabound gold mineralisation occurs in the **Glengawna Formation** (Table 2.1) of the **Dalradian Supergroup** in the Sperrin Mountains. Throughout the formation numerous grab samples contain gold in

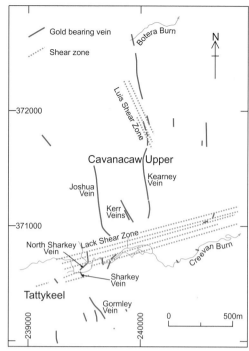

Figure 21.4
Vein and shear zone distribution in the area of the Lack gold deposit (4).

the 20-100ppb range. However, the most notable occurrence is at Glenlark Lodge [H595 901] where semi-massive and disseminated iron, zinc and lead sulphides are associated with significant precious metal grades. The host rock is chloritic-talc schist, typical of that found throughout the Glengawna Formation, which may represent a hydrothermally altered protolith. The widest interval sampled contained 2.55g/t Au over 21m including a section of 2m grading 7g/t Au and 42g/t Ag. The gold mineralisation outcrops as massive and disseminated sulphides, (sphalerite, galena and pyrite), lying parallel to the transposed foliation of the schists and was deformed in the same tectonic event as the host rock. The significance of this occurrence is that, being stratabound and possibly originally stratiform, it may represent a syngenetic or syn-diagentic style of mineralisation. There are also small cross-cutting veinlets of coarse-grained massive sulphide which are manifestly post-tectonic.

Volcanogenic gold occurrences

The **Tyrone Igneous Complex** lies to the south of, and structurally beneath, the Dalradian rocks of the Sperrin Mountains (Chapter 3). The complex comprises a core of sillimanite grade gneissic basement, dated at 640Ma, which is overlain by metabasic igneous rocks, interpreted as an early Ordovician obducted ophiolite dated at 472±4Ma (Arenig-Llanvirn) (8). Overlying the ophiolite and beneath the Omagh Thrust Fault is the Tyrone Volcanic Group. Igneous rocks within the group range in composition from basaltic andesite to rhyolite and are interpreted as having formed in a subduction-related island arc environment. The volcanic rocks are cut by intrusions of calc-alkaline granite and tonalite.

The Tyrone Igneous Complex is highly prospective for gold and base metals. The Cashel Rock prospect [H589 802] in Co. Tyrone comprises a silicified rhyolite with disseminated gold

scale bar = 1mm

Photograph 6
Alluvial gold grains from the Sperrin Mountains.

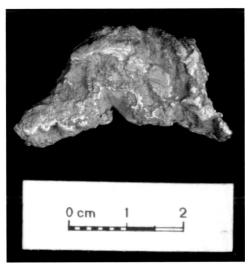

0 cm   1   2

Photograph 7
Clay Lake nugget from south Co. Armagh. (Weight 30.05gm; gold content 28gm). (Photograph reproduced with the kind permission of the Trustees of the National Museums and Galleries of Northern Ireland).

in intervals of up to 3.63m grading 30.1g/t Au and 43.3g/t Ag (including 1.23m at 86.2g/t Au and 122.4g/t Ag). Geochemical base metal anomalies and siliceous ironstone (of probable exhalative origin) occur in the Tyrone Volcanic Group and suggest the presence of a volcanogenic style of mineralisation. This area of Co. Tyrone represents the eastern extension of the island arc system that hosts the Buchans volcanogenic massive sulphide deposits in Newfoundland.

Gold prospecting in the 1980s, in the southern part of the Fintona Block, north of the Clogher Valley showed that Devonian volcanic rocks of andesitic composition (Chapter 6) contain minor gold occurrences associated with wallrock alteration. Little is known about the geology and genesis of this style of gold mineralisation.

Alluvial Gold

Alluvial gold is found in streambeds as native metal alloyed with silver. Gold is eroded from weathered bedrock occurrences and dispersed into streams. Owing to their very high specific gravity, gold grains (Photograph 6) become differentiated from other mineral species and are trapped in areas of reduced stream flow. Although alluvial gold is unlikely ever to become an economic source of gold in Northern Ireland, it does provide physical evidence of the presence of gold in bedrock. Insofar as alluvial gold is common in areas where vein gold is not presently known, the occurrence of gold in bedrock may be much more widespread.

Alluvial gold occurrences are scattered throughout Counties Armagh and Down and therefore suggest that other gold occurrences remain to be discovered. One of the most spectacular finds in recent years is the Clay Lake nugget, now exhibited in the Ulster Museum (Photograph 7). Gold can also be panned in the Hilltown area of Co. Down (9).

A note on the potential for other styles of gold mineralisation

There are several potential gold exploration targets that have yet to be examined in detail in Northern Ireland. As research has strongly suggested that Carboniferous basinal brines have remobilised gold, there is a possibility that receptive horizons and structures older than the Carboniferous fluids could act as traps for gold mineralisation. Such lithologies in the Dalradian Supergroup include the graphitic and impure limestone associated with the Dungiven Limestone Formation in the Sperrin Mountains and the Torr Head Limestone Formation in northeast Co. Antrim.

Base Metals

Lead and zinc showings are scattered throughout the pre-Mesozoic formations in Northern Ireland. Most are epigenetic vein-type occurrences and are found mainly in the Ordovician and Silurian greywacke and slate of the Southern Uplands-Down-Longford Terrane and in Dalradian schists in Co. Tyrone. Two concentrations of vein-hosted lead are of particular historical significance. Three other areas have been examined more recently to investigate their potential for stratabound base metal deposits.

The **South Armagh-Monaghan Mining District** is centred on the town of Keady in south Armagh. In the GSNI records, 57 shafts and adits are recorded in Co. Armagh. A few of the veins were worked on what was a relatively large scale by the standards of the time. The Derrynoose Lead Mine, [H796 316] abandoned in 1842, comprised 13 shafts and one adit, with one of the shafts reported to be 150 feet deep. Other workings of local significance, which had multiple shafts, were the Clay [H828 310], Creggan [H938 170], Carrickgallogy [H984 289] and College mines [H807 332]. The veins are vertical, and although they have variable strike directions, their trend is believed to be controlled by stress fields associated with the Orlock Bridge Fault. Mineralisation predominately comprises galena, sphalerite, pyrite and chalcopyrite. The gangue is mainly quartz with calcite and barite.

Photograph 8
Chimney and spoil heap at the South Engine Shaft on the Conlig-Whitespots Mine [J492 765], north Co. Down.

The **Conlig-Whitespots Mines** [J492 765] between Bangor and Newtownards (Photograph 8) in north Co. Down, consists of ten shafts which lie along a vertical north-south vein hosted by Silurian greywackes (10). The ore minerals are galena, sphalerite and chalcopyrite in a gangue mainly of quartz-cemented breccia with some barite and calcite. The vein has been re-brecciated and subsequently intruded by a Palaeogene dolerite dyke. Conlig was worked intermittently from at least 1780 until 1899, over which period an estimated 13,500t of lead metal was recovered, making it one of the major lead mines in the United Kingdom in the 19th Century.

Examples of stratabound base metal mineralisation occur in two geological environments in Northern Ireland. At Glenlark [H595 901], in metasediments of the Dalradian Supergroup, significant grades of zinc and lead (up to 9.8% Zn and 2.9% Pb over 1m intervals) are associated with gold and silver mineralisation (see page 256). Massive, semi-massive and disseminated sulphide mineralisation occurs over a 21m section. Here, the Glengawna Formation has been interpreted as having suffered extensive hydrothermal alteration prior to metamorphism. The formation also contains numerous other base metal showings along strike. To the north of Glenlark other formations in the Dalradian Supergroup have the potential to host stratabound base metal mineralisation. Regional geochemical surveys indicate that anomalous base metal values are present in the Dungiven Limestone Formation and examples of disseminated zinc and lead (1.5% Zn+Pb) and massive pyrite mineralisation have been recorded around Park, Co. Londonderry [C597 013].

The Tyrone Volcanic Group is host to copper, lead and zinc mineralisation at several localities. Occurrences of boulders of chloritic tuff analysing up to 7.6% Zn are recorded south of Greencastle [H586 820]. In the vicinity of Cashel Rock, copper has been recorded in tonalite and rhyolite with grades of 90m at 0.16% Cu intercepted in exploration drilling in the 1970s. The presence of jasperoid horizons of probable exhalative origin and the spatially close occurrence of graphitic pelites within the volcanic package indicates that the Ordovician arc is prospective for volcanogenic massive sulphide mineralisation.

Copper, as malachite and chalcopyrite, is ubiquitous in small amounts in the lead-zinc veins. While it may have been recovered in the 18th and 19th Century mines as a by-product, there is no record of primary copper mining in Northern Ireland. Very small amounts of native copper have also been recorded in amygdales in basalt lava of the Antrim Lava Group (Chapter 14) as a mineralogical curiosity (11).

Other areas of prospectivity for base metals include the Clogher Valley along the trace of the Aghintain Fault where deep overburden geochemical surveys in the 1980s revealed anomalies of lead, barium and silver, together with galena and barite in heavy mineral samples (12). The geological environment of Lower Carboniferous shallow water sediments near a basin margin fault is analogous to sites of mineralisation in the major lead-zinc orefield of the Irish Midlands, (e.g. Navan, Co. Meath).

Tin as cassiterite was found in an outcrop of greisen at Pollaphuca in the Mourne Mountains in the 1980s. Channel sampling returned grades of 0.4% Sn over a 0.3m interval. Given the current economics of tin mining and the location of the occurrence in an Area of Outstanding Natural Beauty, it is unlikely to be explored further.

Diamonds and Semi-Precious Gems

No diamonds or kimberlite intrusions (the most common host rock of diamonds) have been unequivocally shown to exist in Ireland. However, there are intriguing indications that diamondiferous intrusions could be discovered in Northern Ireland.

In spite of the Brookeborough Diamond (Photograph 9), reportedly found in the Colebrooke River, Co. Fermanagh in 1816, no serious attempts were made at diamond exploration until 1996, when an exploration company carried out a programme of heavy mineral sampling in stream sediments in Counties Fermanagh and Tyrone. Although no diamonds were found, they reported that some samples contained an assemblage of grains of garnet, chromite and ilmenite possibly derived from kimberlitic source rocks.

Photograph 9
The Brookeborough diamond, now set in Irish gold. (© Lord Brookeborough).
(Photograph reproduced with the kind permission of the Trustees of the National Museums and Galleries of Northern Ireland).

A range of semi-precious stones is known from various localities in Northern Ireland, although none are of gem quality. Amber has been found in the Lough Neagh Group (13). Beryl and rock crystal have long been known in drusy cavities in granites of the Mourne Mountains (Chapter 15). Tourmaline is widely scattered in Dalradian schists in the south Sperrin Mountains of Co. Tyrone.

Bulk Minerals

Iron ore was extensively worked in Co. Antrim from at least the 18th Century up to the 1920s. GSNI has records of 780 shafts and adits associated with iron ores. Five types of deposits are known.

Lateritic Iron Ores were formed by hydrothermal alteration and chemical weathering of basalt lava of the Palaeogene Antrim Lava Group in a tropical climate directly following lava extrusion (Chapter 14). The main iron ore and bauxite bed is in the Interbasaltic Formation, which formed as the result of a prolonged period of weathering between the eruption of the Lower Basalt and Upper Basalt formations. A comprehensive survey, published in 1912, was the first to recognise the lateritic origin of these iron ores and bauxite (14).

The lateritic iron ores formed when the aluminosilicate lattice of pyroxene, olivine and feldspar broke down to produce clay minerals and iron and aluminium oxides. At ambient temperatures above 20°C, silica passes into solution and is leached out of the soil profile. In general, if rainfall is uniformly high (greater than 1.5m/year), a lateritic clay results from desilication. However, with distinct seasons, minerals concentrate in layers at redox boundaries in the weathering profile. Leaching of silica proceeds with maximum effect during the dry season, while alumina and iron oxides are mobilised during the wet season. The Co. Antrim occurrences are unlike lateritic beds elsewhere in that the iron ore is deposited above bauxite. The term 'lithomarge' is used to describe the purple and red altered basalt spotted and streaked with white kaolin minerals (14).

Iron ore beds are subhorizontal, commonly with a thin (c. 30cm) higher-grade layer, the 'Pisolitic Ore', overlying a thicker and lower grade 'pavement' (up to 2m). The higher grade ore is 30-60% total iron oxides, while the lower grade ore is about 25% iron oxides. The deposits were worked in open-cast or room-and-pillar underground operations (Photograph 10) and it is recorded that 5,000,000t were extracted (15). Such ores could not continue to be economic beyond the 1950s, when the giant supergene-enriched banded iron formation ores of America, Australia and Brazil began to dominate world markets.

Photograph 10
Internal view of an adit in the Palaeogene
Interbasaltic Formation at Parkmore, Co. Antrim.

Although iron ore occurrences are widely scattered over the Antrim Plateau the main mining districts were around Glenravel [D166 196], Parkmore [D184 205], Newtowncrommelin [D140 186], Cargan [D167 179] and Glenariff [D213 195] in mid-Co. Antrim and at Lyle's Hill [J247 829] in south Co. Antrim.

Blackband ironstone was worked at Carrickmore [D165 426], Co. Antrim, within the Ballycastle coalfield. These ores grade about 30% Fe, are up to 75cm thick and lie within a succession of mudstone and coals, passing laterally into coal. They were worked between 1854 and 1879 and calcined on-site.

Cherty ironstone or jasper occurs within the Tyrone Volcanic Group varying in thickness from a few cm up to 2m at Bonnety Bush [H726 888] and Beaghbeg [H674 828], Co. Tyrone.

Haematite, in narrow vertical veins crosscutting the boundary between the Silurian greywacke and slate of the Southern Uplands-Down-Longford Terrane and the Newry Igneous Complex, was worked at Dechommet [J255 435], Co. Down, in the 19th Century.

Bog Iron was extensively worked in Co. Londonderry in the last century (16). It forms when acid water leaches iron oxides from the boulder clay and deposits iron as a thin crust at the redox interface of the B-soil horizon. The process is mediated by bacteria.

Bauxite was formed along with iron ore by lateritisation of basalt lava of the Palaeogene Antrim Lava Group. The Antrim bauxite is a residual clay deposit comprising a mixture of clay minerals of the kaolinite group, together with aluminium hydroxide, gibbsite and boehmite, with variable proportions of quartz, goethite and minor amounts of residual titanium minerals, especially anatase.

An unrecorded, but presumably small, amount of bauxite was extracted along with the iron ore from the Co. Antrim mines until about 1934, when the work ceased. Extraction resumed during the Second World War, when 244,000t were mined. The major mining areas were Newtowncrommelin [D140 186] and Ballylig [D180 094] in mid-Co. Antrim, and Lyle's Hill [J247 829] in south Co. Antrim. Regional surveys have been carried out (14, 15) and bulk samples were collected from Agnew's Hill [D330 010] and Clenagh and Salmon's Drift [D154 202] (15).

No production records of run-of-mine grades are available, although individual samples show that the Co. Antrim bauxite is very variable in composition and some very high grades are recorded. Samples of gibbsite and boehmite with over 62% Al_2O_3 and low silica and iron oxides are clearly of metallurgical grade. A wide range of sub-ore grade samples is also recorded. Locally named varieties are lithomarge (kaolinised basalt), ferruginous red bauxite with 30% Fe_2O_3, and siliceous grey bauxite with more than 20% SiO_2 (15).

Given the abundance of low cost, high-grade bauxite from Australia, West Africa, Jamaica and South America, the Co. Antrim deposits are not competitive. However, ceramic and other properties have not been fully explored. Tests on calcining bauxite were carried out in the 1960s. A small quantity of bauxite is extracted at Clinty, [D102 075] near Ballymena, Co. Antrim, as feed-stock for ferrous aluminium sulphate water purification material.

Industrial Minerals

Northern Ireland has a remarkable variety of non-metallic industrial minerals. While the occurrence of many is of little more than historical interest, others are present in workable amounts and contribute to the economy. There is scope for the expansion of industrial mineral production in Northern Ireland.

Rock Salt (halite) forms beds of variable thickness within the Triassic Mercia Mudstone Group (Chapter 10) and is restricted to the southeast corner of Co. Antrim. Beds formed by the evaporation of seawater which was trapped in restricted basins on a shallow marine shelf. Salt extraction in the Carrickfergus [J393 895] and Eden [J430 895] salt fields commenced in the mid-19th Century (Photograph 11) at several mines but is now being worked at only the Kilroot Mine (10). Access to the Kilroot Mine [J451 891] is by decline and mining is by the room-and-pillar method. In the abandoned salt mines, uncontrolled brining was often employed after extraction by room-and-pillar mining had ceased and this led to flooding of some of the mine workings. Most of these mines, including those at French Park [J392 895], Carrickfergus/International [J428 896] and Maidenmount [J390 901] ceased operations in the 1950s. In the salt fields the halite beds vary in thickness from 9 to 27m. However, in the Larne No. 2 borehole, 15km to the north, the salt beds are 400m thick and are divided into three seam groups representing the Ballyboley (41m), Carnduff (180m) and Larne (179m) halites. A bed of halite 113m thick is also recorded in this borehole in the Permian Upper Marls at a depth of over 1700m (17).

Gypsum and **anhydrite**, the raw materials of building plaster, occur as thin seams and cement in the Mercia Mudstone Group in the Lagan Valley. Historically, anhydrite nodules were hand picked in the Parkview brick pits (18). Massive anhydrite with fibrous gypsum and granular carbonate was found at 111m below surface in a 4.8m thick bed in the Late Permian Connswater Marl Formation (Permian Upper Marls) just above the Magnesian Limestone in the Avoniel borehole in east Belfast. Stratabound beds of gypsum and anhydrite in possibly economic quantities have been intersected in mineral exploration boreholes drilled in the Carboniferous Clogher Valley Formation (Chapter 7) near Fivemiletown [H445 479].

Perlite, the industrial name for volcanic glass, occurs at Sandy Braes [J320 396] southeast of Ballymena, Co. Antrim where it forms part of the Palaeogene Tardree Rhyolite Complex (Chapter 15). A nearby occurrence at Loonburn [J322 395] is a sinuous lenticular deposit formed from an ash flow. The perlite, when fused, froths up and forms an inert, lightweight and porous granular product with a wide range of uses in the construction, insulation, packaging and agricultural industries.

Photograph 11
Underground crushing and screening plant in the Kilroot Salt Mine, Carrickfergus, Co. Antrim. (Published with the kind permission of the Irish Salt Mining and Exploration Co. Ltd.).

Diatomite, also known locally as Bann Clay, occurs in a deposit up to 0.9m thick in the valley of the River Bann between Toome [H990 907] and Portglenone [C980 039]. It was deposited in freshwater lakes during early post-glacial times and consists of the microscopic siliceous skeletons of diatoms. When dry, it is a friable, white, chemically inert powder that can be used as a filler in paint, plastic and rubber manufacture, but also as an absorbent in animal litter, an abrasive for metal polish, an insultant, and as a filtration agent in the food and pharmaceutical industries. Diatomite was extracted manually on a small scale until the late 1960s but is no longer worked.

Barytes, the industrial name for the mineral barite (barium sulphate) is commonly found as gangue associated with lead and zinc veins in Dalradian rocks of the Sperrin Mountains and Ordovician and Silurian greywacke of the Southern Uplands-Down-Longford Terrane. It is also recorded as cement in sandstones and in veins in Carboniferous rocks near Draperstown and in the Clogher Valley. At both locations the barite is associated with major faults that may have acted as the channel for hydrothermal fluids.

Glass sand with a silica content of 95–99.8% is known at two localities in Northern Ireland. Carboniferous quartz sandstones were worked in the 18th Century for glass at Ballycastle in north Co. Antrim. Other quartz sandstones that could be beneficiated to achieve the appropriate specifications were explored in the 1970s at Kildress [H805 768] near Cookstown in Co. Tyrone.

Moulding Sand, for use in foundries has been obtained from the Triassic Sherwood Sandstone Group in the Lagan Valley, southwest of Belfast and from deposits of Pleistocene fluvioglacial sand.

Feldspar, which occurs in pegmatite veins intruding the Moinian Lough Derg Group in west Co. Fermanagh was worked near Castlecaldwell and used in the making of glaze at the Belleek Pottery.

Fireclay from the Carboniferous coalfields at Coalisland in Co. Tyrone and Ballycastle in Co. Antrim was an important by-product of that industry and was used in the manufacture of refractory bricks.

Ball clay occurs in the Oligocene Lough Neagh Group (Chapter 16) and was used in the manufacture of sanitary pipes at Coalisland and on the east side of Lough Neagh near Portmore, Co. Antrim.

Dolomite is found as dolomitic limestone at several localities in Northern Ireland. It can be used as a flux in blast furnaces and in paper making. It may be calcined and used as an abrasive, or crushed and applied directly to farmland to counter magnesium deficiency in livestock. Extensive secondary dolomitisation of the Carboniferous Knockmore Limestone Member near Belcoo [H085 387] in Co. Fermanagh is associated with faulting (19). Analyses of the dolomite showed a high degree of purity (39.5% $MgCO_3$) and it is now worked on a small scale for agricultural purposes. Elsewhere in Northern Ireland, a 5m thick dolomite bed is found in the Carboniferous Derryloran Grit Formation (Chapter 7) near Cookstown, Co. Tyrone.

Chalk from the Cretaceous Ulster White Limestone Formation (Chapter 12) has been worked for many years by Eglinton Quarries at Glenarm, Co. Antrim [D314 153] and has applications as a whitener, or filler and for agricultural lime.

Construction Minerals

Northern Ireland has abundant sources of minerals and rocks for use in the construction industries.

Aggregate in Northern Ireland is derived from a variety of bedrock types and superficial deposits which are capable of yielding high quality, high specification products. The GSNI inventory of quarries lists some 262 quarries and pits widely distributed throughout the country and describes their products (20). Production in 2002 of hard rock aggregate and sand and gravel was 23.5 million tonnes. Categories listed include limestone, basalt, sandstone and sand and gravel. Aggregate production is dominated by basalt, derived mostly from the Palaeogene Antrim Lava Group, closely followed by fluvioglacial sand and gravel. The sandstone category includes the Silurian greywacke (or gritstone) of Counties Armagh and Down which has high polished stone and aggregate abrasion values, making them a particularly good source of wearing course aggregate.

Brickclay was used in the manufacture of bricks at small brickfields in the Lagan Valley and used in the construction of many of the imposing late Victorian buildings in the greater Belfast area in the late 19th Century up to the mid-20th Century. These are stone-free, red, plastic clays derived from the Triassic Mercia Mudstone Group with re-deposition in Pleistocene times (18). Brick clays are also worked from the Carboniferous Rossmore Mudstone Formation in the Dungannon area of Co. Tyrone.

Dimension Stone includes almost every common type of hard rock in Northern Ireland which has been used in the past as a building stone and a few which were quarried as decorative stone. There are no active decorative or dimension stone quarries active at present, although Northern Ireland has a number of well known varieties of decorative stone. The Mourne granites were widely exported and stone cutting is still a significant craft industry in south Co. Down. Some Carboniferous limestones were once also quarried, e.g. the Armagh Red Marble.

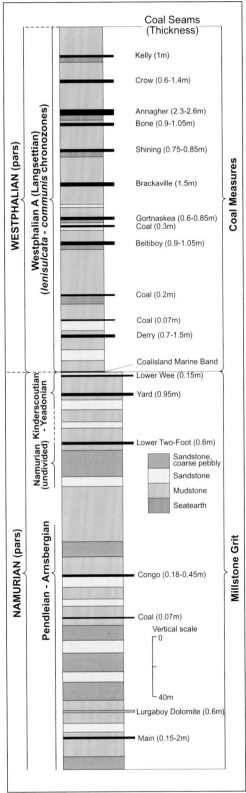

Figure 21.5
Lithostratigraphy of the Millstone Grit (Namurian) and Coal Measures (Westphalian) in east Co. Tyrone.

Fuel Minerals

Hard Coal occurs in two small coalfields that are exposed at surface in Northern Ireland. These are the Coalisland coalfield in Co. Tyrone (Namurian to Westphalian) and the Ballycastle coalfield (Viséan to Namurian) in Co. Antrim (Chapter 7). Coal production in Northern Ireland was significant in the 18th and 19th centuries but now has little economic potential as a source of hard coal. However, it is of interest as a source bed for hydrocarbon generation.

The Coalisland coalfield, lying between Coalisland and Dungannon, is a triangular-shaped, fault-bounded block unconformably overlain by Triassic sedimentary rocks (21). There are two groups of coal seams. In the southwest part of the coalfield the Namurian Millstone Grit succession includes the Main Coal near the base of the succession with a series of thinner, workable, coals above (Figure 21.5). The Main Coal was discovered in 1672 and worked until 1709. The succession in the northeast part of the coalfield comprises the Westphalian Coal Measures with eight seams of workable thickness. The thickest of these, the Annagher Coal, was worked in the 1840s. Records of proximate analyses give ranges of 47.48 - 51.55% fixed carbon, 37.19 - 48.0% volatiles, 4.57 - 11.28% ash and 1.65 - 2.8% sulphur for the Main Coal. The coal rank is therefore high volatile bituminous (B-C) coal with relatively high sulphur. Steep dips of up to 50° hindered production throughout the operating life of the mines and mining ceased in the 1930s. Drilling in 1958 indicated 250,000 tons remaining in the Derry Coal seam.

The Carboniferous rocks of the Ballycastle coalfield (22) are exposed in sea cliffs east of Ballycastle (Photograph 12). While there is archaeological evidence that some coal could have been used in the 13th Century, the main period of development began in 1733 with maximum output of about 15,000 tons per annum. Production declined in the early 19th Century and continued intermittently thereafter, although it was not until 1967 that the last mine was finally abandoned. In the lower part of the succession the Murlough Shale Formation contains ten coal seams (Ballyvoy coals) up to 1.3m thick which are documented in boreholes (Table 7.2). The highest unit in the coalfield, the Ballyvoy Sandstone Formation, contains the most accessible coal seams including the Main Coal and the Hawk's Nest Coal, which provided most of the output (Figure 21.6).

Photograph 12
The Ballyvoy Sandstone Formation at the Gobb Colliery, 4km ENE of Ballycastle, Co. Antrim.

Proximate analyses for the Main Coal report fixed carbon 48.7 - 57.01%, volatiles 27.93 - 36.2%, ash 4.9 - 9.04% and sulphur 0.7 - 1.02%, with calorific values in the range 11,640 - 12,411Btu. It is therefore ranked between Sub-bituminous A and High Volatile Bituminous B Coal, with lower sulphur and ash contents than the Main Coal in Co. Tyrone.

Carboniferous coal is known and suspected to be present at depth elsewhere in Northern Ireland. The Rathlin Basin extends to the north offshore from Counties Antrim and Londonderry. Coal was encountered at 1142m below surface in the Magilligan borehole [C683 353] in Co. Londonderry. Coal is also likely to be present at depth in other sedimentary basins beneath the Antrim Plateau.

Lignite or brown coal was first noted in the Oligocene Lough Neagh Group (Chapter 16) around Lough Neagh in 1757 (21). However, neither the regional distribution of the Oligocene basins nor the quantity of lignite present was appreciated until the 1980s when large deposits were discovered (23). Since then detailed exploration at Crumlin and Ballymoney has revealed a lignite resource of about 1 billion tonnes, with the largest deposit located at Ballymoney. The deposits are potentially mineable although the only currently known use is for power generation.

Deposits of lignite have been found in four areas (Figure 16.1). Near Crumlin, Co. Antrim, two thick seam groups sub-outcrop beneath superficial deposits close to the east shore of Lough Neagh and extend southwest beneath the Lough (Photograph 13). Another group of lignite seams is known between Coagh and the west shore of Lough Neagh in Co. Tyrone, and also between Stewartstown and the southwest shore of the Lough. The largest deposits were found in north Co. Antrim 40km to the north of Lough Neagh, close to Ballymoney.

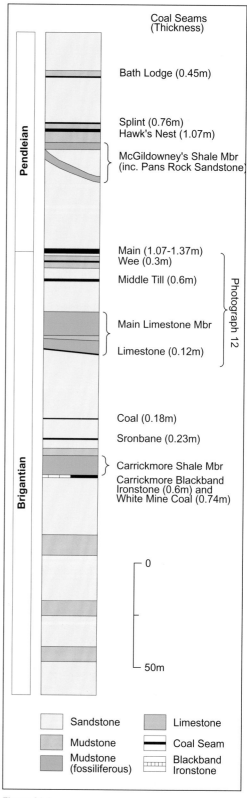

Figure 21.6
Lithostratigraphy of the Ballyvoy Sandstone Formation at Ballycastle.

	Ballymoney	Coagh	Crumlin
Ash (%)	47	39	6.9
Moisture (%)	36.2	39.9	51
Calorific values (Btu/lb)	2674	5704	2834
Sulphur (%)	0.51	0.17	0.2

Table 21.1
Fuel technology (partial proximate analyses) of lignite from Northern Ireland (23).

The lignite beds are flat-lying or shallow dipping within small fault-bounded basins of the Lough Neagh Group. The lignite contains up to 75% carbon and there are two varieties. The woody form contains silicified plant fragments and the non-woody variety is massive and blocky. The beds range from very thin to tens of metres thick and are contained in a succession of sandy clays and silts (24). The coal rank is Lignite B and proximate analyses are given in Table 21.1.

Peat has been hand-dug as a fuel in Ireland from pre-historic times to the present day. Peat bogs in Northern Ireland, being generally smaller, were never developed on an industrial scale for power generation as they were in the Irish Midlands.

Uranium exploration in the late 1970s, driven by escalation in the oil price, identified secondary mineralisation associated with the Mourne Mountains granites and the Newry Igneous Complex. These minerals were deposited on joint faces in the granites by late stage hydrothermal fluids circulating after the granite had solidified.

Photograph 13
Aerial view of part of the Crumlin lignite deposit, Co. Antrim.

References

1) Boate, G. 1652. Ireland's Natural History, London, S. Hartlib.

2) Clifford, J. A., Earls, G., Meldrum, A. H. and Moore, N. 1992. Gold in the Sperrin Mountains, Northern Ireland: an exploration case history. *In*: Bowden, A. A., Earls, G., O'Connor, P. G. and Pyne, J. F. (eds.). *The Irish Minerals Industry 1980-1990. Irish Association for Economic Geology*, Dublin. 77-87.

3) Earls, G., Hutton, D. H. W., Wilkinson, J. J., Moles, N. R., Parnell, J., Fallick, A. E. and Boyce, A. J. 1996. *The gold metallogeny of northwest Northern Ireland*. Geological Survey of Northern Ireland Technical Report GSNI/96/6.

4) Woodham, C., Finlay, S and Holman, R. 1989. Gold exploration in the Dalradian of Northern Ireland. *In: Transactions of the Institute of Mining and Metalogeny. (Sect. B: Appl. Earth Sci.)*, **98**, 63-65.

5) Cliff, D. C. and Wolfenden, M. 1992. The Lack gold deposit, Northern Ireland. *In*: Bowden, A. A., Earls, G., O'Connor, P. G. and Pyne, J. F. (eds.). *The Irish Minerals Industry 1980-1990. Irish Association for Economic Geology*, Dublin. 65-75.

6) Parnell, J., Earls, G., Wilkinson, J. J., Hutton, D. H. W., Boyce, A. J., Fallick, A. E., Ellam, R. M., Gleeson, S. A., Moles, N. R., Carey, P. F. and Legg, I. C. 2000. Regional fluid flow and gold mineralisation in the Dalradian of the Sperrin Mountains, Northern Ireland. *Economic Geology*, **95**, 1389-1416.

7) Morris, J. H., Steed, G. M. and Wilbur, D. G. 1986. The Lisglassan-Tullybuck deposit, County Monaghan: Sb-As-Au vein mineralization in Lower Palaeozoic greywackes. *In*: Andrew, C. J., Crowe, R. W. A., Finlay, S., Pennell, W. M. and Pyne, J. F. (eds.). *Geology and Genesis of Mineral Deposits in Ireland. Irish Association for Economic Geology*, Dublin, 103-20.

8) Hutton, D. H. W., Aftalion, M. A. and Halliday, A. N. 1985. An Ordovician ophiolite in County Tyrone, Ireland. *Nature* **315**, 210-12.

9) Smith, C. G., Smith, R. T., Leake, R. C., Styles, M. T. and Legg, I. C. 1996. *Mineral exploration in the Hilltown and Slieve Croob areas of County Down*. Geological Survey of Northern Ireland. Technical Report GSNI/96/2.

10) Griffith A. E. and Wilson, H. E. 1982. *Geology of the country around Carrickfergus and Bangor*. Memoir of the Geological Survey of Northern Ireland, Sheet 29 (Northern Ireland).

11) Frances, P. and Preston, J. 1974. *Native Copper in the Antrim Basalts*. Irish Naturalists' Journal.

12) Smith, R. T., Smith, C. G., and Legg, I. C. 1996. *Mineral Exploration in the Clogher Valley area, Co. Tyrone. Part1: Follow-up Investigations*. Geological Survey of Northern Ireland Technical Report GSNI/96/3.

13) Shukla, B. 1989. Petrological, geochemical and palaeontological studies of the Lough Neagh Group. Unpublished Ph. D thesis, Queens University of Belfast, Northern Ireland.

14) Cole, G. A. J., Wilkinson, S. B., M'Henry, A., Kilroe, J. R., Seymour, H. J., Moss, C. E. and Haigh, W. D. 1912. *The Interbasaltic rocks (iron ores and bauxites) of north-east Ireland*. Memoir of the Geological Survey of Ireland, Dublin.

15) Eyles, V. A. 1952. *The composition and origin of the Antrim laterites and bauxites*. Memoir of the Geological Survey. Belfast HMSO.

16) Wilson, H. E. 1972. *Regional Geology of Northern Ireland*. HMSO, Belfast

17) Penn, I. E., Holliday, D. W., Kirby, G. A., Kubala, M., Sobey, R. A., Mitchell, W. I., Harrison, R. K.and Beckinsale, R. D. 1983. The Larne No. 2 Borehole: discovery of a new Permian volcanic centre. *Scottish Journal of Geology*, **19**, 333-46.

18) Manning, P. I., Robbie, J. A. and Wilson, H. E. 1970. *Geology of Belfast and the Lagan Valley*. Memoir of the Geological Survey of Northern Ireland, Sheet 36 (Northern Ireland).

19) Mitchell, W. I. 1983. *High-grade dolomite deposits in the Belcoo-Boho area of Co. Fermanagh*. Geological Survey of Northern Ireland Open File Report No. 68.

20) Johnston, T. P. 1996. *Inventory of active quarries, pits and mines in Northern Ireland*. Geological Survey of Northern Ireland Technical Report GSNI/96/5.

21) Fowler, A. and Robbie, J. A. 1961. *Geology of the country around Dungannon*. Memoir of the Geological Survey of Northern Ireland, Sheet 35 (Northern Ireland).

22) Wilson, H. E. and Robbie, J. A. 1966. *Geology of the country around Ballycastle*. Memoir of the Geological Survey of Northern Ireland, Sheet 8 (Northern Ireland).

23) Griffith, A. E., Legg, I. C. and Mitchell, W. I. 1987. Mineral Resources. *In*: Buchanan, R. H. and Walker, B. M. (eds.). *Province, City and People: Belfast and its Region*. 43-58. Greystone Books, Belfast.

24) Legg, I. C. 1992. *Tertiary Lignite Deposits of Northern Ireland. In*: Bowden, A. A., Earls, G., O'Connor, P. G. and Pyne, J. F. (eds.). The Irish Minerals Industry 1980-1990. *Irish Association for Economic Geology*. Dublin, 359-68.

Chapter 22

Oil and Gas

D. M. REAY

Introduction

Exploration for oil and gas in Northern Ireland began in 1965 and whilst gas has been
detected it has not been discovered in commercial quantities. Despite this initial lack of
success the rocks beneath Northern Ireland may yet be found to contain undiscovered
accumulations of oil or gas.

The two most prospective areas are in the Lower Carboniferous rocks of Co. Fermanagh
and south Co. Tyrone and the Carboniferous to Triassic rocks beneath the Antrim Plateau
(Figure 22.1). The former has a history of gas shows from a small number of exploration

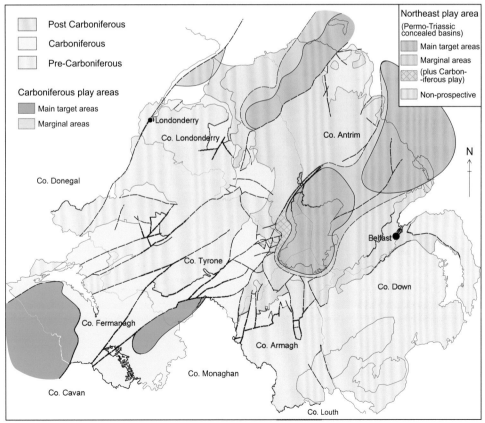

Figure 22.1
Petroleum exploration areas.

273

wells but the prospectivity is reduced by the poor quality of the low permeability **tight gas sandstone** reservoir rocks. Similar **unconventional gas resources** are exploited in North America by hydraulically fracturing the reservoir to stimulate gas flow rates. The latter area is even less well explored because of the technical difficulties in imaging the geological structure beneath the thick cover of Palaeogene basalt lava (Chapter 14). Consequently only five exploration boreholes were drilled between 1971 and 2001. The underlying geology has many similarities to that of the East Irish Sea Basin which hosts the 'giant' Morecambe Bay gasfield (1) (Figure 17.1).

The prospectivity of the two areas may be assessed on the basis of the nature and distribution of the potential source, reservoir and seal rocks. Basin evolution is also important in that its history affects the maturation of the source rocks and the expulsion of hydrocarbons, the reservoir quality and creation of traps, and the relative timing of these processes.

Early Carboniferous basins in Co. Fermanagh and south Co. Tyrone

This area covers the Carboniferous outcrop that extends from Co. Fermanagh eastwards through south Co. Tyrone to Co. Armagh (Figure 22.1). Westwards it extends to Counties Cavan, Leitrim, Sligo, Monaghan and south Co. Donegal in the Republic of Ireland. In Counties Fermanagh and Cavan, the Early Carboniferous section comprises 3500m of marine sedimentary rocks that include organic-rich mudstone and sandstone which are potential hydrocarbon source and reservoir rocks respectively. Late Carboniferous rocks of the Fintona Block and in the Coalisland area of east Co. Tyrone contribute to a cumulative maximum thickness of *c.* 7000m of Carboniferous strata (Chapter 7).

Five wells were drilled in 1965-1966, resulting in gas shows at Dowra and Macnean in Co. Cavan and at Big Dog and Owengarr in Co. Fermanagh while the Glennoo No. 1 well, in the Slieve Beagh area of Co. Tyrone, was dry. Interest in the area lapsed when testing of the wells produced non-commercial gas flows. Dowra No. 1 was re-entered in 1981 and the reservoir interval was hydraulically fractured producing a tenfold increase in flow-rates to 250,000 cubic feet of gas per day (250 mscfg/day) from the Dowra Sandstone Member of the Bundoran Shale Formation (Table 7.8). This led to further exploration which combined a seismic reflection survey with the drilling of wells at Slisgarrow and Kilcoo Cross in Co. Fermanagh and Macnean No. 2 and Drumkeeran in Co. Cavan in 1984-85. Gas shows were again encountered but the wells did not flow to surface when tested.

In 1996, licences were awarded for the area between Co. Fermanagh and the west shore of Lough Neagh. Six wells were drilled in 2001, four in Co. Fermanagh and two in the Republic of Ireland. The reservoir intervals were hydraulically fractured and extended well tests performed. Unfortunately, the fractures did not propagate as well as had been hoped and this, combined with low formation pressures, led to low gas flow rates of <100 mscfg/day. The wells were considered non-commercial given the high drilling costs and lack of infrastructure in the area. Horizontal drilling of the reservoir may be the key to the successful future development of this play.

Play Model

The main **reservoir** target is the Mullaghmore Sandstone Formation (Chapter 7). About 55% of the Formation is composed of sandstone but, even in the best wells, only 20% reaches tight gas sandstone reservoir quality. The Dowra Sandstone Member of the Bundoran Shale Formation is a deeper reservoir target of restricted distribution. The calcareous mudstone of the Bundoran Shale and Benbulben Shale formations are moderate to good **source rocks**. Vitrinite reflectance (R_o) and Conodont Alteration Index (CAI) values indicate that the

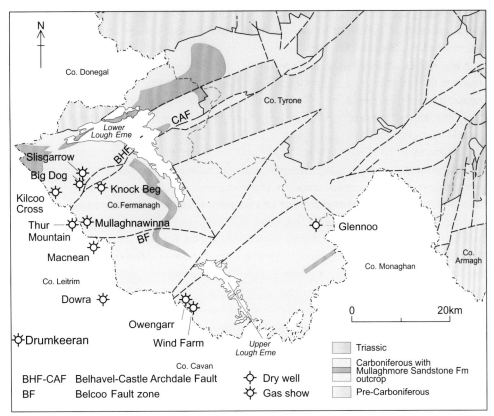

Figure 22.2
Distribution of exploration wells in the area of Co. Fermanagh - south Co. Tyrone and Co. Leitrim.

source rocks are **mature** for oil and gas at surface and for wet or dry gas at depth (2, 3). The Benbulben Shale Formation forms an effective and widespread **seal** to the underlying Mullaghmore Sandstone reservoir. Structural **traps** may be associated with gentle flexures within the basin or tighter, pop-up or flower structures adjacent to major faults such as the Castle Archdale Fault Zone. The widespread occurrence of gas shows and hydrocarbon residues in the cuttings samples may be an example of 'basin-centred gas' and indicate that structural trapping is not an essential factor because of the poor poroperm characteristics. **Migration** from the source rocks into the adjacent reservoirs is not seen as problematical.

Reservoirs
The Mullaghmore Sandstone Formation normally consists of fine- to medium-grained sandstone and siltstone deposited in a delta complex which prograded southwards into the basin. It is about 200m in Big Dog No. 1 but thins southwards to less than 50m in Drumkeeran No. 1 where it comprises a silty mudstone (Figure 22.2). It also thins and shales out in the Upper Lough Erne area where the Formation is represented by thin, sandy siltstone in Owengarr No. 1 well and could not be recognised in Wind Farm No. 1. Further east, on Slieve Beagh, it is present in outcrop and in Glennoo No. 1 is >200m thick. In the basinal wells five major lithological cycles have been recognised in the Mullaghmore Sandstone Formation starting with a basal cycle of pro-delta to distal delta slope mudstone and siltstone (4). This is succeeded by four cycles coarsening-upwards from delta slope to platform facies with channel and inter-channel deposits. Each cycle is terminated by a

fining-upward trend to fine-grained sandy oolitic limestones deposited in a shallow shelf setting (Figure 22.3). Through the Mullaghmore Sandstone Formation there is evidence of increasing water depths leading to the deposition of the Benbulben Shale Formation. Thus reservoir characteristics reflect the changing sedimentary environments with the quality and thickness decreasing from north to south and the better reservoir quality confined to channel sandstones.

Measured and calculated **porosities** in the Mullaghmore Sandstone Formation range from 0% to 10% in boreholes and up to 15% in outcrop samples (5). Petrographic (4,5) and combined petrographic/SEM studies reveal that the major cement components are ferroan carbonate (calcite and dolomite) and/or quartz overgrowths, together with feldspar-replacing illite (6). It appears that primary porosity was totally occluded by the matrix and pore-filling cements. Secondary porosity created by dissolution of grains and cements by meteoric water, associated with periods of uplift, is usually insignificant. However, locally developed secondary porosity filled with hydrocarbons suggests an important

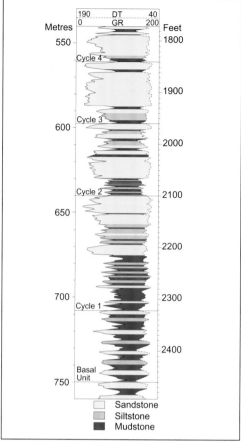

Figure 22.3
Mullaghmore Sandstone Formation gamma-sonic log in the Slisgarrow well showing coarsening upwards cycles.

dissolution phase prior to hydrocarbon migration. Later brittle fracturing of the sandstone may also have created secondary porosity although these fractures are often filled with carbonate cement. The higher outcrop values reflect near-surface leaching of carbonate cements and are not relevant to the reservoir quality of the deeper targets. The irregular distribution of secondary porosity translates into low **permeabilities**, often <0.1mD.

Gas shows and **hydrocarbon fluorescence** are recorded from various intervals in the wells with the best in the Dowra Sandstone Member in Dowra No. 1 and the Mullaghmore Sandstone Formation in Big Dog and Slisgarrow No. 1. The best shows were in cycle 1 (brown oil staining and streaming cut fluorescence in Big Dog No. 1) and cycle 2 (moderate gas show and slow streaming white fluorescence in Slisgarrow No. 1).

Source rocks

The best quality and most mature potential source rocks in the area are Viséan organic-rich mudstone and Namurian mudstone and coal (2, 3, 7, 8, 9), although the latter are too high in the sequence to provide a source for the Mullaghmore Sandstone Formation. Lower Palaeozoic black mudstone in the Pomeroy and Lisbellaw inliers have vitrinite reflectance values in the oil or gas windows but with very low Total Organic Carbon (TOC) content are poor potential source rocks (10).

276

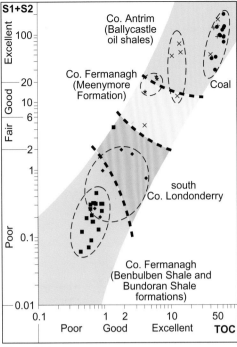

Figure 22.4
Source rock quality: Total Organic Carbon (TOC) vs
Hydrocarbon generation potential (S1 + S2).

Quality

Measured TOC content for the
Carboniferous lithologies of <1% in
exploration wells ranks them as poor
quality source rocks (Figure 22.4). However,
Rock-Eval and maturity indicator analyses
show that they have generated most of
their potential hydrocarbons (7). Original
TOC content would thus have been at least
twice the present values making them
originally good to excellent source rocks.
The organic content consists of marine lipid
and terrigenous humic organic matter
which yield mostly wet and dry gas with
minor oil or condensate (Figure 22.5). At
outcrop, a TOC of 6.32% has been recorded
in the Meenymore Formation (Table 7.9)
which is the source of most of the surface
oil shows (8). This Formation is, however,
stratigraphically too high to be a source
rock for the Mullaghmore Sandstone
Formation.

Maturity

The **vitrinite reflectance** values (R_O) of
potential source rocks in well samples are
generally between 1.45 and 2.75 indicating
that they are below the oil floor $(R_O <1.4)$
and above the dry gas preservation limit
$(R_O >3.2)$ in Co. Fermanagh. Big Dog has the
least mature R_O-depth profile and this is
consistent with the live oil shows in the
well. Rock-Eval analysis indicates that little
hydrocarbon-generating capacity remains.
Kerogen maturity $(R_O$-depth) profiles
indicate that substantial uplift and erosion
has taken place. Projecting the maturity
profile back to a near-surface value of
R_O=0.2% gives an estimate of 3,500-4,500m
of uplift. It appears that hydrocarbon
generation has been suspended since soon
after major uplift and erosion began.
Although these maturity characteristics
extend eastwards to the Glennoo No. 1
borehole, around Lough Neagh vitrinite
reflectance values at outcrop and in
boreholes decrease significantly
(Figure 22.6).

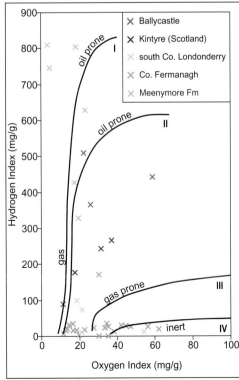

Figure 22.5
Source rock type and hydrocarbon generation
potential (modified Van Krevelen diagram).

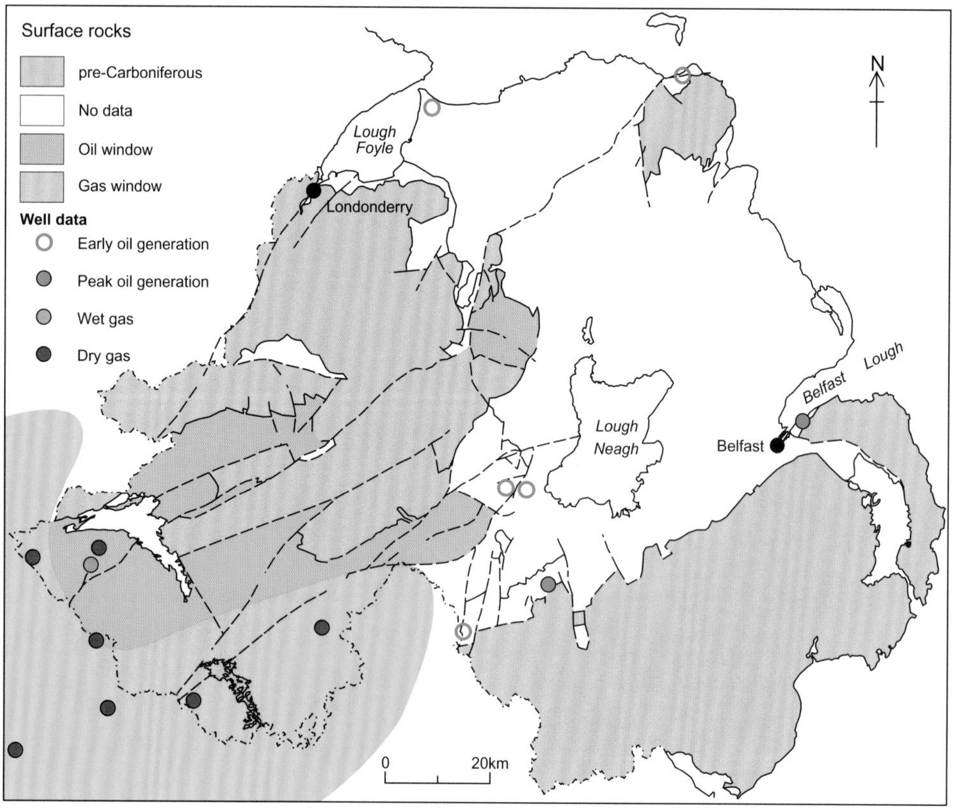
Surface rocks
pre-Carboniferous
No data
Oil window
Gas window
Well data
Early oil generation
Peak oil generation
Wet gas
Dry gas
Lough Foyle
Londonderry
Lough Neagh
Belfast
Belfast Lough
N
0
20km

Figure 22.6
Carboniferous source rock maturity map, based on vitrinite reflectance studies (8, 9, 10 and 11).

Seals

The Benbulben Shale Formation provides an effective seal for any hydrocarbons trapped in the Mullaghmore Sandstone Formation. Although the seals may have been ruptured as a result of Variscan faulting (Chapter 8), leakage of hydrocarbons would have been very low due to the diagenetic reduction in the permeability of the reservoir. The Bundoran Shale Formation acts as a seal for the Dowra Sandstone Member reservoir target.

Burial history, hydrocarbon generation and trapping mechanisms

Understanding the burial history of a rock sequence is critical to defining the relative timing of hydrocarbon generation and migration, the diagenetic reduction of porosity and permeability, trap creation and breaching, and subsequent escape of hydrocarbons. These processes are the key to the formation and preservation of oil and gas accumulations.

In Co. Fermanagh the high maturity of Lower Carboniferous rocks indicates a significantly greater depth of burial than at present. In Northern Ireland, major unconformities correspond to episodes of uplift in the late Westphalian to Early Permian (Variscan Orogeny), Early Jurassic to early Late Cretaceous (Cimmerian), latest Cretaceous to early Palaeogene (Hebridean Uplift), Eocene to late Oligocene and mid-Neogene (Alpine) intervals (Figure 22.7). Structural trap formation is most likely to have occurred during the Variscan, Cimmerian and Alpine orogenic events. Younger strata, which could have covered the early Carboniferous basin, include up to 3000m of Namurian to Westphalian rocks,

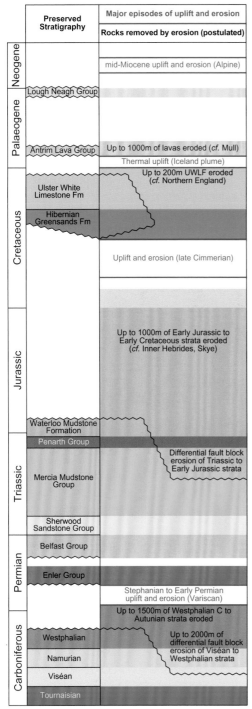

Preserved Stratigraphy	Major episodes of uplift and erosion		
	Rocks removed by erosion (postulated)

Figure 22.7
Northern Ireland Carboniferous to Neogene stratigraphy, showing rocks removed by episodes of uplift and erosion.

3000m of Permian to Lower Jurassic rocks and 1000m of Upper Cretaceous sedimentary and Palaeogene volcanic rocks. In Co. Fermanagh and south Co. Tyrone, it is calculated that up to 1800m of late Viséan and perhaps 1500m of Westphalian strata were removed by erosion (Chapter 8). Estimates of palaeotemperature and palaeogeothermal gradients for the Carboniferous strata from vitrinite reflectance data indicate moderate geothermal gradients (35-50°Ckm^{-1}, mean 44.7°Ckm^{-1} from 4 wells) at the time of peak palaeotemperatures (11). The timing of peak maximum burial and palaeotemperature was probably in the pre-late Mesozoic but could have also preceded the Variscan or Cimmerian episodes of uplift as well. Apatite fission track data from an offshore well west of Ireland, predicts c. 1900m of post-Middle Jurassic to pre-early Palaeogene (late Cimmerian?) uplift. Modelling of onshore apatite fission track data gives estimates of post-early Palaeogene denudation greater than 2500m (12). This last scenario would be favourable for the preservation of hydrocarbons, with generation probably persisting until the Alpine event, allowing hydrocarbons to migrate into structures formed during all three orogenic phases (Table 22.1).

It is likely that Carboniferous source rocks were mature for oil, and wet and dry gas, prior to Variscan uplift. Renewed subsidence in the Permian and Triassic returned the source rocks in most of the basin to the wet gas/dry gas windows. Late Cimmerian uplift possibly suspended hydrocarbon generation but Alpine (mid-Neogene) uplift certainly did.

Permo-Triassic basins

In Northern Ireland, two main areas of thick Permian and Triassic sedimentary rocks are located in the Rathlin and Foyle basins, north of the Highland Border Ridge, and in the Lough Neagh and

Time Interval	Dominant structural processes	Effect on petroleum system
Pliocene	Uplift and erosion.	Loss of hydrocarbons.
Miocene	Alpine compression - uplift and erosion.	Secondary migration and possible seal failure. End gas generation.
Late Cretaceous - early Palaeogene	Extension and minor subsidence prior to Hebridean volcanism.	☀ Final pulse of gas generation? Source rocks depleted.
Late Jurassic - Early Cretaceous	Stable period culminating in mid-Cimmerian uplift and erosion.	Secondary migration into new structural traps. Gas generation suspended?
Permian to Early Jurassic	ENE-WSW extension, normal faulting and subsidence.	☀ Renewed gas generation and migration.
Late Carboniferous to Early Permian	Transpression, and uplift and erosion associated with end-Variscan deformation.	Oil and gas migration, trap formation, seal failure. Gas generation suspended.
Late Carboniferous	Thermal subsidence followed by transtensional and transpressional strike-slip faulting.	☀ Start of oil and gas generation. Continued deposition, burial and reservoir porosity reduction.
Early Carboniferous	Transtensional and transpressional strike-slip faulting followed by N-S extension, normal faulting and subsidence.	Deposition and burial diagenesis of source, reservoir and seal rocks.

Table 22.1
Summary of the history of the Carboniferous petroleum system in Co. Fermanagh.

Larne basins, to the south (Chapter 17) (Figure 22.1). The succession comprises up to 3000m of Permian and Triassic volcanic and sedimentary rocks (Figure 10.2) and includes lithologies that are good potential reservoirs and seals, similar to those in the Morecambe Bay gasfield and in oilfields in the East Irish Sea Basin. The area is poorly explored primarily because of the difficulty in obtaining good quality seismic reflection data through the thick cover of Palaeogene basalt lava (Chapter 14).

In 1971, the Newmill well was drilled in the Larne Basin on the basis of surface structure and nearby offshore seismic data. It encountered good reservoir rocks and seals but no significant hydrocarbons. In 1981 and 1983, the Northern Ireland Government commissioned Vibroseis™ seismic reflection surveys in east Co. Antrim and west of Lough Neagh which demonstrated that sedimentary rocks beneath the basalt lavas could be imaged moderately successfully. Integration of that seismic data with gravity data and the results from deep boreholes sought to produce exploration models with the aim of stimulating further exploration (13, 14). Since then further seismic exploration has been carried out and four (dry) wells have been drilled, two in the Larne Basin and two in the Lough Neagh Basin. Slight gas shows were found in the Ballytober Sandstone Formation in Newmill and Larne No. 2, and oil-staining in Annaghmore No. 1 (Figures 9.2 and 9.5) indicates the presence of hydrocarbons in these basins. No exploration wells have been drilled in the Rathlin Basin where the quality of seismic data is poor although deep boreholes, drilled for mineral and geothermal exploration, provide valuable information about the succession there.

Play Model

The concealed basins of Northern Ireland contain three potential plays. The best-defined plays are within the Permian and Triassic rocks, with secondary potential in the Carboniferous. The Triassic play fairway occurs where reservoir rocks of the Early Triassic Sherwood Sandstone Group are sealed by the Mercia Mudstone Group. The Permian play is prospective where mudstones and evaporites of the Late Permian Belfast Group cap Early Permian Enler Group reservoir rocks. Both plays rely on an underlying Carboniferous source. Limited data are available for Carboniferous source, reservoir and seal rocks in the deeper parts of the basins but this play may have more potential in the western part of the Lough Neagh Basin where they occur at shallower depths.

Reservoir

The Sherwood Sandstone Group is a prolific reservoir in the Morecambe Bay gasfield and occurs in the Rathlin, Foyle, Lough Neagh and Larne basins.

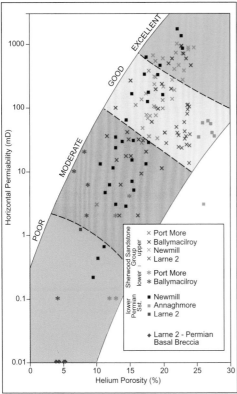

Figure 22.8
Reservoir quality: Porosity - permeability crossplot for Sherwood Sandstone Group and Permian sandstones in Northern Ireland wells (17-21).

Sandstone in the upper part of the Group has the best reservoir parameters based on log and core analyses, with porosities of 15-25% and permeabilities between 10mD and 1000mD (Figure 22.8). The lower part of the Group is more argillaceous and includes a 'silicified' zone with lower poroperm values.

Although sandstone occurs above and below the Late Permian Magnesian Limestone the better potential reservoir target is in Early Permian sandstone which is thicker (up to 450m) and more widely distributed. Sandstone located above the limestone is known only in the Lough Neagh Basin. Measured and calculated porosities and permeabilities in the Early Permian sandstone range up to 23% (average 15%) and 1705mD (average 212mD) respectively in Newmill (Figure 22.8). A particularly clean, relatively well-sorted, orange, fine- to medium-grained sandstone recognised in boreholes at Annaghmore, Ballynamullan, Ballymacilroy and Ballytober, at the top of the Early Permian Sandstone, may represent the marine reworking of fluvial sediments at the onset of the Bakevellia transgression (Chapter 9). In the Larne Basin the Early Permian succession includes aeolian and fluvial sandstone overlying a volcanic and volcaniclastic succession and a basal breccia that has no reservoir potential (Figure 9.5).

Source rocks

The most likely source rocks for these plays are early Carboniferous organic-rich mudstone and oil shale and late Carboniferous coal. However, because the Carboniferous is only proven in the Magilligan borehole in the Foyle Basin (22), source rock properties are

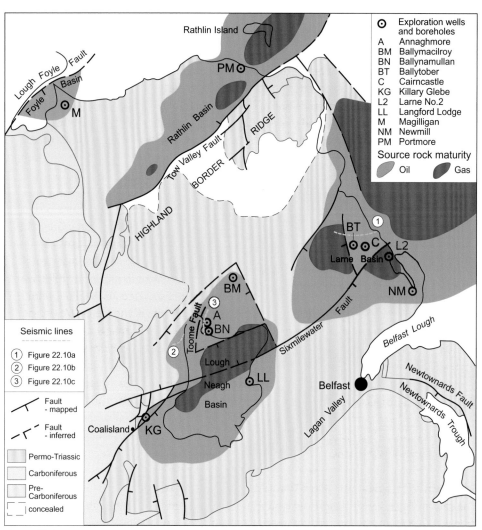

Figure 22.9
Modelled maturity of Carboniferous source rocks in Permo-Triassic basins.

extrapolated from Carboniferous rocks elsewhere in Northern Ireland and Scotland. Namurian and Westphalian coals occur in the Coalisland, Ballycastle and Ayrshire coalfields, and the early Carboniferous source rocks of Co. Fermanagh and south Co. Tyrone could occur beneath the Antrim Plateau.

Coal samples from Coalisland and Ballycastle have TOC contents of 42-66% and contain mainly gas prone organic matter (Figures 22.4 and 22.5). Cannel coal is present in both coalfields and this can typically generate oil as well as gas. The Ballycastle coalfield also contains oil shale with TOC contents in excess of 12%. The early Carboniferous strata may be thinner and more carbonate-rich than in Co. Fermanagh but good TOC values of 1.5-1.8% are recorded from the Rossmore Mudstone Formation in the Lough Neagh Basin. The Early Jurassic Waterloo Mudstone Formation is organic-rich but is immature for hydrocarbons.

Maturity

Vitrinite reflectance values (R_o) from 0.5-0.6, marking the onset of oil generation, have been determined for coal samples from Coalisland, Ballycastle and the Magilligan borehole. If the maturity profiles for these source rocks are extrapolated to depth then source rocks in the basin depocentres probably have R_o values in the oil or gas windows. The oil trace in Carboniferous sandstone in the Magilligan borehole may indicate early oil generation. At present depths and temperatures gas generation is either suspended or confined to the deepest parts of the basins but there may have been several pulses of hydrocarbon generation in the basins since the Carboniferous.

Seals

The Mid- to Late Triassic Mercia Mudstone Group overlies the Sherwood Sandstone Group in the Rathlin, Foyle, Lough Neagh and Larne basins. While the Mercia Mudstone Group is usually between 300-500m thick in boreholes the 951m recorded in Larne No. 2 may be more typical of deeper parts of the Larne and Lough Neagh basins. In the East Irish Sea Basin a thickness of 300m for this Group has been found sufficient to provide an effective seal and significant hydrocarbon accumulations have been discovered at a shallow depth of 600m below seabed (16). Halite enhances the sealing capacity of the Mercia Mudstone Group but is only known to occur in the Larne Basin, south of the Sixmilewater Fault. However, an interpretation of seismic data suggests that there may be halite present north of that fault, both west and east of the Ballytober Horst (Figure 22.10a).

Late Permian mudstones may seal underlying Permian reservoir sandstones although these potential caprocks are variable in thickness and quality, particularly in the Lough Neagh Basin where sandstones are recorded (Annaghmore No. 1 and Ballymacilroy wells). In the Larne area, a thick Late Permian halite should prove an effective seal (Figure 9.5) to the Early Permian sandstone.

Burial history, hydrocarbon generation and trapping mechanisms

The Rathlin, Foyle, Lough Neagh and Larne basins are the preserved remnants of a basin complex that originally extended eastwards through the North Channel, Peel, Solway and East Irish Sea basins into the north of England (16). Permian and Triassic rocks, restricted now to the area of the Antrim Plateau, may have been almost continuous to the offshore basins west of Ireland. Carboniferous strata are preserved in Northern Ireland to the west of the basin complex and, to the east, they are found in the Midland Valley of Scotland.

The evidence from preserved sequences elsewhere in Northern Ireland, the Midland Valley of Scotland and in the Solway Firth suggests that a thick sedimentary pile of variable lithologies was originally deposited during the Carboniferous and then subsequently partly eroded during the Variscan Orogeny. The early Carboniferous succession thins from Co. Fermanagh eastwards to Ayrshire in Scotland. In contrast, the late Carboniferous succession is thicker in Ayrshire, where sedimentary and volcanic rocks up to Westphalian D age are preserved, than in Counties Fermanagh and Tyrone. The Carboniferous succession beneath the Antrim Plateau is expected to be intermediate between that of the two areas described above. An original total thickness of between 2000m and 4000m of Carboniferous strata will have been reduced by uplift and erosion associated with the Variscan Orogeny. The amount of uplift probably diminished to the north and east, although the effects of tectonism are still evident in differential uplift of fault blocks southwest of Lough Neagh (23).

In outcrops on the north side of the Highland Border Ridge, on the margins of the Rathlin and Foyle basins, there is a gap in the sedimentary record between the Tournaisian Roe Valley Group and the late Viséan-early Namurian Ballycastle Group (Table 7.1). South of the Highland Border Ridge the unconformity extends from the early Chadian to the late Asbian (Table 7.4). Although this gap may also occur in the Rathlin and Foyle basins it is possible that later deposition was almost continuous from the late Asbian through to the Westphalian. The Machrahanish Basin in Kintyre has 700m of Namurian to Westphalian clastic sedimentary rocks whilst over 1000m of Carboniferous strata have been interpreted on marine seismic sections west of Rathlin Island in the Malin Sea (24).
A preserved Carboniferous fill of 1500 to 2000m in the deepest parts of the Rathlin Basin is not unrealistic.

Gravity, seismic and well data indicate that Permo-Triassic basins are controlled by NNW-SSE, northwest-southeast and northeast-southwest fault trends (Chapter 17). The Larne and Lough Neagh basins also occupy a northeast-southwest (Midland Valley) belt although they are internally segmented by both Caledonoid structures (e.g. Sixmilewater Fault) and north-south faults (e.g. Ballytober and Toome Bay faults). To the southeast many of the Permo-Triassic basins are preserved as half-grabens bounded by NNW-SSE faults that originated as Caledonian shears (e.g. Portpatrick and Stranraer Basins). The Southern Upland Fault Zone (SUFZ) separates the strongly asymmetrical, eastward thickening Portpatrick basin and the more symmetrical, westward thickening Larne Basin and appears to have acted as a transfer zone during ESE-WNW directed Permo-Triassic extension (16, 26). The Sixmilewater Fault, at the northern margin of the Ballantrae-south Co. Antrim magnetic basement zone (Chapter 19), may be a similar transfer zone en-echelon with the SUFZ onshore in Northern Ireland.

Seismic reflection data is of variable quality, generally poor in the Rathlin-Foyle basins and poor to moderate in the Larne and Lough Neagh basins. The presence of thick, high velocity, high acoustic impedance basalt lava of the Antrim Lava Group, with inter-flow weathering surfaces and an irregular top and bottom surface, degrades the seismic response from the underlying sedimentary rocks. The most important reflectors are the Top Sherwood Sandstone Group (SSG) and Top Magnesian Limestone (ML) which define the structure at the top of the main reservoir intervals. In the Rathlin Basin, because the Magnesian Limestone is not developed and the Top SSG reflector produces a small acoustic contrast, structure definition is poor. West of Lough Neagh reflector quality is moderate but structure mapping is hindered by the prevalence of faulting. North of Lough Neagh two-way time (TWT) maps on Top SSG and Top ML can be constructed in the vicinity of Toome but reflector quality diminishes to the north and east.

The Larne Basin is divided by the Sixmilewater Fault with the thickest Permo-Triassic section in the Larne area (Figure 22.9). Both the Magnesian Limestone to Sherwood Sandstone Group interval and the Mercia Mudstone Group appear to thicken northwards towards the Sixmilewater Fault. The presence of Permian halite and possible thickening of the Sherwood Sandstone Group causes the increase in thickness of the lower interval. The better developed thickening of the Mercia Mudstone Group is confirmed by detailed palynological studies on well sections either side of faults and is the result of syn-depositional Late Triassic extension (27, 28). Evidence for Early to Mid-Triassic extension is more equivocal although seismic data show that the Sherwood Sandstone Group thickens across the Ballytober Fault (Figure 22.10a). The structure north of the Sixmilewater Fault is dominated by the north-south trending Ballytober Horst, mapped at both Top SSG and Top ML level. To the east the reflectors dip and step down towards the

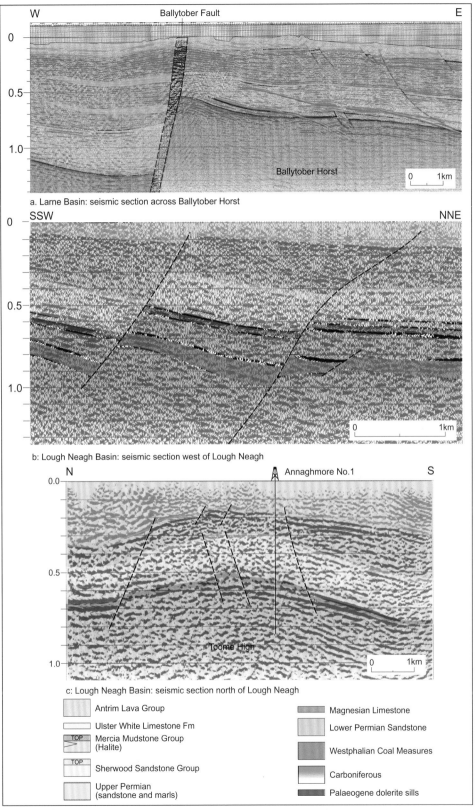

W   Ballytober Fault   E

0

0.5

1.0

Ballytober Horst

0   1km

a. Larne Basin: seismic section across Ballytober Horst

SSW   NNE

0

0.5

1.0

0   1km

b: Lough Neagh Basin: seismic section west of Lough Neagh

N   Annaghmore No.1   S

0.0

0.5

1.0

Toome High

0   1km

c: Lough Neagh Basin: seismic section north of Lough Neagh

Antrim Lava Group

Ulster White Limestone Fm

TOP Mercia Mudstone Group (Halite)

TOP Sherwood Sandstone Group

Upper Permian (sandstone and marls)

Magnesian Limestone

Lower Permian Sandstone

Westphalian Coal Measures

Carboniferous

Palaeogene dolerite sills

Figure 22.10
Interpreted seismic sections across the Larne and Lough Neagh basins.

Time Interval	Dominant structural processes	Effect on petroleum system
Pliocene	Uplift and erosion.	Hydrocarbon generation suspended except in deepest parts of basins. SSG reservoir partly flushed by meteoric water circulation.
Miocene	Alpine compression, uplift and erosion.	Pop-up structural traps, secondary migration and possible seal failure and leakage.
Oligocene	Mid-Oligocene extension and localised subsidence.	☀ Oil and gas generation. Localised fault-controlled subsidence in Lough Neagh and Rathlin basins.
Late Cretaceous - early Palaeogene	Extension and thermal doming prior to Hebridean volcanism, followed by subsidence.	☀ Oil and gas generation. Burial and heat pulse associated with basalt lava pile.
Late Jurassic - Early Cretaceous	Stable period culminating in mid-Cimmerian uplift and erosion.	Migration into new and existing structural traps. Gas generation suspended?
Permian to Early Jurassic	ENE-WSW extension, normal faulting and subsidence.	☀ Oil and gas generation. Deposition of reservoir and seal rocks
End Carboniferous	Transpression, and uplift and erosion associated with end-Variscan deformation.	Trap formation and early oil migration. Disruption of hydrocarbon generation.
Late Carboniferous	Thermal subsidence followed by transtensional and transpressional strike-slip faulting.	● Start of oil generation. Continued deposition and burial of source rocks including coals.
Early Carboniferous	Transtensional and transpressional strike-slip faulting followed by N-S extension, normal faulting and subsidence.	Deposition and burial diagenesis of source rocks.

Table 22.2
Summary of the history of the Permo-Triassic petroleum system in Northern Ireland

(offshore) depocentre whereas on the west it is bounded by the Ballytober Fault with a large downthrow to the west. The dry Ballytober No. 1 well tested a 3-way dip closure, with a large areal extent but small vertical closure, bounded by the Ballytober Fault. Both the Sherwood Sandstone and Mercia Mudstone groups are relatively thin and the former has poor reservoir quality. The horst acted as a positive structural element during the Permian and Triassic.

Trapping styles

Seismic data from the Lough Neagh and Larne basins give an indication of their potential trapping styles. High quality offshore seismic from the Larne and Portpatrick basins also provides better images of potential structural targets at both Top SSG and Top Lower Permian Sandstone levels (16). Four-way dip closures on the footwalls of tilted fault blocks are prime targets, although combined dip/fault closures are more common (Figures 22.10a and 22.10b). Many of the faults appear to have had a polyphase history of movement in both extensional and compressional stress regimes, from the early Carboniferous to the Miocene. Reactivation may result in minor modification of the tilted fault blocks, such as

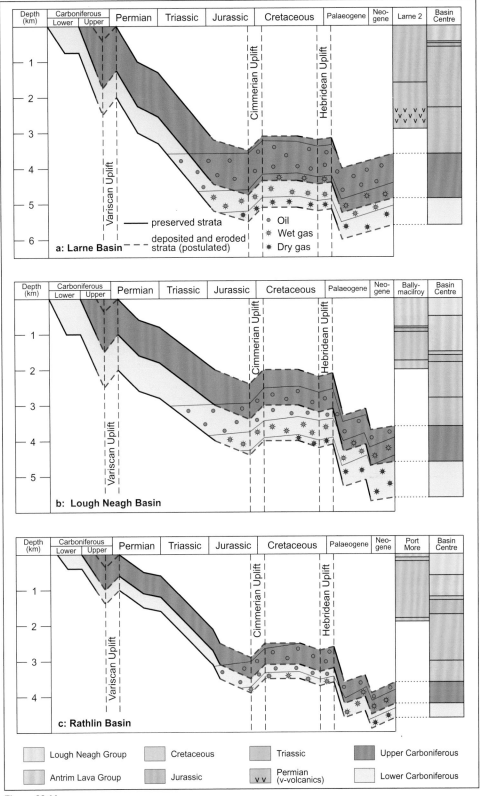

Figure 22.11
Burial history plots for three basins showing modelled generation of oil and gas from Carboniferous source rocks.

footwall uplift and drag, or the formation of more obvious inversion structures (Figure 22.10c). The latter often have the appearance of a flower structure and may reflect transpressional movement. Additional traps recognised offshore are rollover anticlines in the hanging-walls of listric faults, such as the one targeted by the Laggantulloch well in the Portpatrick Basin. Similar structural settings may exist onshore, for example, adjacent to the Toome Bay or Ballytober faults, although seismic data in these areas is either absent or of poor quality.

Although the internal structure of the Rathlin Basin is largely unknown because of poor quality seismic data, geological models based on analogue basins and the succession in the Port More borehole (Figure 10.2) envisage a Permo-Triassic half-graben developing against the Tow Valley Fault. Later movement on transfer faults would form tilted fault blocks and targets include both structural closures and combined stratigraphical/structural traps within the alluvial fan conglomerate-sandstone sequence.

There is little indication of potential trapping styles within the Carboniferous because it is poorly imaged in the Larne Basin. The 1981 and 1983 seismic surveys west of Lough Neagh indicate the presence of small, tilted fault blocks (29, 30) (Figure 22.10b).

The major risks in the Permo-Triassic exploration plays in Northern Ireland are:
- Absence or immaturity of source rocks
- Trap formation after generation and expulsion of hydrocarbons from source
- Breach of trap and leakage of hydrocarbons

Models of the burial history of the different basins are shown in Figure 22.11. They utilise stratigraphical records from deep boreholes and estimates of the possible thickness of strata removed by erosion based on exposed sequences in Northern Ireland and adjacent areas. The estimates of uplift are comparable with those derived from apatite fission track, vitrinite reflectance, density and sonic velocity data. Interpretation of these data is complicated by a lack of knowledge of palaeogeothermal gradients and by the effects of uplift and subsidence since the beginning of the Carboniferous.

If good quality Carboniferous source rocks are present in the deepest parts of the Rathlin, Lough Neagh and Larne basins then subsidence plots indicate that they should have generated gas. Prolonged periods of basin subsidence led to increasing source rock maturation and the generation of hydrocarbons. Intervening tectonic episodes were associated with the formation of structural traps, primary and secondary migration of oil and gas, and uplift leading to the interruption of hydrocarbons generation (Table 22.2).

After the last period of subsidence associated with the Antrim Lava Group subsequent tectonic episodes may have downgraded the prospectivity of all basins by breaching traps and allowing leakage of hydrocarbons to the surface. In addition, it is possible that hydrocarbons may have been flushed from the Sherwood Sandstone Group reservoir by an influx of meteoric water (31). Oxygen isotope data indicates that formation water from those rocks in the Ballymacilroy and Larne No. 2 boreholes is almost identical to that of present-day meteoric water (17). However, similar effects have been recorded in other sedimentary basins with productive hydrocarbon systems, so it does not necessarily suggest that hydrocarbons have been driven out of the reservoirs.

References

1) Department of Enterprise, Trade and Investment. 2000. *Minerals and Petroleum Exploration and Development in Northern Ireland*, 20-25. The Stationery Office Ltd., Belfast.

2) Clayton, G., Haughey, N., Sevastopulu, G. D. and Burnett, R. D. 1989. Thermal maturation levels in the Devonian and Carboniferous rocks in Ireland. *Geological Survey of Ireland Special Publication.*

3) Collins, A. G. 1984. Organic geochemistry of 12 Carboniferous field samples from Northern Ireland. *Robertson Research International Ltd. Report No. 5466P/D.*

4) G. A. P. S. 1986. Correlation of Three Potential Reservoir Sandstones, Lough Allen Basin, Republic of Ireland and Northern Ireland. *G. A. P. S. Report No. J555-2 for Aran Energy plc.*

5) Priority Oil and Gas LLC. 1998. Mullaghmore Formation: Thin Sections and Descriptions. *Priority Oil and Gas LLC Proprietary Report.*

6) Parnell, J. 1991. Hydrocarbon potential of Northern Ireland: Part II. Reservoir potential of the Carboniferous. *Journal of Petroleum Geology*, **14**, 143-60.

7) Dow, W. G. 1997. Geochemical analysis of samples from NW Carboniferous Basin, Northern Ireland. *DGSI Report for Priority Oil and Gas LLC.*

8) Parnell, J. 1991. Hydrocarbon potential of Northern Ireland: Part I. Burial histories and source rock potential. *Journal of Petroleum Geology*, **14**, 65-78.

9) Geochem 1982. Partial geochemical evaluation of a suite of Carboniferous outcrop and core samples from Northern Ireland.

10) Paleochem. 1983. Organic geochemical analyses of Lower Palaeozoic mudrocks from Northern Ireland. Special Report No. 4.

11) Corcoran, D. V. and Clayton, G. 2001. Interpretation of vitrinite reflectance profiles in sedimentary basins, onshore and offshore Ireland. *In:* Shannon, P. M., Haughton, P. W. and Corcoran, D. V. (eds.). *The Petroleum Geology of Ireland's Offshore Basins.* Special Publication of the Geological Society, London, **188**, 61-90.

12) Allen, P. A., Bennett, S. D., Cunningham, M. J. M., Carter, A., Gallagher, K., Lazzaretti, E., Galewsky, J., Densmore, A. L., Phillips, W. E. A., Naylor, D. and Hach, C. S. 2002. The post-Variscan thermal and denudation history of Ireland. *In:* Doré, A. G., Cartwright, J. A., Stoker, M. S., Turner, J. P., and White, N. (eds.). *Exhumation of the North Atlantic Margin: Timing, Mechanisms and Implications for Petroleum Exploration.* Special Publication of the Geological Society, London, **196**, 371-99.

13) Illing, L. V. and Griffith, A. E. 1986. Gas prospects in the 'Midland Valley' of Northern Ireland. *In:* Brooks, J., Goff, J. C. and Van Hoorn, B. (eds.). *Habitat of Palaeozoic Gas in NW Europe.* Special Publication of the Geological Society, London, **23**, 73-84.

14) Robertson Research International Ltd. 1987. A review of the hydrocarbon potential of Northern Ireland: A fresh approach. *Robertson Research International Ltd for Department of Economic Development.*

15) Jackson, D. I., Johnson, H. and Smith, N. J. P. 1997. Stratigraphical relationships and a revised lithostratigraphical nomenclature for the Carboniferous, Permian and Triassic rocks of the offshore East Irish Sea Basin. *In:* Meadows, N. S., Trueblood, S. P., Hardman, M. and Cowan, G. (eds.). *Petroleum Geology of the Irish Sea and Adjacent Areas.* Special Publication of the Geological Society, London, **124**, 11-32.

16) Maddox, S. J., Blow, R. A. and O'Brien, S. R. 1997. The geology and hydrocarbon prospectivity of the North Channel Basin. *In:* Meadows, N. S., Trueblood, S. P., Hardman, M. and Cowan, G. (eds.). *Petroleum Geology of the Irish Sea and Adjacent Area.* Special Publication of the Geological Society, London, **124**, 95-111.

17) Burgess, W. G. 1979. Hydrogeological studies in the Ballymacilroy borehole, Co. Antrim, to investigate the geothermal potential of the Permo-Triassic Sandstones. *Report of the Institute of Geological Sciences, WD/ST/79/17.* Wallingford.

18) Marathon Petroleum U.K. Ltd. and Shell U.K. Ltd. 1971. Newmill No. 1 Final Well Report.

19) Parnell, J. 1992. Hydrocarbon potential of Northern Ireland: Part III. Reservoir potential of the Permo-Triassic. *Journal of Petroleum Geology*, **15**, 51-70.

20) Penn, I. E. 1981. Larne No. 2 Geological well completion report. *Report of the Institute of Geological Sciences, 81/6.* Keyworth.

21) Wilson, H. E. and Manning, P. I. 1978. *Geology of the Causeway Coast.* Memoir of the Geological Survey of Northern Ireland, Sheet 7 (Northern Ireland).

22) Bazley, R. A. B., Brandon, A. and Arthurs, J. W. 1997. *Geology of the country around Limavady and Londonderry.* Geological Survey of Northern Ireland. Technical Report GSNI/97/1.

23) Geological Survey of Northern Ireland 1960. Dungannon, Northern Ireland Sheet 35. Solid Geology. 1:63,360 (Southampton: Ordnance Survey for the Geological Survey of Northern Ireland).

24) Fyfe, J. A., Long, D. and Evans, D. 1993. *United Kingdom offshore regional report: the geology of the Malin-Hebrides sea area.* London: HMSO for the British Geological Survey.

25) Anderson, T. B., Parnell, J. P. and Ruffell, A. H. 1995. Influence of basement on the geometry of Permo-Triassic basins in the northwest British Isles. *In:* Boldy, S. A. R. (ed.). *Permian and Triassic rifting in Northwest Europe.* Special Publication of the Geological Society, London, **91**, 103-22.

26) Shelton, R. 1997. Tectonic evolution of the Larne Basin. *In:* Meadows, N. S., Trueblood, S. P., Hardman, M. and Cowan, G. (eds.). *Petroleum Geology of the Irish Sea and Adjacent Areas,* Special Publication of the Geological Society, London, **124**, 113-33.

27) Ruffell, A. and Shelton, R. 1999. The control of sedimentary facies by climate during phases of crustal extension: examples from the Triassic of onshore and offshore England and Northern Ireland. *Journal of the Geological Society, London*, **156**, 779-89.

28) Warrington, G. 1995. The Permian, Triassic and Jurassic in Northern Ireland: A palynological study with special reference to the hydrocarbon prospectivity of the Larne-Lough Neagh Basin. *Geological Survey of Northern Ireland. Technical Report GSNI/95/7.*

29) Illing, L. V. 1982. Vibroseis Survey in Northern Ireland, November–December 1981: a geological assessment of its significance in the exploration for petroleum. *Geological Survey of Northern Ireland. Open File Report No. 66.*

30) Papworth, T. P. 1983. East Tyrone and North Armagh Seismic Survey. *Geominerals Exploration Inc. Report for Geological Survey of Northern Ireland.*

31) Bennett, J. R. P. 1983. The sedimentary basins in Northern Ireland. *Institute of Geological Sciences.*

Chapter 23

Geohazards

M. R. COOPER

Introduction

Geological hazards or geohazards is the study of the interaction of physical Earth processes with people and environments at different scales. Geohazards represent a source of danger from the ground conditions and may pose a risk to human health and/or the environment with associated cost and disruption. They very often represent a consequence of an adverse combination of ground conditions.

The public's understanding of the implications of adverse ground conditions on the stability of their property, with the associated impact on property values, is growing. Consequently, there is an increasing demand from the public and commercial interests for information about geohazards to address and understand the interaction between land use and the environment. There is therefore an increasing need for detailed data that is related to the identification and assessment of potential geological hazards in Northern Ireland. These datasets will be used to highlight areas that require further study and help quantify risk associated with development. Geohazards and their potential impact can be incorporated into procedures for land use planning and to help ensure sustainable development in a safer environment.

Subsidence

The ground people stand on, and which supports our buildings and roads, is mostly stable. However, each year millions of pounds is spent repairing the damage caused by subsidence of the ground surface. Relatively small, differential movement of the ground has the capacity to cause problems to man-made structures such as buildings, or may cause unevenness or disintegration of roads and disruption to water, electricity and sewage systems. Commonly, the geological conditions that cause the problem are related to the superficial deposits at a particular site and only rarely may the cause be attributed to natural conditions in the bedrock geology.

Compressible Ground

In Northern Ireland, the most commonly occurring compressible materials include deposits of peat and lacustrine clay and, in low-lying parts of Belfast and Londonderry, estuarine clay referred to as 'sleech' (Figure 18.4). All of these materials can allow subsidence if foundations are inadequate, or if through time they fail. A classic example of the effect of subsidence due to failure of inadequate foundations and to the presence of the sleech is the leaning Albert Clock Tower in Belfast [J342 745] (Photograph 1). Remedial action has stabilised the tower and prevented an increase in the angle of lean which reached a maximum of 1°, equivalent to 0.77m of movement from the vertical (Doran Consulting, pers. comm, 2003). In the Belfast area (Figure 18.2), the distribution of the sleech is representative of the former extent of the estuary of the River Lagan and Belfast Lough in early post-glacial times. It is over 15m thick in the docks area of the city and 3-10m in the commercial and inner city areas (1). Other examples of superficial deposits that are naturally soft or loose or prone to flow, and as such are compressible, include alluvial deposits associated with river floodplains, windblown sand, and deposits of fluvioglacial sand and gravel.

Geotechnical information on the distribution, thickness, and physical and chemical properties of superficial deposits and bedrock is essential at the earliest planning stage of a development. Datasets held by the Geological Survey of Northern Ireland contain relevant geological and site-specific information on ground conditions. This includes geological maps at a variety of scales and associated literature, in excess of 40,000 records of boreholes and trial pits in site investigation reports with location maps and the results of geotechnical testing of samples.

Underground cavities

All underground cavities regardless of whether they are natural or man-made pose a potential danger. In the natural environment, because the development of such features is gauged on geological timescales, underground cavities may appear stable. However, in all cases they are evolving and subtle, long-term, changes to their stability may eventually cause collapse and surface subsidence. It is therefore important to understand the processes that lead to the formation of such voids combined with data on their distribution, size, depth below ground level and the bedrock type.

Photograph 1
The Albert Clock, Belfast.

Natural cavities, including caves and swallow holes, are common where there is limestone bedrock, for instance in Co. Fermanagh (Carboniferous) and in Co. Antrim (Cretaceous). Cave systems and surface karst pavements are developed in the outcrop of the Carboniferous Dartry Limestone Formation in Co. Fermanagh (2). Solution of the limestone by acidic water led to the formation of the caves that are still partially utilised by the existing river network. Age dating of flowstone indicates that the caves were mature during the Pleistocene when the calcite was deposited. The most spectacular cave system in Co. Fermanagh is accessed *(inter alia)* at Marble Arch [H121 344] but the underground hydrological network extends for at least 10km to the west towards Shannon Pot in Co. Cavan. In Co. Antrim, cave systems developed in the Cretaceous Ulster White Limestone Formation at the margins of the Antrim Plateau. The most recent cave systems were initiated during post-glacial (Holocene) times and are still forming (3, 4).

Since the arrival of man in Ireland some 9000 years ago the impact of his exploitation of its natural resources has helped shape our present-day landscape. The exploitation of natural resources by underground mining commenced in Northern Ireland about 200 years ago and left a legacy of surface instability above disused mine workings for coal and other minerals. The existence of abandoned mine workings is a serious problem in relation to planning, development and environmental protection. The Geological Survey of Northern Ireland Abandoned Mines Database has information on the location of over 2000 abandoned shafts and adits, the commodity extracted and plans of some of the underground workings (Chapter 21).

Between 1853 and 1958, underground extraction of salt from the Triassic Mercia Mudstone Group in the Carrickfergus area of Co. Antrim made use of the pillar and stall method but later resorted to uncontrolled brining. The resulting caverns vary in size and stability, and many have flooded since the closure of the mines. Progressive collapse of those workings and upward migration of voids has since occurred in a number of them. In 1990 the collapse of pillars at a depth of about 100m in the Tennant Salt Mine [J432 893] near Carrickfergus (5), created an elliptical depression some 8m deep and about 200 x 170m that eventually flooded (Photograph 2). Similarly the Maidenmount Salt Mine collapsed in 2001 (Photograph 3).

Slope stability

Slope stability is a significant issue in Northern Ireland particularly at the margins of the Antrim Plateau. An area of at least 100km² is located on sites of historical landslip and is therefore regarded as potentially unstable because of the risk of further slip (6). Much of the instability occurs naturally but in some cases may be caused or exacerbated by the activities of man. An assessment of ground stability is therefore imperative for such areas that are to be designated for development, if it is suspected that mass movement is a potential hazard.

Landslides

The form, extent and status of landslides depends on factors such as the solid and superficial geology, slope angle, hydrology, hydrogeology and rainfall. As an exacerbating factor, the activities of man can change stable natural relationships between combinations of these factors and thereby promote slope instability.

The margins of the Antrim Plateau often display dormant multiple, large-scale, deep-seated, mainly rotational slumping (7). The evolution of the landslide complexes is related to the stratigraphic succession comprising competent cliff-forming basalt lava and chalk overlying the incompetent and impervious Jurassic Waterloo Mudstone Formation and

Photograph 2
The surface expression caused by the underground collapse of the Tennant Salt Mine [J432 893], 2.6km northeast of Carrickfergus, Co. Antrim. Note the development of concentric tension cracks around the central void.

Photograph 3
The surface expression caused by the collapse of the Maidenmount Salt Mine [J390 901], 3.5km northwest of Carrickfergus, Co. Antrim. Note the absence of concentric tension cracks suggesting that the collapse resembles a crown hole.

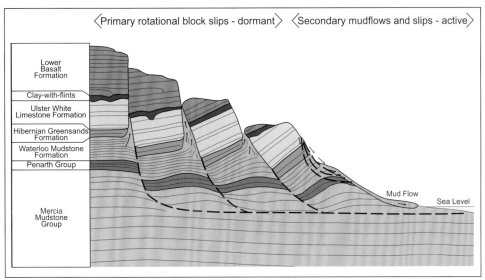

Figure 23.1
Generalised landslip complex associated with the Antrim Plateau escarpment.

Triassic Penarth and Mercia Mudstone groups (Figure 23.1). Undercutting of the basalt and chalk by removal of the underlying incompetent strata by the action of ice sheets led to slumping during and soon after the last Ice Age. Where present, the highly permeable Hibernian Greensands Formation also plays an important role in the landslip process. Movement took place on a vertical or steeply inclined composite surface in the basalt and chalk but assumed a listric form in the underlying high plasticity mudstones. Nevertheless,

Photograph 4
Multiple, large-scale, deep-seated, mainly rotational slumped blocks of white Cretaceous chalk and black basalt lavas. Garron Point [D312 242], 6.5km north of Carnlough, Co. Antrim.

Photograph 5
Multiple landslip of masses of basalt lava. Binevenagh [C692 302], 7km north of Limavady, Co. Londonderry.

Photograph 6
Mud slides and flows of liquefied Jurassic mudstone. Minnis North [D339 137], 3.25km southeast of Glenarm, Co. Antrim.

the impact of secondary activity such as rock falls, shallow slumps and translational slides and mudflows, some triggered by man-made excavations, is still evident.

The sense of backwards rotation on the spectacular masses at Garron Point in Co. Antrim is emphasised by the disposition of the contact between the black basalt and white chalk (Photograph 4). At the escarpment edge their contact is almost horizontal but in the slumped blocks it is steeply inclined into the hillside. Other examples occur in Co. Antrim at White Park Bay (8) and along the coast south of Glenarm (9, 10) where the area of rotational landslip is at least 1.5km wide, in Co. Londonderry at Binevenagh [C692 302] north of Limavady (Photograph 5) (11) and at Benbradagh [C722 113].

Southeast of Glenarm at Minnis North [D339 137], mud slides and flows of liquefied Jurassic mudstone periodically cascade down-slope in well-defined and deeply incised chutes (10). Remedial measures including retaining walls and under-road drainage are occasionally overwhelmed by the quantities of mud involved in the flows (Photograph 6).

Rock falls and accumulations of block scree are associated with cliffs and are promoted by rainfall, frost action and the growth of roots. The majority of scree accumulations are associated with cliffs around the Antrim Plateau, for example Fair Head in north Co. Antrim (12). In Co. Fermanagh, cliffs of Carboniferous limestone produce scree consisting of small blocks while early Namurian sandstone forming the summit cliffs on the north face of Cuilcagh Mountain (13) produce large accumulations of active block scree above Lough Atona [H110 293]. However, in most cases the scree is stabilised by vegetation.

Erosion, deposition and flooding
Rivers channel excess water from catchment areas and drain both the land surface and sub-surface aquifers. In the upper reaches of most catchment areas the rivers are eroding their bed and banks, transporting the material downstream to be redeposited on flood plains. All flood plains in Northern Ireland have developed in post-glacial times and are associated

Photograph 6
Flooding of the River Strule in 1987. Newtownstewart, Co. Tyrone.

with areas of alluvium. In upland regions such as the Sperrin Mountains, alluvial flood plains are typically narrow and are confined by the steep sides of valleys. In contrast, rivers such as the Bann develop extensive flood plains up to 2km wide such as west of Ballymoney in Co. Antrim.

The incidence of severe flooding in many parts of the British Isles is becoming more frequent (Photograph 7). While this is often blamed on climate change there is also a consequence of improving drainage in upland catchment areas, increased ground cover through urbanisation and over-compaction of soils in agricultural land. Whatever the cause or causes, urban development on flood plains in major cities is a potentially intractable problem.

At coastal locations the impact of even small rises in sea level will be significant for a large proportion of the world's population. It would also threaten the integrity of strands, dune systems, estuaries and tidal flats and, as in early post-glacial times, could undermine cliff sections possibly causing renewed landslides, increased erosion and rock falls around the coast of Northern Ireland.

References
1) Geological Survey of Northern Ireland, 1971. Special Engineering Geology Sheet. Solid and Drift. (Reprinted 1984). 1:21,120. (Keyworth, Nottingham; British Geological Survey).

2) Jones, G. Ll., Burns, G., Fogg, T. and Kelly, J. G. 1997. *The caves of Fermanagh and Cavan*. The Lough Nilly Press, Florencecourt, Co. Fermanagh, Northern Ireland.

3) Barnes, S., 1999. Karstic groundwater flow characteristics in the Cretaceous Chalk aquifer, Northern Ireland. Quarterly Journal of Engineering Geology, **32**, 55-68.

4) Kelly, J. G., Fogg, T. and Enlander I., 1996. Holocene and Tertiary karstification in the Ulster White Limestone Formation (Cretaceous) of the Garron area, County Antrim, Northern Ireland. Cave and Karst Science, **23 (3)**, 93-100.

5) Griffith, A. E. 1991. Tennant's ills. *Ground Engineering*, November.

6) Manning, P. I., Robbie, J. A. and Wilson, H. E. 1970. Geology of Belfast and the Lagan Valley. *Memoir of the Geological Survey of Northern Ireland*. Sheet 36 (Northern Ireland).

7) Forster, A. 1998. The assessment of slope instability for land use planning: A case study on the northeast Antrim coast. *British Geological Survey Technical Report WN/98/8*. (Keyworth, Nottingham).

8) Wilson, H. E., and Manning, P. I., 1978. Geology of the Causeway Coast. *Memoir of the Geological Survey of Northern Ireland*, Sheet 7, HMSO, Belfast.

9) Carney, J. N., 1974. A photo-interpretation of mass movement features along the Antrim Coast of Northern Ireland. *British Geological Survey Technical Report WN/EG/74/13*.

10) Hutchinson, J. N., Prior, D. B. and Stephens, N., 1974. Potentially dangerous surges in an Antrim mudslide. *Quarterly Journal of Engineering Geology*, **7**, 363-76.

11) Bazley, R. A. B., Brandon, A., and Arthurs, J. W., 1997. Geology of the country around Limavady and Londonderry. *Geological Survey of Northern Ireland Technical Report GSNI/97/1*.

12) Geological Survey of Northern Ireland 2002. Ballycastle, Northern Ireland Sheet 8. Solid Geology (second edition). 1:50,000. (Keyworth, Nottingham: British Geological Survey).

13) Geological Survey of Northern Ireland 1991. Derrygonnelly, Northern Ireland Sheet 44, 56 and 43. Solid Geology. 1:50,000. (Keyworth, Nottingham: British Geological Survey).

Index

A

Abandoned Mines Database 293
accretion 7, 53, 59
accretionary prism 5, 7, 26, 43, 55
actinolite 23
Acton Inlier 44, 46, 49
aeolian 134, 136, 161, 281
aeromagnetic anomaly 236, 241
Aeronian 39, 40
agglomerate 170, 181, 188, 190, 195
aggregate 90, 256, 267, 268
Aghafad 36
Aghintain Fault 263
Aghnadarragh 216-218
Aghnadarragh Interstadial 216
Aghyaran Formation 20
Agivey 200, 201, 203
Agnew's Hill 176, 265
Ailsa Craig 216
air-fall ash 164
Albert Clock Tower 291
albite 22, 23
alder 214, 223
Alderwood Mudstone Formation 102
algal laminated 96, 100
Alla Glen Limestone Member 19
alluvial fan 69, 77, 115, 122, 127, 141, 288
alluvial gold 256, 261
alluvial plain 79, 115, 122, 298
Alpine Orogeny 278
Altachuile Breccia 157
Altagoan Bridge 86
Altagoan Formation 86, 110
Altalacky River 86
Altmore Anticline 20, 22
Altmore Formation 21
Altvenagh 101
aluminium 264
amber 264
ammonite 141, 146-148, 153, 154, 157, 196
ammonoid 83, 94, 99, 100
amphibolite 11, 12, 20, 23, 27
amygdales 172, 263
andesite 75, 194, 260, 261
Anglesey 192

Anglesey Mountain 191
anhydrite 86, 128, 131, 136, 266
Anisian 136, 138, 142
Annacramph 92
Annagher Coal 269
Annaghmore 280, 281, 283
Anneeter Beg 201
anorthosite 182
antiform 12
antimony 259
Antrim 173
Antrim Lava Group 163, 168, 170, 192, 194, 201,
    205, 209, 229, 230, 243, 244, 251, 263, 264, 265,
    268, 284, 288
Antrim Plateau 125, 138, 145, 150, 161, 168, 170, 176,
    177, 194, 205, 206, 219, 220, 231, 235, 240, 247,
    251, 265, 270, 273, 282, 283, 293, 297
Antrim-Down Lineament 235, 241-243
Antrim-Galway Line 237, 240
apatite fission track 279, 288
aplites 189
aquifer potential 252
aquifers 249, 250, 252-254, 297
Ardglass 62, 193
Ardglass Formation 53
Ards Peninsula 49, 65, 242, 251
Arenig 3, 26, 30, 33, 260
arenite 14, 16, 51, 53, 75
Argyll Group 12, 13, 14, 16, 20
Armagh 90, 113, 114, 130, 134, 268
Armagh Group 90, 93, 103, 113, 121
Armoy 242, 243
Armoy Moraine 220
Arnsbergian 114, 121
Arran 237
arrowheads 224,
arsenic 257
arsenopyrite 259
arthropod 136
Artigarvan 16
Arundian 84, 98, 102, 105, 108, 111, 112, 119
Asbian 87, 90, 93, 99, 100, 103, 110, 112, 114, 120, 284
ash cones 170
ash-flow tuff 163
Ashgill 34, 35, 49
Atlantic Canada 79
Atlantic Ocean 207
Atlantic Period 224

Belfast Group 125, 131, 281

Belfast Harbour Evaporite Formation 126

Belfast Lough 50, 110, 207, 225, 231, 292

Belfast Marls Member 153

Belhavel Fault 120

Bellaghy 211

Bellanaleck quarry 98

Bellavally Formation 100, 113, 121

Belleek 98

Belleek Pottery 12, 267

Belmore Mountain 100

Belshaw's quarry 165

Benbradagh 297

Benbulben Shale Formation 98, 102, 103, 108, 112, 274-278

Benburb 102, 103, 114, 214

bentonite 36, 41, 46, 53, 101, 114

Beragh 211

Beragh 32

Bernisk Glen 219

beryl 186, 264

Bessbrook 65

Big Dog 274-277

Bin Mountain Sandstone Formation 105, 110

Binevenagh 177, 219, 297

Binnagapple Sill 196

Binnawooda Spring 105

biotite 12, 17, 18, 20, 22, 23, 32, 186, 187

biotitite 62

bioturbated 83, 107, 146, 155

birch 222

Birkhill Shale Formation 46, 48

bisaccate pollen 201

bismuth 259

bivalves 35, 36, 86, 103, 126, 127, 130, 138-141, 146-148, 153, 154, 203, 216, 223

Black Head 172

Black Rock 28, 65

blackband ironstone 265

Blackstones Bank 168

Blackwater Limestone Formation 103

Blaney 98

block scree 297

Bloody Bridge 187

boehmite 265

Boheeshane Chalk Member 155, 157

Bonds Glen Limestone Member 19

Bonnety Bush 30, 265

Boreal 216, 222-224

Bouguer anomaly 180, 207, 228, 235, 236

Bouguer gravity 207

boundstone 104

Bovevagh Till 216

brachiopods 34, 35, 36, 83, 92, 93, 98, 101, 103, 106, 148, 153, 154, 155, 159

brickclay 268

bricks 92

Brigantian 82, 83, 88, 90, 93, 100, 102, 114

brining 293

Briscloonagh Sandstone 114

Bristol Channel 168

Brockley 225

Brookeborough Diamond 264

Broughderg 30

Brougher Mountain 88

Broughshane 177

bryozoa 35, 130

Bundoran Shale Formation 98, 102, 103, 105, 106, 111, 274, 278

burial history 278

Burrelian 34

burrows 102, 106, 146

Butterlope Glen 14, 16, 219

by-pass quarry 39

C

calcrete 71, 84, 104, 115

calcsilicate 181, 195, 196

caldera 181, 187, 190, 245

Caledonian 3, 5, 9, 12, 22, 23, 58, 61, 67, 117, 125, 199, 205-207, 209, 284

Caledonian Orogeny 12, 69, 257

Caledonides 1, 7, 41

Cam Lough 189

Cam Lough quarry 65, 189

Cambrian 5

Camderry Member 101

Camlough Breccias 189

Camlough Fault 189

Campanian 152, 155, 156, 165

Cappagh quarry 73

Caradoc 33, 34, 49

carbonate platform 114

Carboniferous 9, 20, 70, 77, 79-115, 117, 125, 134-145, 150, 176, 181, 193, 196, 199, 205-207, 216, 231, 235, 236, 241, 243-245, 247, 251, 252, 257, 262,

Cushendall Porphyry 77

Cushendun 33, 74, 223, 237, 240, 242, 244

Cushendun Formation 74

Cushendun Granodiorite 33, 244

Cushleake Mountain 33

cyanobacterial 96, 104

D

dacite 28, 29, 31, 33, 194

Dalradian 5, 9, 12, 14, 16, 20, 22, 74, 82, 84, 88, 96, 104, 111, 133, 134, 150, 152, 156, 176, 193, 216, 231, 235, 237, 241, 243, 244, 251, 257, 259, 260, 262, 264, 267

Dalradian Supergroup 9, 12, 23, 257, 260, 262, 263

Danesfort 225

Danian 166

Dart Formation 16

Dartry Limestone Formation 98, 99, 102, 112, 121, 293

debris flow 218

Dechommet 265

deglaciation 218

delta 112, 114, 216, 275

dendrochronology 212

density 152, 180, 227, 288

Dergvone Shale Formation 101, 114

Derraghadoan quarry 94

Derreens Limestone Member 100

Derry Coal 269

Derrygonnelly 97, 98, 99, 111

Derryinver 199, 203

Derryloran Grit Formation 93, 267

Derrynoose Lead Mine 262

Derryvore 101

Derryvree 216, 217

Desertcreat Group 34

Desertmartin Limestone Formation 87

desiccation cracks 71, 74, 88, 134, 136, 139, 141

Devlin's quarry 164

Devonian 3, 5, 36, 41, 61, 69-77, 79, 92, 117, 193, 203, 231, 236, 237, 251, 252, 261

dextral strike-slip 79, 115, 117, 189, 193

diachronous 5

diamict 216, 208-220

Diamond Rocks 186

diamonds 263, 264

diatomite 223, 267

diatoms 203, 223, 267

dimension stone 268

Dingle 117

dinoflagellate cyst 141, 165

diopside 181, 196

diorite 63, 65, 176

dip slip 118, 200, 205

disconformity 157

dolerite 13, 25, 146, 148, 177, 180, 188, 193, 195, 196, 224, 245, 263

doline 93

dolmens 225

dolomite 126, 259, 267, 276

Donaghadee 46, 54

Donald's Hill 163

Donald's Hill Ignimbrite Formation 163, 164

Donegal-Kingscourt dyke swarm 192, 235

Doobally Sandstone Member 100, 114

Doraville Dyke 191, 193

Downpatrick 225

Dowra 274, 276

Dowra Sandstone Member 98, 274, 276, 278

Drain 19

Drapersfield quarry 134

Draperstown 86, 110, 113, 114, 220, 241, 245, 267

Draperstown Lineament 241

Dromore 176

Dromore High 236, 237

Dromore Sandstone Member 106, 112

dropstones 219

Drumahoe 241

Drumard Member 86

Drumarg Conglomerate Formation 130

Drumchorick Siltstone Formation 106, 112

Drumgivery Limestone Member 88, 115

Drumkeeran 108, 274, 275

drumlin 41, 211, 219, 220

Drumlish Conglomerate Formation 88, 115, 122

Drummahon Burn 105, 106

Drummahon Lane 106

Drumman More Sandstone Formation 90, 103, 112, 121

Drummangarvagh Member 100

Drummond quarry 103

Drumowen Sandstone Member 105

Drumquin 105

Drumskinny Sandstone Member 106

drusy cavities 186, 264

Duckmantian 122, 123

Dunaghy borehole 200

Dunaghy Formation 200, 201, 203

Dunbar 58

Dundalk 190

Dundalk Bay 219

Dundonald 50, 58, 195

Dundrum 223, 242

Dungannon 93, 112, 136, 268, 269

Dungarvan 117

Dungiven 14

Dungiven Limestone Formation 14, 16, 20, 21, 262, 263

Dunloy 220

Dunnamanagh 19

dwarf willow 222

dyke swarm 169, 181, 191-193, 235

dykes 28, 31, 58, 62, 65, 165, 169, 182, 192, 195, 208, 209, 230, 237, 241-243, 245, 252, 263

E

early gabbro 181

early granophyre 181

Early Permian Sandstone 281, 283

East Irish Sea Basin 274, 280, 283

Eastern Mournes Centre 182, 186, 187, 194

echinoid 154, 155, 159

Eden 266

Edenvale beds 36

Ederney 105, 108

Ederney quarry 106

Ederny Limestone Member 105, 111

Eglinton 216, 267

Eglish Sandstone Formation 82

electrical conductivity 227

electrum 258

elm 222

emergence 111, 114

Emsian 70

England 3, 192, 283

Enler Group 125, 127, 131, 132, 281

entablature 174, 175

Eocene 168, 199, 278

Erne basin 218, 219

Ervey 19

esker 211, 218, 220

Eskermore 211

estuarine clay 291

European Plate 205

eustatic 111

evaporite 86, 102, 104, 126, 281

F

Faeroe Islands 192

Fair Head 82, 83, 196, 297

Fair Head Sill 196

Fair Head-Clew Bay Line 5, 9, 26, 237

Famennian 70

Fardross 102

Farragandoo 196

Fearnaght Formation 101

feldspar 264, 267

felsite 29, 67, 179, 194

fenestral micrite 102, 106

Fermanagh Highlands 100, 231

Fermanagh Stadial 215-217

ferruginous laterite 174

fiammé 164

Fintona Block 70, 80, 87, 92, 110, 112, 119, 122, 193, 203, 231, 240, 251, 261, 274

Fintona Group 36, 70

fireclay 82, 94, 267

fish 136, 138, 141, 165

fissure eruptions 169

Fivemiletown 102, 266

Flandrian Transgression 223, 224

flint 155, 157, 159, 161-164, 195, 216, 224

flood plains 292, 297

flower structure 120, 275, 288

flow-ploughing 176

flowstone 293

fold envelope 55

foraminifera 83, 84, 90, 93, 98, 102, 105, 106, 107, 108, 211, 216, 221

fore-arc basin 26

fore-arc trench 43

Forkill 61, 188

Foughill 190

Foyle Basin 244, 247, 279, 281, 283, 284

Foyle Fault 244

fractional crystallisation 182

Frasnian 70

French Park 266

Fruitfield Formation 218

Grey Point 50, 54

Grey Point Formation 48

greywacke 37, 39, 42, 50, 53, 59, 61, 67, 113, 176, 262, 263, 265, 268

grikes 162

groove marks 37

Groundwater 111, 249-254

Groundwater Chemistry 225, 252

Groundwater Vulnerability 249, 253, 254

Guadalupian 131

gypsum 86, 128, 136, 266

H

haematite 162, 163, 265

half-graben 113, 121, 205, 207, 208, 235, 284, 288

halite 86, 128, 131, 136, 141, 142, 245, 266, 283, 284

hardgrounds 157, 159

hawaiite 180

Hawick Group 44, 53, 55

Hawk's Nest Coal 269

hazel 214, 222

Hebridean Uplift 278

Heinrich event 1 219

Hekla 224

Helen's Bay 46, 48, 50

Henry's Bridge Member 16

hessite 258

Hettangian 141, 145-148

hexactinellid sponge 156

Hibernian Greensands Formation 150, 153, 156, 208, 295

Highland Border Complex 26

Highland Border Ridge 125, 134, 152 156, 235, 237, 240, 242-244, 279, 283

Highland Boundary Fault 5, 9, 26, 69, 237, 240

Hillsborough 176, 193

Hilltown 261

Hirnantian 35

Holkerian 90, 93, 102, 108, 112, 119

Hollow House 88

holly 214

Hollymount 216, 217

Holocene 212, 222, 293

Holywood Group 83, 110

Homeville 39

hornblende 11, 17, 22, 31, 67

hornfels 63, 187, 195, 196, 225

Horse Rock 46, 48

hyaloclastite breccias 30, 175

hydraulic conductivity 252

hydrocalumite 195

hydrocarbon fluorescence 276

hydrocarbon generation 278

hydrogeology 249, 252, 293

I

Iapetus Ocean 3, 5, 7, 13, 31, 43, 44, 61

Iapetus Suture Zone 6, 61

Ice Age 295

ice marginal lakes 218, 220

ice sheet 212, 216, 219, 220, 222, 295

icebergs 219

Iceland 168

Iceland Plume 167-169

ice-wedge casts 211

ignimbrite 163

illite 59

illuvium 161

ilmenite 264

industrial minerals 255, 266

Iniscarn Formation 86

Inishowen 244

Inisway 98

inoceramid bivalves 154

insect 166, 211, 217

Interbasaltic Formation 169, 174, 176, 194, 225, 264

intergranular flow 249, 250

interstadial 212, 215, 216

Inver Volcanic Formation 131

Ipswichian Interglacial 214

Ireland 6, 7, 26, 81, 117, 145, 149, 168, 192, 194, 211, 212, 222-225, 240, 254, 263

Irish Sea 215

Irish Sea Basin 218

iron 260, 264, 265

Iron Age 225

iron ore 225, 255, 264, 265

ironstone 83, 146, 203, 265

Irvinestown 193

Irvinestown Dyke 193

Irvinestown Segment 70

island arc volcanic complex 5, 260, 261

Island Magee 154

Island Magee Siltstones Member 154

Isle of Man 236

lateritic iron ores 264

latite 176

Laurentia 3, 13, 79

Laurieston Fault 44

Layered Complex 190

leachate 253

lead 255, 260, 262, 263, 267

Leadhills Supergroup 44, 50, 259

Leaghany River 20

Leambreslen Conglomerate Member 37

Leckpatrick Green Bed Member 22

Leitrim Group 87, 94, 99, 100, 101

Lessans Cottage 48

Letterbrat 14

Lewisian 231, 244

Lifeboat House 77

lignite 166, 176, 200, 201, 203, 209, 255, 270, 271

Lilstock Formation 138, 141

Limavady 9, 136, 139, 146, 150, 216, 218, 219, 297

Lime Hill beds 36

Limerick Point 77

Lisbellaw 33, 37, 70

Lisbellaw Formation 37

Lisbellaw Inlier 25, 112, 119, 276

Lisburn 150, 211, 218, 241

Lislea Granophyre 191

Lisnaskea 101, 102, 110, 111, 220

listric faults 288, 295

lithic arkose 104

lithomarge 172, 174, 200, 264, 265

Little River 35, 36

Little River Group 34, 35, 36

Littletonian Stage 222

Llandeilian 46

Llandovery 36, 42

Llanvirn 26, 30, 33, 46, 260

load casts 136

Lockhovian 70

Londonderry 19, 291

Londonderry Formation 19

Londonderry shelf 152, 155, 159

Long Gilbert Flint Band 159

Loonburn 266

Lopingian 131

Lough Atona 297

Lough Derg 9, 193

Lough Derg Group 9, 12, 22, 97, 267

Lough Derg Inlier 9, 12, 20, 231, 235

Lough Derg Slide 9, 20, 22, 231

Lough Fea 220

Lough Foyle 84, 205, 216, 223, 225, 231, 235, 241, 245

Lough Foyle Basin 205

Lough Foyle Syncline 19

Lough Neagh 199-201, 218-220, 223, 228, 231, 235, 236, 245, 267, 270, 274, 277, 280, 283, 284, 288

Lough Neagh Basin 205, 206, 245-247, 279-283, 286, 288

Lough Neagh Group 199-201, 203, 209, 236, 245, 247, 264, 267, 270, 271

Lough Tay Limestone 21

Loughaveema 219

Loughgall 90

Loughgall Limestone Formation 92

Loughguile Basin 243

Lower Basalt Formation 169-171, 173, 174, 176, 177, 240, 264

lower colonnade 174

Lower Hartfell Shale Formation 46

Lower Lough Erne 9, 98, 121, 236

Lower Permian Sandstone 286

Ludlow 42

Lundy Island 168

Lurgan River 100

Lyle's Hill 265

M

Maastrichtian 155, 159, 160, 161, 165

Machrahanish Basin 284

Macnean 274

Maghera 243

Magherameena Limestone Member 98

Magherameena quarry 98

Magilligan 223, 224

Magilligan borehole 114, 134, 138, 205, 206, 244, 270, 281, 283

Magilligan sill 245

Magnesian Limestone 123, 125, 126, 129, 130, 266, 281, 284

magnetic anomaly 193, 230, 235, 236, 241, 242, 245

magnetic susceptibility 227

Maguiresbridge 217

Maguiresbridge Till 218

Maidenmount 266, 293

Main Coal 83, 269, 270

Main Limestone Member 83

malachite 263

pelite 14, 16, 17, 18, 19, 257

Penarth Group 133, 137-141, 153, 207, 295

Pendleian 94, 101, 114

periclinal fold 196

peritidal 110, 119

peritidal limestone 102, 105

perlite 256, 266

permafrost 215

permeability 252, 254, 276, 278, 281

Permian 73, 77, 83, 115, 119, 123, 124, 125-132, 133,
    143, 205-207, 250, 252, 266, 278-281, 283, 286

Permian Upper Marls 130, 266

Pettigoe Fault 9, 97

phosphatic nodules 165

phytoclast 73

picro-dolerite 193

pillar and stall 293

pillow lavas 13, 14, 16, 26, 29, 32, 43, 46, 175

pine 214, 222, 223

pisoliths 137

pisolitic grainstone 93

pisolitic iron ore 264

pitchstone 67, 193

Plaister quarry 103

playa lakes 114

Pleistocene 211, 212, 267, 268, 293

Pliensbachian 145, 148

plugs 177, 192, 194, 225, 245

Plumbridge 14, 219

Pollaphuca 263

pollen 166, 211, 214, 217, 221, 222

pollution 253, 254

Pomeroy 5, 32, 93, 220

Pomeroy Inlier 25, 33, 236, 240, 276

poplar 222

porcellanite 195, 224, 225

porosity 276, 278, 281

porphyritic felsite 188, 189, 208

porphyritic granitoid 28

porphyritic granophyre 188, 189, 191

porphyritic rhyolite 193

porphyry 194

Port Calliagh 160

Port Calliagh Chalk 160

Port More borehole 132, 134, 136, 145, 146, 148, 288

Port na Spaniagh Member 176

Port Noffer 176

Port Obe 75

Portadown 164, 176

Portaferry Tract 44, 53

Portavogie 55

Portbradden Fault 242

Portglenone 223, 267

portlandite 195

Portmore 267

Portnaloub 82

Portpatrick Basin 284, 286, 288

Portrush 148, 155, 170, 196, 241

Portrush Chalk Member 159

Portrush Sill 148, 169, 196

Portstewart Strand 224

Pragian 73

precious metals 256, 260

Pre-Dalradian Basement 9, 231

Prehen quarry 19

prehnite-pumpellyite facies 59

Pre-*planorbis* beds 139-141

Pridolí 70

primary porosity 276

protalus ramparts 222

protolith 190, 260

protomylonite 58

proximate analyses 269-271

psammites 11, 12, 14, 16, 17, 18, 19, 21

pteraspid 70

pteridophyte 164

pull-apart basin 115, 122, 199

pumice 163

pyrite 257-260, 262, 263

pyroclastic flow 163, 170, 176

pyroxene hornfels 181

pyroxenite 62, 195

Q

quartz diorite 32

quartz trachyte 193

quartz vein-hosted gold 257

quartz veins 257, 259

quartz-feldspar porphyry 194

quartzite 14, 37, 74, 75, 106, 257

quartz-porphyry 244

Quaternary 211, 214, 252

R

radiolarian chert 46

raised beach 218, 223

Ramore Head 196

ramp 112

Rampark 181

Randalstown 221

Rasharkin 244

Rathlin Basin 155, 156, 159, 205, 206, 244, 247, 270,
    279-281, 283, 284, 288

Rathlin Island 146, 157, 170, 205, 225, 284

Raveagh Sandstone Formation 73

Rawtheyan 35

recumbent folds 55

Red Arch Formation 74, 77

refractory bricks 267

regional gravity 180, 205, 228

regolith 125, 212

regression 103

restraining bend 120

Retreat Siltstone Formation 89

Rhaetian 141

rhizoliths 106

Rhuddanian 40

rhyodacite 176

rhyolite 26, 29, 31, 33, 65, 114, 170, 176, 193, 260, 263

riebeckite-microgranite 216

ring dyke 169, 181, 186, 188-191

ring fractures 186, 189, 208

Ringboy Point 65

Ringburr Point 65

ripples 71, 84, 88, 134, 136

River Bann 223, 267, 298

River Blackwater 103

River Foyle 218

River Lagan 219, 223, 292

River Main 250

River Roe 14, 19, 218

roadstone 51

roche moutonnées 216

rock crystal 264

rock falls 297, 298

rock glaciers 222

Rock Road quarry 92

Rockall 192

Rockall Trough 168

Rockdale Limestone Formation 93

Rock-Eval analysis 277

Rockfield quarry 102

Roe Valley Group 84, 110, 284

rogen moraine 218-220

rollover anticlines 288

roof pendants 186

room and pillar 264, 265

Rossmore Mudstone Formation 94, 114, 122,
    268, 282

rotational slumping 293

Rough Island 221

Rowreagh Formation 53

Runabay Formation 22

Rushindoo Oolite Member 105

S

sabkha 106, 112, 141

Sallagh Braes 219

Salmon's Drift 265

salt 255, 256, 293

sand and gravel 250, 268, 292

sandstone dykes 100, 122

Sandy Braes 176, 266

Santonian 151, 153, 155, 156

Scalp 27

Scawt Hill 195

scawtite 195

schist 5, 11, 16, 20, 75, 260, 262, 264

Scotland 5, 7, 9, 12, 13, 14, 16, 20, 26, 34, 42, 44, 55,
    69, 167, 168, 207, 216, 220, 224, 231, 234, 237,
    240, 259, 282, 283

Scrabo 136, 195

Scrabo Sill 195

Scraghy quarry 104

secondary porosity 276

Seeconnell 62

seismic reflection 227, 236, 247, 274, 280, 284

seismic refraction 227

seismic surveys 288

seismic velocity 227

Selandian 166

serpulid 104, 153, 154

Shanaghy Formation 20

Shane's Hill Intrusion 176

Shanmaghery Sandstone Formation 73

Shanmullagh Formation 70

Shannon Pot 293

Shanvin 106

shear zones 257, 260

turbidity current 43

Turonian 153, 154

Tyrone Group 84, 86, 88, 93, 96, 101, 102, 103, 110, 119

Tyrone Igneous Complex 5, 12, 22, 25, 33, 92, 120, 203, 207, 231, 236, 237, 240, 244, 245, 257, 260

Tyrone Plutonic Group 12, 25, 26, 32

Tyrone Volcanic Group 26, 28, 30, 260, 261, 263, 265

U

Ulster White Limestone Formation 139, 150-152, 154, 155, 208, 251, 267, 293

Ultramafic-Intermediate Complex 62, 234

ultramylonite 58

underground cavities 292

Unnamed beds 36

Upper Basalt Formation 169, 176, 177, 192, 194, 199, 240, 264

upper colonnade 174, 175

Upper Hartfell Shale Formation 46

Upper Lough Erne 101, 119, 275

uranium 271

V

Variscan 5, 73, 79, 110, 115, 125, 196, 205, 279, 283

Variscan Mountains 79, 123, 126, 141

Variscan Orogenic Cycle 117, 124, 257, 278, 283

vent agglomerates 170, 181, 189, 195

vesicle cylinders 172

vesicles 172, 193

Viséan 70, 80, 90, 92, 101, 269, 276, 279, 284

vitrinite reflectance 274, 276, 277, 279, 283, 288

volcanic arc 26, 31, 33, 42

volcanic breccia 29, 31

volcanic vent 194

volcaniclastic 13, 14, 16, 22, 26, 28, 31, 59, 111, 122, 229, 281

volcano 176, 188, 224

Vulcanists 196

W

Wales 3

Wallace's Rocks 65

Washing Bay 199, 203

Waterloo 136, 138, 141, 146, 147, 157

Waterloo Mudstone Formation 133, 138, 141, 146, 147, 153, 196, 207, 282, 293

waulsortian 98

Wenlock 42

Westbury Formation 138

Western Mournes Centre 182, 186

Westphalian 88, 92, 94, 115, 122, 269, 278, 279, 282-284

Whiskin Rocks 51

White Brae Mudstone Formation 131

White Glen 106

White Mountain 84

White Park Bay 148, 156, 297

White Rocks 170

Whitehead 172

Whitehead Flint Band 155, 157

Wilson's Bridge borehole 89

Wilson's Bridge Limestone Formation 92

WINCH survey line 227

Wind Farm 275

wollastonite 181, 195, 196

Woodbrook Cottage 173

Woodgrange Interstadial 221, 222

Wordian 131

X

xenoliths 28, 32, 33, 64, 67, 194, 196

xonotolite 195

Y

Yates Corner 48

yew 214

Z

zeolite 59, 172, 193, 200

zinc 260, 262, 263, 267

zircon 186

Publications of the Geological Survey of Northern Ireland

Maps

1:50,000, one-inch and larger scale

The main scale for publication of geological maps is 1:50,000. These have supplanted maps at a scale of one-inch to one mile (1:63,360). Most maps of Northern Ireland appear in two editions. In the Solid (Bedrock) edition only the pre-Quaternary geology is coloured. The Solid and Drift (Bedrock and Superficial Deposits) edition shows linework and symbols that illustrate both the Quaternary (Superficial Deposits) and pre-Quaternary (Solid) geology. In the Solid and Drift edition the Quaternary and the Solid (Bedrock) geology are both coloured.

Most of the maps are based on surveys at 1:10,560 (six inches to one mile) or 1:10,000 although some are compiled at 1:25,000 scale. Copies of the 1:10,000, 1:25,000 and 1:10,560 maps can be consulted or purchased in the Survey's office.

Smaller scales

The Solid geology (1997) and Quaternary geology (1991) of Northern Ireland are published as separate maps at 1:250,000. Also published at 1:250,000 is a Bouguer Gravity Anomaly Map of Northern Ireland. A Magnetic Anomaly Map of Northern Ireland is published at a scale of

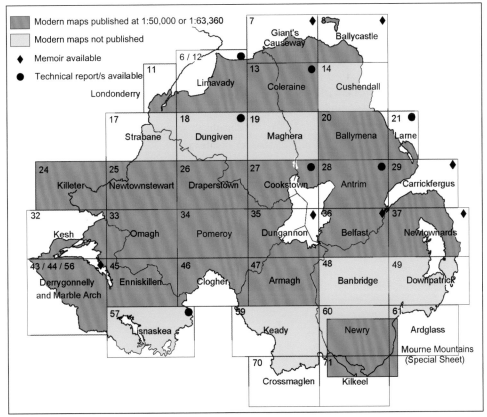

Availability of geological maps, memoirs and technical reports from the Geological Survey of Northern Ireland.

317

1:253,440 (Quarter-inch to One Mile). The Hydrogeological Map and Groundwater Vulnerability Map are published at the 1:250,000 scale and are accompanied by an explanatory booklet describing the Hydrogeology of Northern Ireland. Aspects of the geology of Northern Ireland are covered in the British Geological Survey's 1:1000,000 Series, by the Industrial Mineral Resources Map of Britain, and, in the 1:500,000 Series, by the Metallogenic Map of Britain and Ireland and the Tectonic Map of Britain, Ireland and adjacent areas.

Other publications

Detailed descriptions of the geology of some 1:63,360 and 1:50,000 sheet areas, as depicted on the index map, are published as *sheet memoirs*. A series of Technical Reports describing the geology of individual 1:10,000, 1:25,000 and some of the published 1:50,000 maps are also available.

Popular publications

The **Walk Series** consist of walking packages that explore the geology and natural history of Ireland's 12 northern counties in particular the areas of the Bann and Roe Valleys, Cuilcagh, Donegal, Mourne/Gullion and Cooley, Sligo/Leitrim, Sperrins and South Ulster. The **Explore Series** explore the geology and natural history of the Bann and Roe Valleys, Cuilcagh, Donegal, Lough Neagh, Mourne/Gullion and Cooley, Oriel, South Antrim, Sperrins, Upper Erne, West Breifne and West Sligo. **A Story through Time** (1999) describes the formation of the rocks and scenic landscapes of Ireland (North). Told in non-scientific language, the book is aimed, not at the specialist, but at those who have a curiosity about where our surroundings, and we, really come from. Popular style 1:50,000 geological maps of the Causeway Coast (1998) and Ballycastle (2002) areas explore the landscapes and rocks for the non-specialist but also provide the professional geologist with an overview.

Sources

Maps and books of the Geological Survey of Northern Ireland may be purchased from the Survey's office listed below and from the sales offices of the British Geological Survey. The publication of new maps and books by the Geological Survey of Northern Ireland will be notified by the issue of brochures.

Sales Office

Geological Survey of Northern Ireland,
20, College Gardens,
Belfast BT9 6BS
Tel: 028-90-666595
Fax: 028-90-662835
Email: sales.gsni@detini.gov.uk